From the Ground Up

From the Ground Up

Richard & Lorna; 12/09
    May your Journey
ontinue to be happy healthy
wealthy.
    Your a great man & Godly.

From the
Ground
Up

It's Not Just Business!

May your life together Be
always filled by with happiness
John L. Hoich every Day
God Bless Rich & Norma;
Enjoy life to the fullest.
    John Lee Hoich

TAPESTRY PRESS
WYOMISSING, PENNSYLVANIA

jhoich@hoich.com
    www.johnhoich.com

Tapestry Press
1401 Parkside Dr. North
Wyomissing, PA 19610
610-375-1422   www.tapestrypressinc.com

Printed in Canada
09 08 07 06 05 1 2 3 4 5

Library of Congress Cataloging-in-Publication Data
Hoich, John L., 1958-
  From the ground up : it's not just business! / by John L. Hoich.
    p. cm.
  Summary: "Autobiography of John Hoich, who endured an abusive father
and his mother's death when he was seventeen years old. To survive, he
started a lawn mowing business and built it into a multimillion-dollar business. Includes his principles for success in life and in business"—Provided by
publisher.
  Includes index.
  ISBN 978-1-930819-53-5 (trade paper : alk. paper) — ISBN
978-1-930819-52-8 (hard cover : alk. paper)
  1. Hoich, John L., 1958- 2. Businessmen—Nebraska—Biography. 3.
Lawn care industry—United States—Biography. 4. Real estate business—United States—Biography. 5. Adult children of dysfunctional families—Biography. 6. Successful people—United States—Biography. I. Title.

HC102.5.H65A3 2007
338.7'6359647092—dc22
[B]
                                        2007005869

A portion of the receipts from sales of this book will be donated to:
    The Stephen Center: The John L. Hoich Center for Recovery
    Lakeside Hospital Foundation
    The Westside Schools Foundation: The John L. Hoich
        Scholarship Fund
(all located in Omaha, Nebraska) and
    Rotary International Foundation, Evanston, IL

Cover design by David Sims

Book design and layout by
D. & F. Scott Publishing, Inc.
N. Richland Hills, Texas

To my mom
Becky Leona Williamson Hoich
and
my four sisters and deceased brother
and
my twin sons
Jeremy and Justin
and
to all who will join me in the journey to
overcoming adversity and insecurity

Contents

Preface

Whon I was ten years old, I felt like giving up. I lived in fear of an abusive father who beat me, my mother, and my sisters. I alternated between fear and depression. Then one night I had a dream. I was in a barn on a hill. Inside the barn were my father and a lot of other people. I can't remember precisely who they were, but I believe that they were all mean people I knew who hurt others. The barn was burning and I was up on one of the rafters trying to escape the flames when Jesus came into the barn, took my hand, and led me out of the barn. As it continued to burn, we walked up a hill and, as we walked, Jesus told me that he had saved me because he had a plan for my life. I asked, "What's the plan? What should I do?" But he just said, "You'll see.

I woke up in the middle of the night and could remember all the dream (and still do). It was like God had wakened me. From that night on, my life took a different direction. I was filled with resolve and confidence because the experience of the dream was so real that I knew without a doubt that there is a God and that God loves me and has a plan for my life. I realize now that the barn was a metaphor for our home, which was a burning hell that Jesus would save me from—and he did. God's plan for my life was not just to make a lot of money. My business success has simply provided me with the resources to help family, friends, the community, and those in need. This book is partial repayment of the debt I owe to God for saving me from that burning barn/home. I hope that it will help to encourage others who think that having a successful life is out of their reach. It's not likely you'll have many more cards stacked against you than I did, but if I could do it, so can you.

In addition to the great debt I owe to God, I also want to thank The Toro Company. One of their mowers was the first business purchase I ever made and it served me well. Ever since, I have used Toro equipment whenever I could. In fact, it was Toro, through my local distributor, Midwest Turf and Irrigation, who sort of got me started. When I was in high school, I participated in Toro's Young Entrepreneur Program and they gave me 50 percent off all my purchases, charged me no interest for a year, and provided me with a thousand-dollar grant for college. Under that program, I was the western regional winner and the first runner-up at the national level. To me, that Toro was more than a lawn mower: It was a relationship that continues to this day. I can honestly say that without the support of Toro and Midwest Turf and Irrigation during those early, very difficult, years, it is unlikely I would have survived that initial business venture.

I also want to thank other business relationships that contributed to my journey of success.

Joe and Ada McDermott—Loveland Lawns and parental guidance

Len Johnson, Jim Johnson, Bob Pease, and Dan Poore—Midwest Turf and Irrigation, Inc.

Joseph M. Smith—My friend since 1970 and my first business partner in Green Star Lawn Care, from 1974 until 1979

George Allison and Bernie Marquardt—M & A Enterprises Inc.

Maurice and Joan Udes—Friend and business partner

Steve Durham—Partner, friend, and client

Jerry Slusky—Partner, Slusky/Hoich Real Estate and my friend for a lifetime

Fritz Stehlik—My attorney of twenty-five years

Jim Jandrain—My CPA for fifteen years

Kirby Clarke—My friend since four years old

David O. Janke—Twenty years of inspiration

Prologue

So I was taking a shower and I got to thinking about the last time I was at the beach. I remembered watching the waves. They had an irregular but rhythmic sort of pattern that somehow reminded me of life—always advancing and moving forward as the tide came in, but not without an occasional retreat. My God, how did I get to be forty-nine so quickly? I began to think about my life—I get all my best ideas in the shower. I like to focus on the future, but I wonder sometimes if I'm always advancing towards the future or just running from the past.

Well, it's certainly been a successful life. I've founded several companies, helped out a lot of people and causes, and made millions of dollars—mostly by mowing lawns! But there have also been setbacks and costs to pay. Still, when I think about it, a lot of people would probably think that my life is a sort of miracle. Considering how it all started out, conventional wisdom would suggest that I'd probably wind up as a failure, a child abuser, or worse. Yet that didn't happen. I wonder what it was—determination, hard work, luck, good friends, the hand of God? Somehow, I suspect that it was a bit of all these.

Well, I've got the second half of my life in front of me and I've learned some valuable lessons that should help. I'm going to simplify my life. I'm going to apply the 80-20 rule that I've always used for business to the rest of my life as well.

I think the first thing I'll do is write a book and share what I've learned. Perhaps it will give me some closure. Perhaps it will encourage someone who thinks they don't have a chance. Yes, the future looks promising.

But it wasn't always so . . .

Part I

My Story

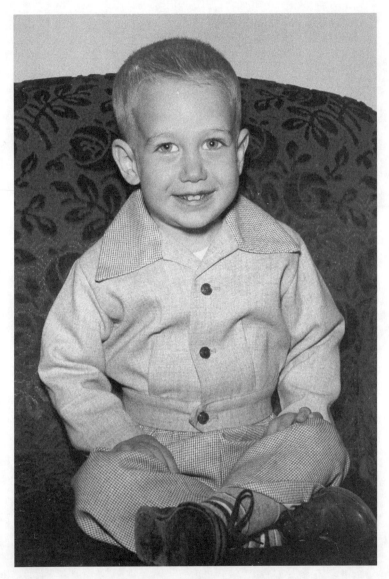

Johnny Lee Hoich, Age Three

Growing Up

My mother was a troubled woman. She was born and raised on a farm in Crookston, Minnesota as the second youngest of fourteen children. She had been abused as a child and wound up marrying an abusive drunk. She suffered from nervous breakdowns and had to be hospitalized from time to time as a result. My father was a violent alcoholic who sexually abused my sisters. When Dad wasn't beating me or Mom, he would call me a worthless bastard. When I was eighteen, I found out that he was half right. Mom had been pregnant with me when they met. I have no idea who my biological father is, though I've searched as hard as I can. I would like to meet him some day just to find out what he is like.

When I was eleven, Dad moved out. In one way, it was a great relief; but, over the years, he never paid more than a few hundred dollars of child support or alimony. So we were very hard pressed to survive. The pressure was often too much for Mom, and when she'd have to be institutionalized, we children would be placed with family or neighbors or foster parents. My sister Susan was put in a state-run group family. During one of these times, I was in a foster home where the man was sexually abusing me. I couldn't bear it and ran away. The next day I went to school and after school I just sat at my desk. The teacher asked me why I didn't leave and I told her that I didn't know where to go. She called the police and, not knowing what else to do, they sent me to a juvenile detention facility. That night two of the older inmates nearly raped me. I was saved by a guard before they could carry out their intentions, but it was terrifying. I was there for two weeks—the worst days of my life.

Then, when I was fifteen, everything finally began to work out. Mom came home to stay. I was working several jobs and we had enough money to get by. Mom and I chipped in together and bought a Sears Craftsman lawn mower. One of the ways I earned money was by mowing lawns. I also had a couple of paper routes and did some babysitting for Mom to earn the fifteen dollars a week that I needed to make payments on a little 125cc 1969 Honda motorcycle that I had bought for 195 dollars. I remember those two years as one of the happiest times of my life.

Then, without warning, it all ended.

My sister Susan was staying in a group foster home, having just given up a baby for adoption. The day before, she had visited us and was very excited because she was going to be coming home for good. It was a wonderful visit. Mom had cooked her favorite dish—curry chicken, but it was the last meal Mom would ever cook.

As Susan got into the car, she heard Mom's voice, very quiet and emotional. Mom said, "Susan."

Susan turned around, annoyed that Mom was still talking to her as she got into the car, and she responded with that sing-song, mockingly defiant voice that teenage girls have perfected over the centuries. "What now?" asked Susan.

"I love you," answered Mom.

On September 25, 1974, the morning after Susan left, Mom was the first one up. She stopped by the children's rooms and flashed the lights, a signal for us to get up, and then she went down the hall to the kitchen to make a pot of coffee. It was her most enjoyable time of the day. Except for the noise the children made as they got ready for school, the house was quiet, and she had the kitchen and living room to herself. Every morning, like clockwork, she poured herself a cup of coffee and sat on the couch to smoke a cigarette. I don't know what she thought about when she was in the living room all alone, but it must have been something special, because it was what she looked forward to the most every morning.

I was the first one to see her in the living room that morning. When I walked past her, she was already on the couch. She asked, "What did you do last night?" I told her I had been to Alateen, an organization for teens with alcoholic parents, and then stopped by a restaurant to help them wash the dishes. Although only sixteen, I had been working for six years, first as a paperboy and then at a restaurant and a gas station.

With her curiosity satisfied, Mom got up without saying anything and went into the kitchen for a refill of her coffee. It was not until she walked past me on the way back to the couch that she spoke again, saying, "Well, that's really nice." Then she sat down on the couch, her mind a million miles away.

"You know, it's really nice that you had a nice time."

Mom didn't say anything else. She exhaled, the way she did when she was tired, resting her head on the back of the couch. She often went to sleep while she had her coffee and I didn't think anything about it. After that, Aunt Elouise, who was visiting, got up and helped the children with breakfast. As the kids walked past Mom, they reached over and tickled her, saying things like, "Mom, get up!"

Sometimes she was really asleep. Other times she faked it to give us kids a hard time, like she was dead or something. It was sort of her idea of a joke. It was such a common thing that Cathy wrote a poem about it titled, "Becky, Don't Fake It." Usually, when she was faking it, she raised up like a movie monster and said: "What would you do if I really died? See, when you're mean to me or say bad things to me and call me names, you're going to regret it one day if I don't wake up."

We didn't know whether she was really asleep or faking it, so we all went back to get ready for school. I was in my bedroom for only a few minutes, when Aunt Elouise came to my door and asked, "What's Dot Wheeler's phone number?" Dot Wheeler was the lady next door who taught me how to drive a car, pitch a tent, ride a bike and all that. I gave my aunt her phone number and asked, "Is something wrong with my mom?

"I'm not sure, honey," she answered. "I think she might be sick."

I went back and saw Mom tipped over to the side. I said, "Bye Mom, I love you," and about that time my friend Kirby Clarke walked into the house and asked, "How are you, Mrs. Hoich?" When she didn't answer him, I said, "Oh, she's just faking it. She's acting like she's sleeping." I reached over and pulled her up straight and then put my ear on her chest to see if she was breathing. I couldn't tell whether she was breathing or not, but I wasn't really worried because it was the sort of thing that she did all the time. She didn't say anything, so I kissed her on the lips and went out the door with Kirby—and we rode our motorcycles together to school.

By the time my eleven-year-old sister Donna came into the living room, I was already gone. Donna walked past Mom on the couch and noticed that there was just something different about the way she looked. "Being a beauty operator, and a very beautiful woman, she always kept herself looking a certain way," says Donna. "So I knew something was wrong by the way she was scrunched down on the couch. She had false teeth and they were hanging out of her mouth and I remember knowing that wasn't right for my mother to lay like that with her underwear showing. But I walked right past her and didn't do a thing about it. Nowadays people call 911, or they administer CPR. Sometimes I wonder if I could have saved her. Why didn't I call someone immediately?"

Donna got something to eat and then went back to finish getting ready for school. When she came back, little Michael was sitting on Mom's lap, hitting her. "Quit faking, Mother!" he screamed. "Wake up!" Recalls Donna: "Mother was quite a jokester. She would be at work all day long and then when she came home, we would clean the house and she would say, 'Call the ambulance, the house is clean and I'm dying!' I remember getting my aunt out of bed and telling her that something was the matter with my mother. She called the neighbor, Dorothy Wheeler, and as I went to school, Mrs. Wheeler was heading over to the house. I remember, as we walked to school, hearing the ambulance. I remember praying that I would go home and everything would be okay."

Everything wasn't okay, of course. Our mother was dead and each of us had walked past her without doing anything to help her. Was she already dead then, as we got ready for school, or was she desperately in need of our help? If we had acted, would we have saved her life? That's a question that no one will ever be able to answer. Each of us will take that question to the grave.

Donna, who was eleven, was pulled out of math class at 10:30 AM by the school secretary, who explained to her that our neighbor would be picking her up at school. The same thing happened with Michael, who was six; Cathy, who was twelve; and Angela, who was ten. I remember hearing my name being called over the loud speaker, asking me to report to the principal's office. At the time, I was talking to a friend with whom I was in a peer-counseling group, and I told her that my mom had not been feeling well and I thought my being called to the principal's

office had something to do with that. After hearing my name, I ran all the way to the principal's
office. When I got there, the principal told me that
I needed to go home because Mom was sick. He
didn't tell me that she was dead, only that I
needed to go home. I remember driving down
Westridge Drive on my motorcycle and pulling up
onto the lawn of the house, allowing my bike to
go into the bushes as I jumped off and ran into
the house.

"What happened?" I asked, when I saw everyone gathered together in the living room and
kitchen. "What's going on? Where's my mom?"

One of our neighbors said, "Your mom has
died."

I sat down and started crying. A few minutes
later, my brother and sisters arrived. Recalls Donna:

> People were flocking in like you wouldn't
> believe. We had a yard full of people. We went
> into the house and the pastor and his wife
> were there. John was sitting there and he had
> been crying. Looking at him, I knew some-
> thing was wrong, but I still denied it to myself.
> The minister's wife was a nurse. The minister
> said, "If you will pay attention, my wife will tell
> you how your mother went." I remember
> those words very clearly. When I heard how
> my mother went, I still couldn't believe it and
> I said, "Do you mean my mother's dead?" She
> said, "Yes, honey." John lost it and went into
> the bathroom and then I don't remember any

more about John at that point. Our relatives were coming in and out, fighting over possessions we didn't have.

Susan was the last to find out what happened. When they told her at the girls' group home, she was devastated. Mom had promised to bring her back into the family—and then she had died without doing so, her final words to Susan, "I love you," lingering in her memory like the remnants of a bad dream. "It was like having a carrot stuck out in front of your face," says Susan, "and just about the time you get close enough to get a bite of it, it is ripped away from you. That was a huge thing for me."

There are no words to express the fear I felt when Mom died. What was going to happen to us? Would I be able to finish high school? How would I make a living as an adult? I reestablished a relationship with Dad, but that was not very satisfying because I had a very difficult time getting over their divorce and the abuses that had taken place in our home. My motivation was to get help for myself and my siblings from the one person who should care more than anyone else, but something inside me held me back and kept me from doing what needed to be done.

Instead of stroking Dad's ego and trying to impress him, I asked him questions like, "Why did you beat Mom?" Or "why did you drink so much and hurt us kids?" Or "Why did you and Mom get divorced?" As fearful as I was about life, I desperately needed answers for the past. I know now that it was beyond Dad's capacity to provide all of those answers.

When Mom died, the pastor asked me to sit on the couch so that he could talk to me. His intentions were good, but he imposed a weight on me that no sixteen-year-old should have to bear. The pastor said: "John, no longer can you be a young man. You need to become a full fledged man now. You have to be a dad, a brother, a leader, a grown-up, for your brother and sisters—and you have to start today. God has a plan for your life. We don't know why He plans these things, but this is what you are going to have to do for your sisters and your brother, who need you now more than ever before. You know that your father is incapable of giving to you and the state won't let you live with him. So, you're it, buddy, and I'm going to pray for you right now."

With the pastor leading us, I dropped to my knees, along with my brother, Michael, and my sisters, Cathy, Donna, and Angela, and we pulled each other into a circle and prayed a long prayer that I would help lead the family.

At the funeral, Donna looked at our mother laid out in the coffin in a beautiful dress and she wondered where the beautiful dress had been when she was alive. Seeing her like that made her feel bitter and angry. I looked down at Mom in the casket and sort of saw my entire life pass before my eyes. She was only thirty-nine—and they said she died of a heart attack. No one's mom dies of a heart attack at thirty-nine. I had never even heard of such a thing. Why was our mom dead? It just didn't make sense to any of us. After all we had been through, how could we be so unlucky as to lose our mom?

Feeling an enormous sense of responsibility to my brother and sisters, I leaned over the casket and whispered, "Mom, I'll do everything I can for the other kids. I'll try to see that they're good and become good adults. I'll be a millionaire by the time I'm thirty–and I'll take care of everyone."

I was only sixteen, but as the casket lid was lowered, I felt the weight of the world on my shoulders.

Bob and Sammy Smith

Getting Started

After Mom died, the biggest problem facing us as a family was where we would live. Bob and Sammy Smith solved that problem right away by taking us into their home, as they had done so many times before. But that was only temporary, since our family was just too large for any one foster family to take in. The Smiths ended up with me, Michael, and Angela. Cathy and Donna went to live with separate foster families, while Susan remained in the girls' group home in Geneva, Nebraska.

My new life got off to a shaky start, not because of anything the Smiths did, but because less than a week after Mom died, I was in an accident with my motorcycle. I was driving home from school when a lady turned in front of me. I slid my motorcycle down on the ground and went underneath her car. Luckily, I was wearing one of those helmets with the bubble on the face.

As I went underneath her car, I bit a hole in my tongue and blood filled up the bubble, which must have been a fearsome sight to the woman, who jumped out of her car, looked at me—and screamed, "I killed him! He's dead!"

I heard her screaming and wondered if maybe I was dead, like maybe there is a point after you die when you continue to hear the voices of the people around you. I certainly was hurting badly enough to be dead, I knew that much. When they got me to the hospital, they discovered that I was all right, except for the hole in my tongue and a torn cartilage in my knee, and I was greatly relieved not to be dead, though the accident did put me at a disadvantage as a gymnast at Westside High School in Omaha.

I had tried wrestling for a year, which seemed like a good idea at the time, but the more I thought about it, the more I realized that I didn't really want to do anything that Dad had done, so I decided to become a gymnast. Parallel bars were my specialty. I won the state championship and that was a big deal for me; but after the motorcycle accident, I had to drop out because of the pain in my knee.

Life settled into a routine at the Smith household, but I was sixteen and upset over losing my mom and over the fact that I had a dad that didn't want to be a dad and I was difficult to deal with sometimes, especially living with a foster father who only had one way of doing things—*his* way. I remember one time when I told Sammy that she was a bitch. That didn't go over too well with Bob, who told me that, if I ever said that again to his wife, he would knock me so far down the hallway that I wouldn't know what hit me.

Of course, being the rebellious wise guy that I was, I looked at Sammy and said, "Bitch!"—and he immediately slugged me, sending me down the hallway and into the back wall. Today, if a man did that to a teenager, he would go to prison, but back then it happened, right or wrong. One thing's for certain: I never, ever, called her a name again. After that, he had my full respect. I never forgot what happened because I understood that I had no right calling her that. I really cleaned up my act after that.

Bob Smith changed, too, while we lived with him. He quit drinking. He joined Alcoholics Anonymous. And he found Jesus in his heart. When my dad took me fishing, he always just dropped me off at the lake and said, "See ya, kid," as he would enter the bar next to the lake. Bob wasn't like that. When he took me fishing, he stuck with me the entire time. I'll never forget those early Saturday mornings when we got all our fishing gear together and headed out for the lake, the two of us singing

Gordon Lightfoot's "If You Could Read My Mind." That's the sort of thing I never got to do with Dad. I'll never forget those precious times. Today, whenever I hear that song, it just melts my heart because those were some of the best times of my life. Bob Smith was a friend to me—and a teacher—when I needed those two things in my life the most. I still consider him one of my best friends.

The Smiths later were named outstanding foster parents of the year by the Douglas County Social Services Department because of their devotion to us—and they deserved that award because it is a rare thing for foster parents to take in a child with severe health problems. In some way, I guess they were touched by God.

The severe health problems that I mentioned belonged to my younger brother, Michael. Two of his heart chambers were in reversed positions, and the two major blood vessels that carry blood to and from the heart were transposed, which meant that there were two holes between the chambers. Doctors also found that he had an obstruction between his heart and lungs, a second obstruction between his heart and his aorta, and a leak in one valve. To look at Michael, you would not know anything was wrong with him, but the doctors all said that his days were numbered without surgery to correct his congenital heart defects. His situation, however, had not become critical until we were living with the Smiths.

He desperately needed surgery. The only problem was that there was no surgeon in Nebraska qualified to do such a complicated operation and there was no money to pay for surgery outside the state. Talk about red tape nightmares! Of course, Mom had known about this before she died. She made the rounds of all the public and private agencies, but no one was willing to help. It makes you wonder, doesn't it? What are all these agencies for, if not to help out a little boy with two holes in his heart?

He was scheduled for an operation at the University of Alabama in Birmingham in February 1975. The surgery was to be performed by Dr. John Kirklin, an internationally famous heart surgeon. But there was still no money.

On February 2, a little more than three weeks away from the scheduled surgery, the *Omaha World-Herald* came to the rescue with a page one story that told Michael's story under two well-placed headlines:

BOY, 6, HAS MESSED-UP HEART

and

BOY'S HEART SNARED IN RED TAPE.

Overnight, we had a celebrity in the family. Michael looked cute as a button in the newspaper photograph, not like someone facing death, but the public response was immediate and overwhelming.

An account was set up at the Omaha State Bank for donations and, thanks to the newspaper article, the money started pouring in and all the needed funds were donated before the operation was held.

One of the most interesting donations was the use of a twin engine Piper Navajo for the three-and-a-half hour flight to Birmingham. The airplane was owned by Freeman Decorating Company. A year earlier, Buck Freeman, the company's chairman of the board, was flying over Birmingham when he started having heart problems. The pilot made an emergency landing so that Freeman could rest at a local hotel. When the seventy-one-year-old business executive's symptoms grew more ominous, he was rushed to the University of Alabama Medical Center for tests. The results were a shock, to say the least. Freeman had a hole in his heart, a defect that probably had existed since birth. The surgeon who repaired his heart was Dr. John Kirklin. When Freeman read about Michael's predicament—and then realized that they had the same surgeon—he offered the use of his company's airplane. (Later, I purchased the same model airplane myself.)

Michael's operation was successful and he returned, healthy, but with a "zipper"—a long scar that ran from his throat to his navel. He was very proud of it.

Since Mom's death, we had overcome two major problems—where to live and Michael's health. There was still a third one. We were practically penniless and needed some financial base. My mom's lawyer had sold the house and settled with all the creditors, and set it up so that each of us five kids would get $3,300 when we reached twenty-one. After all the bills were paid, the only thing left was the two-year-old Sears Craftsman lawn mower. Mom and I had bought that lawn mower so that I could cut the grass at our home and also make money cutting other people's lawns. So I asked my friend Joe Smith (not related to my foster parents) if he wanted to start up a lawn-mowing business with me, and we founded Green Star Lawn Care.

At that time, a lot of people thought that the lawn business was no big deal. If you wanted your grass cut, you did it yourself, recruited your son or daughter to do it, or you simply waited for someone to come along with a lawn mower. I thought that any service that people would pay good money for was a big deal.

Before starting up the lawn business, I had worked at many jobs near my home in Omaha: forty hours a week at the House of Pies, pumping gas at a Texaco, pouring concrete for sidewalks, washing dishes at Mr. Up's Restaurant (where I also helped cook and seat people), making pizzas at Godfather's Pizza and Shakey's Pizza, and helping out at the VIP car wash at the Phillips 66 station (my final job before getting into lawn care). It was an all-around job. I pumped gas, washed and dried cars. I have always been a hard worker.

Joe is about four years older than I am, so when we first met, it seemed unlikely that we would become friends, with him at the advanced age of seventeen and me at thirteen (a big gap in teen years), but we hit it off for some reason, even though I was in junior high school and he was in high school. I had the Sears Craftsman lawn mower that I had bought with my mom. He had an old Montgomery Ward lawn mower that belonged to his parents and a 1960s-something pickup truck with a stick shift that we used to haul our equipment around in. Recalls Joe:

> John was pretty good at talking to people
> and getting business. He was very personable.
> He would say anything to anybody. Relating to

people is his strongest point. He would just walk up and start talking and make a deal. So we were strong on the public relations end. But neither of us had any money to throw into the business. We didn't have money for anything and when things went wrong it was always disastrous. My truck had a bad radiator, so I'd drain it during the winter every night and put water in it during the day. John knew that, but one day he forgot and grabbed the pickup and took off and there was no water in it and it burned the pickup up.

Joe always accused me of getting out of the work by spending my time selling jobs, instead of mowing lawns, but we had to have the job orders or else there would have been no work. We were like a Laurel and Hardy show. The challenge of building the company was in going out and finding the customers, doing the work, coming home late at night, getting the bills out, sharpening the mower blades for the next morning, making repairs on the equipment, getting the vehicle gassed up early in the morning or late at night and, finally, loading the back of the truck with the grass we cut and then dumping it somewhere (not always at authorized sites).

Building a business from the ground up, even a business as basic as lawn care, requires a lot of strategic planning and I didn't have much experience to fall back on, except for what I learned from the jobs I held as a paperboy and in the food service and automotive industries. By the time Mom passed away, I already had six years experience working. I had to try to remember what I learned on those jobs to create a day-to-day knowledge for operating my own business. The greatest challenge was simply cash flow—having enough money to buy gas for the vehicle, having enough money to eat lunch, those types of things. That startup period was so humbling and so difficult.

Joe had asthma so bad that he wheezed and wheezed, and had to take his medicine constantly throughout the day. I had hay fever pretty bad, but it was nothing like what Joe went through, especially when we were out on a job. Breathing in the pollen and the grass particles made him miserable, which is why after about one year of our partnership I bought him out for four hundred dollars. He kept a new pickup that he had bought and I took the equipment. Joe was enrolled at the University of Nebraska in Omaha at that point and had his eye set on law school. Later, I joined him at college for a short while.

Around the time that I bought out Joe's interest in the business, Bob Smith gave me a riding lawn mower and I bought my first pickup truck for $575. The Omaha State Bank gave me a loan for the truck. "How are you going to pay for this?"

they asked, to which I answered, "I don't know, but I promise I will."

During that time, I made my first business purchase—a Toro lawn mower, a twenty-one-inch self-propelled model that lasted forever. This was my first encounter with a company that would stand by me for the next thirty-one years.

After I bought out Joe, I realized that I needed to multiply myself if I was ever going to get any-where. I took on two young men who were former neighbors of mine as employees. I focused on getting contracts. Meanwhile, other people started coming to me and asking for work. Within five years, I had more than fifty employees and had annual sales of about a half million dollars.

In 1976, two years after starting Green Star, I graduated from Westside High School. It was a big day in my life. I received two tassels—one that was red and black, the school colors, and another one that was red, white and blue, to celebrate America's bicentennial year. I still have those tas-sels. Needless to say, I was very proud when I took the tassels and the diploma home to show my foster parents, Mr. and Mrs. Bob Smith. Un-fortunately, my celebration was short-lived, be-cause the next day Bob kicked me out of his house, saying that it was time for me to be out on my own. I hated his guts for doing that to me, but I now understand that he did me a favor and I love him for that. He kicked me out of the nest so I could grow my wings and learn to fly.

I owe a lot to the Smiths. Each time Mom had a nervous breakdown, we were sent across the street to live with Bob and Sammy Smith, a married couple who had children of their own. Since they lived across the street, they witnessed almost everything that happened to us over the years, good and bad. Bob remembers the first time he met me:

> I was working on my car in the driveway, and this seven or eight-year-old from across the street comes over and his name is John. He asks questions and he isn't shy about it, either. I mean he wants to know everything. I'm trying to explain the basics of the internal combustion engine to him, but after about an hour of that he's starting to get on my nerves. I knew he was too young to understand, but he had just tons of questions and I hated not to answer them, so, finally, I say "I hear your mother calling you," and he says, "no, she's not." Of course, I insisted that she was. John takes off across the street, and I'm thinking he will probably get distracted when he gets home and forget to come back, because that's the way most children are, but his mind doesn't work that way Five minutes later he comes back, saying "She wasn't calling me!"

So he stays another half hour or so. He's just very curious. He had gone with his father to the gas station to get work done on the family car, but no one there answered his questions and I guess he just figured that I would.

I met Bob's wife Sammy much the same way. I just sort of appeared in her kitchen one day. She was cooking or doing work of some kind and I just walked in and sat down at the kitchen table. That wasn't a very childlike thing to do, and I think it surprised her that this little boy from across the street that she didn't know very well at all, wanted to have a conversation with her at her kitchen table. Grownups keep telling children to be a "big boy" or a "big girl," but when children do that, it always seems to unnerve them and make them uncomfortable. At that point in my life, I was an old man in a little boy's body, because of all the craziness and troubles that I had seen in my life.

I counted on people like Bob and Sammy Smith to keep me grounded. I remember one day when I was having a hard time with the little girl who lived next door. Every time I went outside to play, she made it a point to join me, but she wasn't as interested in playing as she was in picking on me. That little girl just seemed duty bound to pick a fight with me every time we made eye contact.

Once, while Bob Smith was watching from across the street, she started hitting me, slapping me, clawing at me like some kind of a wild cat. I took as much as I could and then I hit her back, which sent her running back into her house in tears. About that time, I heard Bob Smith's authoritative voice: "Johnny!" I knew I was in trouble, just by the determined way he walked across the street over to where I was standing. "Sit down a minute, buddy," he says. "I want to talk to you."

"Okay."

"John, there's one thing that you cannot do in your lifetime," he said. "You cannot whip a girl, not ever again. You can't do that. Men don't do that."

I knew that wasn't true because I had seen Dad whip Mom many times, but there was something about the way he said that that made me want to believe that it was wrong. I could tell by looking at Bob Smith, by the expression on his face, that he would rather die than ever hit a girl and it made me want to be just like him.

I don't know if it was Mr. Smith's influence, or the violence I saw in my family, but from a very young age I decided I was a lover, not a fighter. The only real, knock-down, drag-out fight I ever had left me in a shambles. While I was in junior high school, Mark Bro, a fellow student, challenged me and my buddy, Don Reagan, to fight each other. We told him we weren't interested in fighting. He said that if we didn't fight, he was going to kick the crap out of both of us.

Getting Started

So, we fought one day after school. Because I had heard people say that Don had a bad knee, I kicked him there several times and watched him drop to the ground. By then, I was crying and I picked him up and he started crying, and I made up my mind then and there never to get into another fight. Later, I learned karate and wrestled in high school, but I never again got into a fight.

That first summer after graduation is mostly a blur now, and I don't remember much about it, except that I worked very hard to raise money so that I could attend the University of Nebraska in Omaha that fall. Not long after I started school, I met an older woman—let's just call her Mrs. Robinson. She had three children and was in the process of getting a divorce from a well-known Omahan.

She took me home one day for coffee and introduced me to her friends. We hit it off right away, so she made me an offer that I couldn't refuse: If I would agree to help her out around the house, she would let me live in her basement, free of charge. By "helping her out around the house," I assumed she meant she wanted me to keep her lawn mowed and make repairs about the house.

Mrs. Robinson was a beautiful woman—about five-seven, with silky black hair and a great figure—and I felt very fortunate that a thirty-eight-year-old woman with so much going for her would invite me into her life. As you may have guessed, she wanted more from me than good lawn care. It was like something out of that 1967 Dustin Hoffman movie *The Graduate*. Even today, I can't hear that Simon and Garfunkel song, "Mrs. Robinson," without thinking about her.

We were discreet about it so the kids wouldn't know, but it went on for a long time, about six months. She was really good for me and I think I was really good for her, because she had just gone through this divorce and was trying to find out if she was still attractive. All through that time I kept in touch with Dad, and with Mom's brother Cliff Williamson, who had moved to New York. When I told him about Mrs. Robinson, he invited me to visit him in New York—and he sent me two tickets, one for me and the other for Mrs. Robinson. Uncle Cliff, who was single and wealthy, was quite taken with Mrs. Robinson and romanced her the entire two weeks we were there. I told him I needed money for college. He loaned me $385 and charged me interest for the loan. He obviously got a lot more out of the visit than I did.

Before Mrs. Robinson and I left, we all went out to a nice restaurant. At some point, Uncle Cliff and I went to the restroom together and it was there, in the restroom, that he told me that my dad was not my biological father. "You don't need to worry about helping your dad anymore," he said, his voice slurred by alcohol.

"What do you mean? He's my dad."

"You don't need to help that bastard anymore. He's not your father. In fact, you are a bastard. You don't even know who your real dad is. John Hoich is not your dad."

"Yes, he is!"

"No, he's not. Go see your Aunt Marge. She'll tell you."

I was stunned. Why had everyone kept that a secret from me for all these years? Was it even true? Or was Uncle Cliff simply rattling my cage? As soon as we returned to the table, I told Mrs. Robinson what Uncle Cliff had told me. She seemed surprised—and then she didn't seem surprised. Perhaps he had shared that secret with her during one of their intimate moments.

Not long after we returned to Omaha, I got in touch with Aunt Marge and asked her to tell me the truth. That's when I found out that Mom had asked her sisters and brothers to keep it a secret forever. If Uncle Cliff had not had too much too drink that night, I might still not know the truth about my birth. Of course, I immediately confronted Dad with that information. He got angry and said that Mom's sisters and brothers didn't know the truth and were saying that to get back at him for some reason.

By the time Dad met my mom, he already had lived a full life. He was an athlete of athletes—a pole-vaulter, a diver, a gymnast, and a professional wrestler. He was only five-feet-six inches, but he weighed 260 pounds and had a stocky build. It was while he was working as a wrestler that he met Frank Faketty, the son of an Omaha packinghouse "hog sticker." Before becoming a famous wrestler named Karl Von Hess, Frank was a 1941 Golden Gloves champion who worked as a lifeguard at a local swimming pool at Morton Park, where they sometimes called him Tarzan because of his muscular build.

Perhaps it was because of his nickname that Frank became a Navy frogman and demolitions expert in the South Pacific during World War II. In 1943, before being recruited for the elite underwater demolition team, he was awarded a Navy commendation for "courageous performance" while under enemy attack.

It was when Frank returned to Omaha after the war that he decided to become a professional wrestler. He went by various names—Tarzan,

Frank Congo of the Panama Canal, and Mara Duba the South American Assassin—but it took several years of hard living on the road before he found an identity that enabled him to stand out from the other wrestlers on the circuit. Although he was a genuine war hero, he adopted the persona of a violent, half-crazed German Nazi named Karl Von Hess, complete with a monocle, a goatee, and an upturned moustache that made him look like the stereotypical Nazi.

Almost overnight, Von Hess became a national sensation as he snarled and grunted his way to the top, some years earning more than $150,000, which was very good money in the late 1940s and early 1950s. He was so convincing as a villain—he never spoke in public, so as not to betray his Nebraska upbringing—that he was investigated by the FBI as a possible fugitive war criminal. For a time, he was the most hated villain in professional wrestling, so much so that he sustained more injuries from irate fans than from his challengers in the ring. By the time he called it quits in 1967 to operate a trailer park near Atlantic City, New Jersey, he had more than three hundred stitches on his body, most of them from "fans" with broken bottles or knives.

Dad and Frank met at Morton Park while they both were in their teens (Frank was three years older) and became lifelong friends. In fact, the year that Dad died, Frank lost his son, a loss that perhaps influenced his decision to legally adopt me.

Dad never made it as a big-time wrestler, so it was a good thing that he had an inheritance to fall back on. In 1949, his brother was killed in an automobile accident on his way to the dog tracks and left him with two bars and a half million dollars in cash. It was a fortuitous event for my dad because he didn't really have a direction in his life. He had a loud and gregarious personality, and the kind of appearance—he always laughed a lot and had this big, round face that reminded me of actor Jackie Gleason—that perfectly fit the image of a bar owner. Sometimes I think I must have modeled my extroverted approach to life on Dad's personality. We are a lot alike in the way that we approach life.

Dad's problem at the time that Mom showed up in Council Bluffs was that he was going through a contentious divorce. His wife left him to go to Chicago to start a new life and she left him with their three daughters—Jeannie, DeeDee and Linda—until she could send for them. He must have sounded pretty desperate when he went into the Birdcage Lounge and talked to Aunt Marge about his problems, because it gave her the idea that the solution to everyone's problems would be for him to take Mom and myself into his home so that she could help him with his daughters. He swore that there'd be no funny business. All he wanted was someone to help out with the kids.

Aunt Marge had no idea that his wife had left him because he abused her and inflicted mental torture on his daughters, so when she called Mom and asked her to drop by the lounge to meet him, it was done with the best of motives. In fact, she was pretty proud of herself for solving two desperate people's problems with very little effort. Although he was about fifteen years older than Mom, John George Hoich was a respected businessman, the father of three daughters— what could possibly go wrong? It looked like a good deal for everyone involved.

I was less than six months old when we moved into the home with John George Hoich and his three daughters. We weren't there long, maybe six months, before his wife returned and took their daughters back with her, which left Mom and me alone in the house with him. I don't think his daughters ever saw him again, but by then he had pretty much made up his mind to start a new family with my mom. My sister Susan was born on February 13, 1960, a little more than a year after the girls left the house. They didn't get married when Susan was born, and I don't know whether that was her idea or his idea, or whether his divorce had not gone through.

After Susan was born, it seemed like all that Mom and Dad did for the next seven years was have more children. Catherine was born on March 13, 1962; Donna was born on March 19, 1963; Angela was born on September 4, 1964; and Michael was born on February 5, 1968. No one ever explained to me that they were my half-siblings, but I remember asking, at a very young age, why Dad was named John George Hoich and I was named John Lee Hoich. Their response was always, "Well, we just named you that way." I don't know if they ever planned to tell me the truth. Do parents really believe that they can keep secrets like that from children, or do they hope that they will be dead and gone when the child finds out so that they will never have to explain it?

I was very young when I realized that Dad was physically abusive to my mom on a regular basis. He had a real bad drinking problem. Later, I found out that he drank twenty-seven screwdrivers a day, but then I didn't know enough about alcohol to understand the way it affected him when he was at home.

Mom was always crying. It was hard on her, the way Dad treated her, and most of the time she was always overwhelmed. Always hurting, always filled with pain. I hugged my mom a lot. I was the father, the husband, the son. I was everything to her. Even today, I can reach back in my memory and hear my little boy's voice: "What's wrong, Mom? I'll take care of you." Even then, I was a caretaker.

I hardly ever saw Mom and Dad being affectionate to one another, except when they were posing for pictures. When he came in from work, he was usually drunk. He would see visions and all that stuff. He was always saying, "You kids be quiet, I've got work to do." He was always too busy for us, or too drunk. He smoked three packs of cigarettes a day, Old Golds—and he just sat there in his chair, drunk, allowing the cigarette ashes to fall to the floor and burn the carpet. There were hundreds of cigarette burns around his chair. It was terrible.

One incident in particular had a profound impact on me. To this day, I still have nightmares about it. One night Dad came home late, around 11 o'clock. He was drunk, as usual, and when he got out of the automobile, he swayed all the way to the door, a case of soda pop perched precariously in his arms. Right before he reached the door, he tripped over my bicycle and dropped the soda pop, breaking all of the bottles.

Furious at me for leaving my bicycle where he could stumble over it, he stormed into the house, awakened me, and dragged me by the hair into the kitchen, where he grabbed a steak knife, and then dragged me outside and showed me the soda pop that he dropped because of my bike. He said he was going to teach me a lesson so that I would never do it again. He smacked me a few times and then grabbed me by the hair again and dragged me over to the bicycle and threw me down to the ground.

"This is the lesson you are going to learn!" he screamed.

Then he took the steak knife and chopped up the bicycle tires. For years, I could remember the air rushing out of those tires. If I had to identify one thing in my childhood as a contributor to my distrust of adults, it would be the bicycle incident.

Not all my memories of Dad are like that, though. Once he played on the baseball team with me, and he volunteered to be an assistant coach for a few games. He had his moments when he went through the motions of being a father. I also remember him taking me fishing at Grover Street Lake, which was a bullhead fishing spot next to a neighborhood bar. After a few minutes, he'd leave me and go off. Every time I caught a fish, I'd run it in to him at the bar, where he was usually surrounded by a bunch of drunks.

"Daddy, look, I caught another bullhead!"

"Oh, my boy caught a fish! Go get another one, kid.!"

There was nothing in the world I wanted more than to please him and catching those fish was my way of doing that, except he never gave me credit for catching the fish. When he bragged to his friends, it was *his boy* who caught the fish, as if it was really him who caught the fish through his son, like I was just something he owned, like the fishing tackle. Looking back, I wonder why it was so hard for him to ever give me credit for anything. It was like it was a competition between us and he always had to win.

The greatest memories I have from early childhood are about what happened on Sunday nights after our baths. Mom laid each of us on her lap, and took lotion and Q-Tips and cleaned out our ears. She'd say, "There's a big potato, I'll get it!"

Those times were when I felt the most secure, when I was on my mom's lap, with her cleaning out my ears and telling me how many potatoes were growing in there. Those were probably the funniest, most loving times in my life. It made me feel calm and secure. During those times, she would always give me some words of wisdom. A lot of those things I carry with me today. One of them was, "Honey, if you don't ask questions you will never know the answers." She did her best for a wife who was abused as much as she was, and when I look back at her now, it is with total amazement.

A little more than a year after they got married, Dad legally adopted me as his son, although no one told me that at the time. It was all pretty hush-hush.

Judging by the timing of it, I think it probably had more to do with legally changing my name before I started to school so that teachers would not be asking a lot of embarrassing questions.

The first school that I went to was Paddock Road Elementary School. It was only three blocks from our home where I lived from the time I was two until I was sixteen. That school seemed huge to me at the time. My first teacher was Mrs. Kay Kerwin Ogle, a twenty-something woman, not very tall, with blondish brown hair. She made me feel warm all over. She made me feel loved. I'd hold a book and not only did she look at the book with me, she explained it to me. She had a depth of caring that I had never before experienced. One day I went to school, crying, upset over something that Dad had done, and she said, "It's OK, honey. Everything will be fine."

The school had lots of halls, which are always intriguing to small children. Hallways imply direction and security, and if you are a child, you follow them faithfully because you somehow know that they are there for your protection. If only life had hallways that could safely see you through to the end of your journey.

Paddock Elementary had a big old gym where tables could be pulled out of the walls so that the children could eat lunch there everyday. From the time I was in third grade or so, I always took the dust mop and mopped the floor after the kids ate and then again at the end of the day. I did that because Ernie the maintenance man gave me an extra piece of cake and a little carton of milk to help him clean the gym. I didn't consider it work. I loved cake and helping with the floor made me feel important. Besides, Ernie was my buddy and I wanted to help him out.

Of course, a school is just a building. It's the teachers that make it special. I knew when I went to school each day that I would receive a lot of compassion and understanding. Mrs. Ogle knew that I had a bad relationship at home with my father, but a great relationship with my mother, and when I went to school with bruises, she knew that he had beat me. I felt worthy because of her attention and she loved me at a time when I needed love more than anything else.

I guess you could say that the school was my first real home, in the sense that a child thinks of home as the place where he is the safest. I never felt safe at home, only at school. I have no memory of the first house that Mom and I lived in, but the second house, where we lived for six months, I do recall, mainly because the next-door neighbors were the Volceks, a family that meant a lot to me. Jean Volcek, whom I called Aunt Jean all my life, always reminded me that was where I lived when I was born. It was a small, three-bedroom house that probably had less than eight hundred square feet.

The third house was larger, probably a thousand square feet. It had a beautiful patio with a brick bar-b-que that my dad built himself. He built it so that there was a place for plants in the center and a metal awning over the grill and smoker. Inside, the house had three bedrooms and a basement that Dad finished off with nice paneling. I never helped him with the work because he wouldn't let me. He was the sort of person who had to do everything himself. Mom loved that house and felt happy there.

But enough reminiscing. To get back to my story—after moving out of Mrs. Robinson's home, I had nowhere to live, so I went to Mom's attorney, Michael Dugan, and asked him to petition the court to get me the $3,300 from the sale of our family home prior to my twenty-first birthday. He was successful doing that, and I took $1,500 and purchased a truck for my lawn-care business and I took $1,500 and used it as a down payment to purchase a $6,500 house. P. J. Morgan's father, Paul Morgan, sold it to me and convinced me that real estate would be a good investment for me. It was my first investment of any kind. (P.J. later became mayor of Omaha.)

The house needed lots of repairs, so I made a deal with my Pi Kappa Alpha fraternity brothers at the University of Nebraska at Omaha that if they helped me with the repairs they could use the house on weekends for parties. Then I made a deal with a carpet layer at this apartment complex where I mowed the lawn to give me the good used carpet that he tore out. I took that used carpet, which still looked pretty good to me, and carpeted the entire house. I lived there for two years while I fixed it up and then I sold it for $13,500 to a woman who made her monthly mortgage payments directly to me.

Meanwhile, I moved into the Boardwalk Apartments with a friend named Scott Cernick (who become a lifelong friend) and lived there for a couple of years while I pursued my studies at the University of Nebraska at Omaha. I'm afraid that I was not a very good student. I like to tease Joe Smith that we were both on a dean's list. He was cited as a top scholar at the Creighton University Law School. I, on the other hand, was on a different sort of list—a list of those who did not have a 2.0 grade point average at the end of their second year. Consequently, I did not continue into a third year of college. However, for the last eight years, I have served on the UNO College of

Business Advisory Board and endowed a college professorship in real estate.

While I was in college, the woman who bought my house fell so far behind in her payments that I had to foreclose on her. That made her so angry that she burned the house to the ground. She went to jail, but I collected the full value of the house—$13,500—from the insurance and I took $10,000 of that money and used it as a down payment to build a $90,000 duplex. I lived in one side, rented out the other side and used the garage as an office for my lawn care business. I still own it and today it is worth about $300,000.

Dad found out that he had cirrhosis of the liver not long after Mom died, but it took him a long time to die. During that time, I did everything that I could to get closer to him. I wanted to understand him. Long before he was confined to a bed, while he was still going to work, I hung out with him at his bars, always asking him questions about why he did the things that he did to our family.

Just prior to the end, while he was lying on his deathbed, I visited him and told him there was something I needed to tell him.

"What?" he asked.

"My mom's brother, Uncle Cliff, told me that you weren't my dad."

"That's baloney. I don't know why anyone would say something like that."

Our conversation went back and forth like that over many visits. I don't know why he was so resistant to telling me the truth. Perhaps he thought that if he told me the truth I would desert him in his final days. Perhaps he didn't fully understand the truth. It's possible that the truth came to him in bits and pieces that he had to assemble like a model airplane, fitting one piece into another, until he could see the final shape of what his memory was building. That process went on for weeks and weeks, until, finally, he broke down and started crying, telling me that he had met my mom when she was pregnant.

"You didn't have a dad," he said, "so I became your dad, and your mom and I made a decision never to tell nobody. The bottom line is that when you were about five years old, I adopted you. Nobody ever knew any better."

Truth is a funny thing. Before he admitted that he wasn't my father, I told him he couldn't stand the truth, but when he finally faced it and told me what I wanted to know, I discovered that I couldn't stand the truth. There was just something about him saying it after all those years that hit me pretty hard. For days afterward, I walked around feeling sorry for myself, finally understanding that when Dad called me a worthless little bastard throughout my childhood, he was speaking half the truth. I *was* a bastard child.

Dad died on July 3, 1979. I was twenty-one years old. Susan was nineteen. Donna was sixteen. Cathy was seventeen. Angela was fifteen. And Michael was eleven. Most people make it into their fifties or sixties before they lose both parents, but we never made it into adulthood as a family. The question we kept asking was, Why us? What did we do to deserve this? It seemed so unfair.

Not long after Dad died, I asked the University of Nebraska for advice on receiving a Social Security survivor's benefit from his account. The first step was to obtain a copy of his death certificate, a matter I thought would be routine. I should have known better. Nothing in my life has ever been routine. Before they would issue me my dad's death certificate, they requested my birth certificate. That's when I realized that I didn't have a birth certificate.

When I applied for a copy of my birth certificate, I learned that I had two certificates—one in Des Moines, Iowa, that listed my father as John Lee Moreno, and the other in Nebraska, that listed me as the adopted son of John Hoich. Since he never adopted me in Iowa, my birth certificate there listed my last name as Moreno. I was surprised to learn that Dad met Mom after she gave birth to me, not while she was pregnant, as he said—and I was surprised to learn that it took him five years to adopt me.

After I got it all straightened out, I was able to receive money from Social Security for my college expenses. In a way, John Hoich ended up helping me with my education, and for that I have to give him some credit, though it was never his intention for that to happen. Thanks to him, I received my two-year associate degree at UNO.

The Hoich Logo and Ginger

3

Becoming a Millionaire

Hoich Enterprises, Inc., founded in 1979, seemed headed for great things. I had fifty employees and the company was grossing a half million dollars a year. Unfortunately, despite those numbers, the company was barely breaking even. I doubt I would have even been able to break even had it not been for Ada and Joe McDermott, owners of Loveland Lawns, a lawn products supply company that began as a lawn maintenance business and expanded into a multi-million dollar company.

I started buying products from Joe and Ada when I first started my business. I bought fertilizer from them. I bought seed from them. I bought trees from them and then sold them to my customers. They never loaned me money, but they carried me on credit longer than my mom did (she only carried me nine months).

Joe and Ada had a very paternal air about them, and whenever we were at functions together I always introduced them as Mom and Pop. Says Joe: "There's a lot to love about him," to which Ada adds, "He's so enthusiastic all the time. He doesn't look on the downside. He looks on the bright side, and he finds all the good there is to find and makes the most of it."

Bless Ada's heart for recognizing that quality in me, but I have to admit I sometimes get a little too enthusiastic. In 1979, I went into a nursery to buy a bush and ended up talking to the owner who told me that his business problems were so severe that he planned to file for bankruptcy protection within a week or so. What happened next is shocking in retrospect, but you have to remember that I was twenty-one years of age, I had a net worth of over three hundred thousand dollars, and I had never experienced a business setback.

The more I talked to the owner, the more convinced I became that if I were to purchase his nursery I would not only save his life, I would expand my business and elevate my operations to a higher level of profit. Before leaving the nursery that day I agreed to buy it. About a month later, I took over the business, including a significant portion of the owner's debt. He stayed on for a while to show me the ropes of the nursery business, but as far as my education about the business was concerned, it was a case of too little, too late. I should have stayed in the lawn mowing business. I had no idea what I was doing. I was cocky. I was arrogant. I thought I was infallible.

I struggled with the nursery for nearly three years. Then one day I awoke and realized that I was in deep trouble. When I purchased the business, the interest rates were at twelve percent—high, but manageable—but by 1982 they had jumped to twenty-two percent, the highest rate of interest in this country's history. I had nowhere to go but down. I set up an appointment for March 20, 1982, with my attorneys so that I could file the necessary papers for bankruptcy, convinced that I had no other choice.

The day before that scheduled appointment, I drove to Grant, Nebraska, to attend my sister Donna's wedding. She had met a man named Bruce that she wanted to spend the rest of her life with (in this case "life" amounted to only twenty-three years; they were divorced in 2005). At that point, my assets consisted of the duplex, a pickup truck and a boat that was worth about $3,500. I sold the boat to pay for some of Donna's wedding expenses. Recalls Donna:

> He bought my wedding dress and my wedding shoes. It has been in my heart for so long that he wanted to do that for me at a time that he was facing bankruptcy. I don't know how I would have made it through life

without John's knowledge of things, from business to just needing my brother to talk to. That man has a heart bigger than Texas. It makes me cry sometimes to think that this man, who has helped so many out of the goodness of his heart, has been treated really badly in life. He's so forgiving, so forgiving.

After the wedding, I drove home, thinking that my life was over. I prayed for guidance on how to solve my problems. I just asked for His help and His guiding light in finding a way out of bankruptcy. When I got home I went to sleep, still praying for a way out of what I felt was certain destruction. The next morning I got up and went to the lawyer's office. They had all the papers lined up on the table for me to sign. I looked at those papers and started crying.

The lawyer tried to comfort me. "Bankruptcy is like Rolaids—it's instant relief," explained the lawyer. "You won't even know it and seven years from now you'll still be under thirty. Most people that go bankrupt are fifty, sixty, and they can't start over again. It's no big deal. That's what bankruptcy was invented for, situation like yours."

I started signing the paper, but I couldn't get past "John." My hand froze on the page. To my lawyer's surprise, I put the pen down and said, "I'm sorry I got myself into this, but I did—and I'm the only one who can get me out of this."

Let me tell you, 1982 was the equivalent of a Harvard education for me. My feathers got trimmed way back. I learned that cockiness is not the way to run a business. I thought I was infallible and I found out that no one is infallible. Besides that, I was simply in over my head. I didn't know what I was doing. The key to success is to stay in what you know. I blew that rule and probably deserved the hell I went through.

After I left the lawyer's office, I went to see two friends that were in the lawn business. Actually, I had known one of them for a long time. When I started up my lawn business at the age of sixteen, I went to him and asked for his advice since he already had a lawn business in operation. I can still remember the day we sat at his kitchen table and he said, "You're going to need a rake, you'll need your mom's lawn mower, you'll need some gas cans, and you'll need a Weed Eater." I still have that original list of things I would need.

Since I was a friend of one of them, I felt compelled to be the other's friend as well. That day I met with them after walking away from the bankruptcy papers, I told them: "I have half a million dollars worth of mowing accounts. Spring is just around the corner. All I need is equipment. The contracts are all signed. If you'll loan me the money or help me get a loan for the equipment, I can work myself out of this debt, and I'll give you two-thirds of the profit."

To my surprise, they agreed to do it. We went to the bank that day and I set up shop in the rear of their business. We called ourselves Special Mowing, Inc. Two amazing things happened that day: First, they were an answer to a prayer, and second, I sold my building, which enabled me to pay off the mortgage, pay off the bank, settle on the interest, and pay the late fees. Then I went to all my creditors and asked them to give me two to three years to pay them completely off, and almost all of them settled or waived the interest and I paid them all off over the next four years.

Working with my new partners was an education unto itself. They had been partners for so long that they had worked out "good cop, bad cop" roles. Most days my old friend played the bad cop and the other one played the good cop; but sometimes they switched roles, which could be very confusing. I just went with the flow.

Before long, my business grew past theirs, and I was just working out of the room in the back of their shop. Looking back, I think my success bothered them. One day, one of them walked into my office and spit a big wad of chewing tobacco on the floor.

"I put a spit can there for you to spit in, not on the floor."

"This is my building, this is my floor, and I'll spit where I want to."

Then he spit again.

"Don't do that again," I said.

"What are you going to do about it? Kick my ass?"

"No, I don't fight. But just don't do it again."

He spit on the floor again, obviously looking for a fight.

That made me so angry that I told him I wanted to move out of the building.

"Why don't you just do that?"

After four years with them, I bought them out.

That run-in was the best thing that could have happened to me because it gave me the confidence to go out on my own again. This time, I put the cockiness aside and proceeded with common sense, direction, humbleness, and, perhaps most important of all, the power of prayer. I trusted God to lead me in the right direction and I trusted my God-given intuition to keep me out of trouble. People should listen to their intuition. It will pay off every time. It's there for a reason. Don't ever forget that.

After I terminated that partnership, my top priority was simply learning from my mistakes and getting back on my feet again with my own company. Since lawn maintenance is a seasonal business, my challenge, as a businessman, was to maximize my efforts during the growing season and to explore new avenues of profit during the off-season.

As this point in life, I had learned several important lessons:

To balance predictable debt with profit expansion

To diversify whenever possible

To partner up with individuals with track records for success

Now that I was out on my own again, I was determined never to fail again. It was at that point that I got into the lawn sprinkler business. In the mid-1980s, sprinklers were a luxury, not a necessity, so they were a tough sell at first. I worked a lot of home shows and sold my heart out. My line was: "Throw that hose away—buy a sprinkler today."

Once people realized how easy it was to replace hoses with sprinklers—and how it would save them time and enhance the appearance of their property—they embraced the concept with great enthusiasm. We sold so many Toro sprinkler systems that we were able to form a separate corporation named Hoich Irrigation, Inc.

Of course, I knew nothing about actually installing underground lawn sprinklers. In this case, diversification meant partnering up with someone who had experience in that specialized area. Luckily for me, I found a partner who had many years experience installing underground sprinklers and was looking for entrepreneurship opportunities. Since he and I had known each other for about ten years, we felt comfortable becoming partners in Hoich Irrigation, Inc.

In the early 1980s, I had met a successful Kansas City real estate investor named Doug Pugh through his property manager, Mary Fitzpatrick, when I submitted a proposal to mow the grass at four of their commercial properties in Omaha. They hired me and I serviced those properties for nearly a decade.

Only a year or two into the contract, Doug left the company and Mary stayed on as the property manager, but I stayed in touch with Doug and built a social as well as a business relationship with him.

I was already interested in real estate when I met Doug and Mary, and they convinced me that it was something that I should pursue. The major differences between investing in a service industry, like lawn maintenance, and in real estate are risk and profit margin. If I invest a half million dollars in lawn equipment, I have to work that equipment everyday if I expect to make a profit— and the entire time that I am doing that, the equipment is depreciating. If you invest in real estate, the amount of time you invest in securing renters or maintaining the property is only a fraction of what the lawn business requires—and, best of all, your investment grows in value instead of depreciating.

In 1987, I purchased my first eighty acres that once had been used as a ranch for thoroughbred horses. Although I bought the land to house the new corporate headquarters for Hoich Enterprises, one of the first things I did was to get a horse and a dog. One thing led to another, and before I knew what had happened, I had over two hundred exotic animals on the property—enough to establish a petting zoo.

Over the next few years, more than ten thousand children visited the petting zoo, which by then was stocked with llamas, pot-bellied pigs, a zebra, a mouflon ram and a black and white royal palm turkey, to name a few.

In the beginning, the idea was simply to build a petting zoo for my family, but once people in the community found out about it, everyone wanted to bring their children out for a visit. And who could blame them? The concept snowballed and before we knew it we had over two hundred exotic animals on display for an unending stream of children and parents. We opened the doors to countless fundraisers for groups such as the Boy Scouts, Girl Scouts, Cub Scouts, softball teams, high schools, and political parties. More than ten thousand children have visited the petting zoo. It's something I'm very proud of.

In 1992, I entered into a real estate partnership with Jerry Slusky and Steve Durham. We purchased a 144-unit apartment complex, which was really the launching pad to my first big real estate ventures. Steve ended up selling out to me and moving to Dallas, Texas, to pursue other interests, but Jerry hung in there with me and we ended up building a strong partnership that continues to this day. I jokingly tell him that instead of "Starsky & Hutch," we became "Slusky & Hoich."

So, by the early 1990s, I was involved in both lawn care and real estate. But those weren't my only business ventures. In the mid-1980s, Dr. John Allely and I had commissioned Michael Anthony Ricker, a Colorado artist who is considered one of the most accomplished pewter sculptors in the world, to make a sculpture of a humanitarian reaching out to the youth of the world. Several sculptures by Ricker were sold to Rotarians. More than one hundred thousand dollars was raised and the profits were given to Rotary International to help eradicate polio in parts of the world where it was still active.

Dr. John Allely, a very prominent Nebraska anesthesiologist, owned a store in Omaha that featured Ricker's work. I considered Dr. Allely a mentor and he taught me much about common sense and about simplifying my adversities. Each time I visited Dr. Allely, I always left with great ideas that I thought were mine—and only in retrospect did I realize that they were really his ideas. He had a knack for making people feel special.

Most of the time, his ideas were stellar. He once encouraged me to collect Ricker's work as an investment. As an artist, Ricker had a wonderful reputation. He was one of the most collected artists in the world, with special commissions from Presidents Reagan and Ford, and from Pope

John Paul II. In 1985, he made a piece named after me called "Johnny Lee—The American Cowboy." It depicted a cowboy shaving while looking into a mirror in a cactus.

Over the years, I've collected more than a half million dollars worth of Ricker's pewter sculptures. I have them all over my house and in my rental properties. He became a good friend and I love him dearly. We sometimes played golf with John Ashton, an actor who's played in several movies, including Beverly Hills Cop. Sadly, Ricker had a heart attack and passed away in January 2006 while I was out of the country. I wrote a eulogy and sent it to John who read it at Ricker's funeral. I think of Michael Ricker every day and will miss him forever.

Collecting Ricker's work was a wonderful idea, and I thank Dr. Allely for that. It's what I did with that idea that caused me grief.

I opened a retail store with another Ricker collector. We figured we would make a nice profit selling Ricker's work. It didn't turn out that way. We lost a few hundred thousand dollars in the venture. Ricker's work is not cheap and we quickly learned that selling expensive sculptures was not easy. It was a dumb mistake because I would have been better off just buying more sculptures instead of opening up a store and trying to run it along with everything else I was doing.

I didn't stay in my own game. Warren Buffett, the Omaha Oracle, says, "Invest in what you know and understand." I thought the store would be a good opportunity and I quickly learned I didn't know Jack about retail, advertising, or how to market retail items. It was a good example of taking on too much in an area in which I had no expertise. I can market services with the best of them, but retail sales are a different game. The mistake I made is that I fell in love with a hobby and tried to make it more than that. Today, I own more than a thousand Ricker sculptures, and they are making money for me by simply existing as works of art. In the art world, those who squirrel away prized possessions also are blessed.

Not long after I bought out my partners in Special Mowing, Inc., I bid on a commercial project and learned that mine was the only bid. Since the client needed a second bid in order to issue a contract, I asked my old partners to do me a favor and make a bid so that the client would have two bids on file and would be able to award me the contract. As it turned out, they backstabbed me by making a lower bid and taking the job away from me.

Then, in 1989, I bid on a mowing contract for Offutt Air Force Base. I won the bid, but a spokesperson for the base informed me that my bid was so low that, in the government's opinion, it was doubtful that I would be able deliver the services needed. She said, "I'd rather do you a favor and ask you to back out of your proposal and let us go to the next bidder that we feel is capable. That way, we'll be doing you a favor and you'll be doing the government a favor by not going broke while you are under contract. Why don't you just come back the next time it goes out for bid and maybe understand, between now and then, where you were too low and why you were too low and bid competitively next time around."

No one wants to hear something like that from a client, but I accepted the advice and backed out of the proposal. Two years later, the contractor was let go because he wasn't keeping up with the job and they changed the offer to best value instead of low price. This time I bid much higher because I had studied the situation and figured out what it would take to do the job. I put together a proposal and bid for the contract.

Meanwhile, I learned that my old partners in Special Mowing, Inc. were going to offer a bid as well. Even though I had been pretty upset with them, I still felt that we were friends.

One of my character "flaws," if you want to call it that, is that I am too forgiving. I forgive and forgive and forgive. So, I forgave the initial partnership breakup and the loss of a commerical account. When I found out that they were also bidding on the Offutt contract, I went to them a third time and said: "Look, I'm confident I'm going to win the Offutt Air Base contract without you, but if you want to be part of it, I would consider letting you be a part of the contract, but only if you let me run the business and you run the employees and the equipment."

"I'd love to," one partner said. And so he came into the company.

At the time, I told him that the offer was for him only. I didn't plan to include our previous partner in the deal. I told him: "I'm not going to do a third, third, and third because our past relationship did not work well, but I'll go fifty-fifty, and I want to be president of the company and I want to sign the checks." My feeling was that if you can't have majority control, the second best thing is to have equal control. He agreed to those terms, but then about a month later he returned and said that he had to let the other partner in on the deal. He said that he would give him half of his half. "That's your business," I told him, "but I'm not going to give up any of my ownership. I don't want to go back there. I don't want to go through what we went through all over again."

So that's how my old partners became partners again in a company named U.S. Grounds Maintenance. I had good reason to be angry with both of them, but I forgave them on two occasions, even though I probably shouldn't have. That's just the way I am. It was no surprise to me that we got the contract for Offutt Air Force Base, because I knew that we were the best company for the job and I knew that our price was fair.

We worked hard and four years into a five-year contract, we got renewed. I asked our contracting officer with the air base what it would take to grow our business and she showed me how to search for military procurements. We bid on more projects and won contracts for Columbus Air Force Base in Columbus, Mississippi; Warren Air Force Base in Cheyenne, Wyoming; Ellsworth Air Force Base in Rapid City, South Dakota; the Veterans Administration in Omaha; and Fort Benning in Columbus, Georgia, which is the largest acreage that we mow (with 8,000 acres). With all that work, our business grew to about six million dollars a year. We had it down to a science.

When Mom died, I swore to her that I'd become a millionaire by the time I was thirty— and I had done it!

Looking back, I realize that the major impetus for whatever success I've had in life and one of the reasons that I've always focused on the future has really been my fear of the past. I wanted to escape the world that I knew as a child. I wanted to escape the hurt and the pain of being brought up in a divorced family, an alcoholic family; a father who beat me from five to eleven pretty much every day, one way or another—either by beating me down mentally, or hitting me physically, or throwing my head against the drywall, or telling me I'd never amount to anything; a father who treated my mom terribly, physically, mentally, abusively, putting her down, calling her a worthless human being; a father who hit my sisters, beat my sisters, fondled my sisters, and did things that were just so abusive that it made the entire family stressed emotionally, physically, mentally. His alcoholism, with twenty-seven screwdrivers a day, his two to three packs of cigarettes a day (and even my mom smoked two packs a day) added to the stress. It was just a house filled with negativity from the alcohol to the smoking, to the yelling, to the cussing, to the

John and His Mother, 1958, Council Bluffs, Iowa

Brother Michael and John's Mother

John Hoich, Age Three

1968, Ten Years Old, Horse Camp. John is on the far left.

John's Mother, Becky

John's Mother (Becky), Michael Hoich (John's Brother),
and Angela Hoich (John's Sister), September 24, 1974
(The Night before John's Mother Died)

Joe Smith at John's First Apartment, 1977

Uncle Lewis Mitchell (Left) and John Hoich, Sr.
In front of Mitchell's Home in Esterville, Iowa

John and His Guitar, Age Eighteen

John L. Hoich and Michael Hoich,
Getting Ready for Angela's Wedding

Michael Hoich, Donna Hoich and John L. Hoich,
Ready for Angela's Wedding

John and Siblings With John's Father in VA Hospital before His Death, 1979

John and Brother Michael

Kirby Clarke, John's Friend since Childhood,
Purchased Hoich Enterprises Lawn Division

Rod Strong, First Employee, New Truck and Lawnmower, 1978

John and Mark Morgan, US Grounds Maintenance

Jim Peters, John, Mike Tipton, and John's Twin Sons, Jeremy and Justin at Mancusco Trade Show in Omaha

John's First Tractor Flail Mower for His First Large Commercial
Contract, Connectivity Solutions Factory

1980, John L. Hoich with His Walk-Behind Commercial Mower,
Mowing Chuck and Cyndee Lakin's Lawn

Twin Sons, Jeremy and Justin, 2004

John with Cub Scout Troop

John and Twin Sons, Jeremy and Justin

John L. Hoich in His Home Office

John and His First Horse, 1989

John G. Hoich (John's Father, Upper Left),
Gene Mahoney (Upper Right); Karl Von Hess (Lower Right);
Unknown (Lower Left)

Karl Von Hess, World Champion Wrestler

John L. Hoich and Joe M. Smith,
John's Best Friend Since 1968 (2000)

Cathy Hoich, Donna (Hoich) White, John L. Hoich, Susan Hoich,
Angela (Hoich) Leuschen at John's Wedding,
in the Garden at His Home, 1996

screaming, to the crying. And all those emotions consistently made me only want to do one thing and that was to succeed more. Why? I was weird. Some days I don't understand why I was weird, but it was a good weird, because instead of joining them, I fought to avoid their fate. I tried everything in the world to tell myself daily I would never be like that bastard. I would not grow up and ever hit a woman, and I didn't. I would never grow up and smoke and I didn't. And I would never grow up and do drugs, and I didn't. And I'd never grow up and have a big huge beer gut like my dad, and I don't—but I work at it every day. And I'd never grow up poor. Everything that they were, I didn't want. Everything that they had, I didn't want, because what they had was just nothing but hate and misery. All my life, I've worked to focus on positive attitudes and actions and to avoid negativity.

John's Brother, Michael

Family and Friends

David Janke

In the fall of 1985, after dissolving my partnership in Special Mowing, Inc., I moved into a new building and reestablished Hoich Enterprises, Incorporated. The building was owned by David Janke, who became a very good friend of mine. David had started his career as a plumber's assistant to his dad. One day he had a disagreement with his dad and started his own plumbing company. By the time I moved into his building, real estate had become his passion. For the four years that I leased space in that building, I didn't sleep because Dave kept me up all night. We'd work all day and then go out and party and play at night. I hardly drank because he did enough for the both of us. He had more rum and Cokes in a night than some folks have in a lifetime, but he always had fun cars for me to drive when I took him from bar to bar. He called me five times a day. "What are you doing?" he asked. Later, he would call and ask,

"What are you doing now?" And I would always answer, "I'm doing the same thing I was doing the last time you called, working as usual."

Dave taught me that you could play a lot and still be unhappy. He bought vehicle after vehicle, materialistic thing after materialistic thing. He had one of the biggest homes in Omaha, the same in Florida, the biggest yacht he could find, the nicest jewelry, everything. His wife, Chris, was pretty low key and didn't care about all that stuff. In the end, he learned that money can't buy the things we most need in life.

Dave was diagnosed as a manic depressive and fought depression all his life. I expressed my concern for his use of alcohol with his medication. One day he was driving a golf cart in his front yard when he slumped over and crashed into a tree. He died at the age of fifty of a massive heart attack. I'll always miss Dave. He did a lot of things right, and he did a lot of things wrong, but he taught me that money and hard living cannot buy a long, happy life, and that is something that I will never forget. I love him like a brother. I think the feeling was mutual; he honored me by being a groomsman at my wedding.

My Brother, Michael Hoich

In 1986, when I was twenty-eight, and my brother Michael was eighteen, he moved out of the Smith's home and into the duplex with me. The Smiths had adopted him (along with our sister Angela) several years earlier, thus changing his name to Scott Michael Smith; once he was living with me, he changed his name back to Michael Joseph Hoich. That meant a lot to me and I think he did it as much for me as for himself. At that point in my life, the Rotary Club had become very important to me and I was so pleased that Michael was awarded, on his own merits, the Rotary's Suburban Handicap scholarship.

I was so proud of him. I told him that I would help pay his college expenses, just as I had done with my sisters when they needed me. He accepted my help, but he insisted that we sign a note, an actual note, that he created for everything that I loaned him for college, so that when he graduated he would pay me back.

I certainly didn't need or ask for a note from my brother, but he was insistent that I not give him a free ride and I admired him for taking a business-like approach to his college education. I also bought him his first car, a purple junker that was so ugly—the car was his choice, not mine—that I nicknamed it the Pregnant Car (later the Smiths helped him get a sleek Monte Carlo that he was very proud of). I also purchased cars for my sisters; helping them with their first cars and assisting them with college expenses was a big deal for me and allowed me to fulfill the promise I made to Mom.

When the time came for Michael to choose a college, he decided on Northwest Missouri State in Maryville, Missouri, where he enrolled with a major in accounting. I missed not seeing him everyday, but he came home on weekends and during the summer recess. When he was home, he worked at one of the local movie theaters. He loved movies more than anyone I've ever known and I figured he would end up owning a movie theater later in life.

Michael and I were very different physically. He grew to be six feet tall and was very slender—and I'm neither of those things. He became like my son and my brother, and I was his brother and his dad. We were ten years apart, but he really helped me mature. As a result of spending so much time with my brother, I fell in love with him all over again. It was like a rebirth.

Everything went smoothly the first year, but then not long after he turned nineteen, we learned that he needed another heart surgery. So we had to raise some more money and we all had to prepare emotionally for this because it was a big, big thing for his sisters and me to go through another surgery. The last time I went through anything like this, Michael was six years old and I had lost my mom a month earlier. The last thing I wanted to do was to lose my brother. Mary McGrath, the *Omaha World-Herald* reporter who wrote about Michael's first surgery, did another story about his latest challenge. "When you consider all of the advances that have been made in the last twelve years," Michael told her, "I should be out of the hospital in no time."

When he had his first surgery, a plastic valve and tube were placed from one chamber of his heart into his lungs to bypass the narrow area he had been born with. Over time, the tube had narrowed to the point where he would suffer heart failure if it was not replaced. This time, doctors decided to use an artery and valve from a human donor. The surgery was done at the University of Nebraska Medical Center. It didn't go as well this time because the surgeon made a mistake and cut out some tissue that he shouldn't have.

Even so, doctors told Michael that his heart should be good for at least fifty years. Michael was fitted for a pacemaker and prescribed medication that he was told he would have to take for the rest of his life. Michael was so skinny that the pacemaker stuck out of his skin. It was really hard on him, but he didn't let it slow him down. He was brilliant and determined. He liked law and he got straight-A's in college, despite holding down a job as a security guard at the Kawasaki plant in Maryville, Missouri.

On October 17, 1989, two years after his surgery, Michael was starting his senior year in college and was working as a guard at the Kawasaki plant. That day, while he was at his guard post reading one of his school books, his heart went into defibrillation and he fell to the ground so hard that it cracked his watch. Despite rescue efforts that lasted an hour, he died of a massive heart attack.

I got the call that night at a friend's house and I just went into convulsions and collapsed. It was so hard on me. A few days before he died, he told me that he had given his girlfriend a ring and his letter jacket that he got in college. He was really happy about this girl and wanted me to meet her. He asked if he could borrow my limousine and take her out in it when they got to town Friday. Instead, we used the limo for his funeral. That was heartbreaking for me that he never got to take her for the limo ride. We did get to meet the young lady, and that was a big blessing for us.

Upon his death, I learned things about my brother that I did not know. Prior to his death, we had a fundraiser for his heart surgery and Takechi Jewelry auctioned off a beautiful, very expensive Seiko gold watch. The person who made the highest bid, Irv Holst, was the same person who gave the most money for Michael's first surgery, and he gave the watch to Michael as a gift. As the weeks went by, I noticed that Michael wasn't wearing the watch, so I asked him about it. He made up some excuse for not wearing it, and then a short time later I saw him with the watch.

As it turned out, Michael had given the original watch to a friend at college who didn't have a watch and was too poor to buy one for himself. Michael didn't want me to get upset with him for giving his watch away, so he purchased a new one on the installment plan. At the time of his death, he still owed a few more payments. When I found that out, I was devastated because he had told one of his sisters that he bought the watch because he didn't want me to get upset with him for giving the first watch away. I also learned that he wrote a check for seventy-eight dollars to the American Heart Association a few days before his death. What little money he had, he shared with others; he thought the donation to the AHA would help with research efforts to find a cure that would benefit others with conditions similar to his own.

After his funeral, I displayed the watch that he had bought and the bill that he had paid, and the payments he was making, and the note that he made me sign so that he could pay me back for any money that I gave him for college.

Michael was a greater man than I because he seemed to have his own mission in life. He was the last person that wanted to leave Earth, but now I know that he's in Heaven with Mom. My little brother was my hero.

After we buried Michael, I had a difficult time accepting that he was gone. I was only thirty-one, but I already had lost my mom, my dad and my brother. For the rest of October and then through November, I had a hard time keeping my head above water. I spoke to the pastor at my church, and he said: "You need to go run a mission for me. Be a leader. I want you to go in my place to Cité Solei in Port-au-Prince, Haiti, and help put on a Christmas celebration with two thousand orphans." I was shocked. I seldom left Nebraska, and I had never left the country, but I decided that, instead of feeling sorry for myself, I would go to Haiti and honor my brother by serving God.

Before leaving Omaha, we collected two thousand sacks from McDonald's Restaurants, two thousand coloring books and boxes of crayons from ShopKo, and five thousand dollars in contributions from my lawn customers. Then we went to Haiti and spent ten days at the orphanage with Pastor Al, who was in charge of operations there. Together, we put on a Christmas celebration for two thousand, under-nourished children. As part of the program, I sang a song with Daniel Alexis, one of the young men who went on the trip with us.

Not only did we put on a Christmas program, we painted the orphanage, inside and out. Of course, a building is just a building—the children were the reason for our trip. The children were beautiful. They gave me an entirely new perspective on life. In America we really have no idea what economic and social devastation is all about. We witnessed a lifestyle that would never have occurred to any of us.

When I returned to Omaha, I had a new vision of life. No longer did I feel sorry for myself over losing my brother. Instead, I looked at the lives of people who lost every day of their lives, with no hope for the future—and it made me determined to do more to help those in need. My favorite saying is "Do unto others as you would have them do unto you." It is a great saying to live your life by. If you have been successful in life, the best way to honor God is to pay it forward by helping the less fortunate.

Once I was back at work, I did two things—I hired Daniel Alexis as an intern in my company, and I helped him with school and other expenses, and I threw myself back into the day-to-day operation of my business. The more trauma I encounter in my personal life, the harder I work to escape from that trauma. Other people with that type of personality often escape through alcohol or drugs or domestic violence or whatever. I escape by throwing myself into my work. Oddly, the more pain I encounter in my personal life, the harder I work—and the more money I make. For me, the byproduct of adversity is financial success.

My Biological Father

Ever since I learned that John Hoich was not my biological father, I have felt compelled to locate the man who impregnated my mom and then abandoned her and me to a lifetime of uncertainty and emotional pain. Right now, I don't know what kind of a man he is. He left my mom pregnant, so maybe he wasn't such a good guy, but I'd sure like to find him. Maybe he had good reasons for doing what he did.

The name on my birth certificate is John Lee Moreno. My brother and sisters all told me that Mom told them that John Lee Moreno was Italian, but the spelling is Spanish, so I don't know if Mom knew for a fact that he was Italian, or simply assumed that he was because of the way his name sounded.

In 1990, I got serious about finding my dad. I wrote the Navy. I hired people to do computer searches for either John Lee Marino or John Lee Moreno. I located one man in California who looked promising. His name was John Luna Moreno and he was Spanish, and I thought for sure that he was going to be my dad, even though everyone had always told me that my biological father was of Italian descent. He wasn't my father, as it turned out; DNA testing on him proved negative.

On February 8, 1990, I wrote a letter to my biological father. I have held onto that letter for more than a decade and a half, hoping that I would someday have reason to mail it—that I would have an address. There is not a day that goes by that I don't think about my biological dad. IS THERE ANYONE OUT THERE?

JOHN'S LETTER TO HIS FATHER

Dear Mr. John Lee Moreno:

Here's hoping this letter finds you. I am in great need to find you, just to know who you are. My name is John Lee Hoich, but as you can see from the enclosed birth certificate I was named John Lee Moreno when I was born.

My mother, Rebecca Leona Williamson, moved to Council Bluffs, Iowa around November 1, 1957, from Patterson, New Jersey. She moved in with my Aunt Marge, her sister, and she told everyone that her name was Rebecca Leona Moreno and was pregnant with me. I was born January 19, 1958. She then met a man who became my dad, John George Hoich. They married and had five other children. Later, I was adopted by John George Hoich.

John, on September 25, 1974, Rebecca, known to you probably by the name of Becky Williamson, died of a heart attack at the age of 39. John George Hoich had a severe drinking problem. The courts would not allow him to take the six children after Mom died, so we were split up and put in foster homes. My mother was a very courageous woman and was the best mother I've ever seen. My dad was a different story, mainly because of his alcoholic problem.

On July 3, 1979, John George Hoich, my father, died of cirrhosis of the liver. I supported him and took care of him the last five years of his life, as well as paid for his funeral, just because he was the only father I knew. He never was a father to me or ever spent any time with me.

After John George Hoich died, I applied for Social Security to help me with my college expenses. The Social Security Administration said that I needed a birth certificate. It then dawned on me that I didn't have one. I wrote to the Vital Statistics office in Des Moines, Iowa and they returned my letter to me, saying that there was no such person born January 11,

1958 at 8:02 p.m. in Jenny Edmundson Hospital in Council Bluffs, Iowa named John Lee Hoich. A list was sent to me of the names of the babies that were born on that day and one of them was named John Lee Moreno. Wow!

My Mother and Father are dead. Who do I ask about this one? Well, it has taken me ten years to find out what I know now and I still don't know much. My aunt told me that my mother was deeply in love with you and that she got pregnant. She said the two of you were going to get married but you were afraid of all the responsibilities and that you backed out of the relationship.

John, that's all I know. What can I say except that I'm in great need to find you. Michael, my only brother, died of a heart attack on October 17, 1989. I helped raise him and he was my hero. I miss him so very much. He was only 21 years old. Dad, Mom and Michael are all dead. Now I find out I have someone out there who is still possibly alive that is my natural father. Who are you? What is your nationality? What are your physical drawbacks and medical history? Do I have health like Mom and Michael, or is there another health history I should know about? What do you look like? Are you Italian or are you Spanish? Where are your parents and your grandparents from? Did you love my mom? Did you ever wonder about who I was?

I guess I have lots of questions. I'm not at all angry with you, no matter what took place. I just want to know these things. I'll not interfere with your life or your family. I need you please, to help me with these questions. I don't want money. I have been very successful and I have plenty of money.

I would love to meet you. I'd love to know what you did throughout your life. What kinds of jobs did you have? Did you marry? Did you have children? Does your son look like me?

Please, Mr. Moreno, respond to my letter. I've worked hard to find this information. I'd do anything for you to learn about you. I'll come to see you or fly you to Omaha, if you are interested. If I just received a letter from you I would be honored the rest of my life.

Through the Grace of God, I pray that you respond to my letter.

Respectfully, I await anxiously.
John Lee Moreno
John Lee Hoich

My Wife and Children

It was November 30, 1993, at 2:00 p.m., and I was in the New Era Beauty Shop in Millard, Nebraska, getting my hair trimmed after my customary shampoo, when I looked over to the next chair and saw Roxie the hairdresser pull a head of long, shiny, brown hair from the sink and gently wrap it in a towel.

As the customer sat up, I noticed how beautiful she was: she had one of those unforgettable faces that take your breath away. I thought, "She is beautiful—I'd like to get to know her." So, I started talking to Roxie, joking with her in an attempt to attract her customer's attention. It was like Roxie was reading my mind, because she said to the customer, "Denise, you should go out with us sometime. We have a lot of fun."

"Well, give me a call—I will," said the customer, whose name was Denise Mollner. I've got to hand it to Roxie. As a matchmaker, she worked like a skilled surgeon, cutting through layers of social convention to introduce us in a roundabout way and then to lay the groundwork for a date.

"I'll take her out—I'm more fun!" I blurted out.

"John, be quiet!" Roxie said. Then, after a pause, she added, "But John's right. He is fun. If you go out with him, make him buy you Dom Perignon champagne and lobster." Denise laughed and answered, "I really don't like lobster all that much, but I'll take the Dom."

Denise and I finished up at the same time, so I walked with her to the cash register, where she paused to write out a check. I looked over her shoulder and memorized her telephone number and her address. At that point, my mind and my heart were racing in unison. I knew I had to get to know that woman.

"What do you do?" I asked.

"I clean houses," she answered.

"Wow, that's great! I mow lawns. Let's merge!"

Denise laughed and gave me one of those Marilyn Monroe smiles. You know, the kind I mean: friendly but not aggressive, with just a hint of vulnerability. She was quietly beguiling, and I was hooked on the spot. I walked her to her car and made my move.

"Will you join me for a hot chocolate tonight?" I asked.

"Well, I don't know," she said, lowering her eyes.

"Oh, come on, please—I'd really like to talk to you."

"I'm married," she said.

"Oh." I felt deflated. The moment had been building for ten minutes or more, and then it was over, gone as quickly as it had arisen. I struggled to think of something to say, wondering whether

I should give her my business card or simply break into a run.

It was the longest two or three seconds of my life, but then she brought a smile to my face when she said, "But I'm separated." She paused, and then the words gushed out, "I have been for eight months. My husband moved out. I have the house."

It was wintertime and the air was cold, so I asked a second time. "Why don't we meet for hot chocolate at Village Inn at eight o'clock?"

"That would be wonderful. I'll be there."

Men always react to women. Sometimes in a sexual way, in that we see them as potential physical partners. Other times it is in an emotional way, when they strike a chord with us and we are attracted to them for reasons that go deeper than sex. Looking back, I can see that I was attracted to Denise for both reasons, which makes it inexplicable that I would almost blow something so important to me by arriving late for our date. Ten minutes late, to be exact.

"I was just about ready to leave," she said, once I joined her at her table. "I was already nervous about doing this in the first place."

She didn't say it in a threatening way, and she smiled when she said it, but I could tell that she was unhappy with my tardiness. I apologized and then we talked and had a beautiful visit for a couple of hours. I walked her out to her car and we kissed. When she drove away, she took my heart with her. I was totally smitten with her.

The only other time I was smitten was during a five-year relationship with a real estate agent. The relationship was platonic, both of us waiting for that magic day of marriage. I naturally assumed she was the woman I would marry. She had different assumptions and moved on before I got around to asking her to marry me. I don't really blame her. I had so little free time, between the demands of my work and my responsibilities to my siblings.

When I met Denise I was thirty-five, at a point in my life when I knew I would have to make time for dating if I ever hoped to have a family of my own. She was at a critical point in her life as well. We dated through December and it was a difficult month because it was the first holiday season.

After Christmas, when I saw her again, I asked if she planned to file for divorce, she said no. He was the one who had the affair. Why should she file for divorce over something that was not her fault? It made sense to her, but not to me. I told her that regardless of whose fault it was, divorce was in her best interest. Being the entrepreneurial extrovert that I am, I encouraged her to be more aggressive in resolving the conflict within herself.

In mid-January, I invited a lawyer friend over to my house to meet Denise. He had been my lawyer for more than a decade, and he had helped me through many, many obstacles, so I was optimistic that he would be able to help Denise. I had only known her for sixty days, but I desperately wanted to fix her life for her. Once he heard Denise's story, he agreed to handle her divorce.

In repayment, all I wanted in return from Denise was attention. I have been starved for attention my entire life. I'm a jokester. I'm a comedian. I'm a clown at parties sometimes because I am starved for attention and affection. As my attorney set the wheels of divorce in motion, I helped Denise through the process of discovering herself. She was like a wounded bird in some respects. She owned a housecleaning business and she was undercharging her customers. She only charged ten dollars an hour to clean a house, when I knew that she could have charged twenty. I finally persuaded her to raise her rates to fifteen dollars an hour, and that alone boosted her income from twenty thousand dollars a year to thirty thousand dollars a year.

In some respects she was a mystery to me. She was very educated—she had a college degree in psychology—but she never sought a job where she could use her education. Instead, she started up a housecleaning service, a line of work that calls for street smarts. Unfortunately, she was not blessed with a lot of street smarts or common sense. Why would a brilliant woman with a specialized education reject all that to do something that called for talents that she did not possess?

I felt that God put Denise there for me to help her. She was my assignment, like in the television show "Touched By An Angel." So I took my Hoich wings and spread them over her and helped her through her divorce.

People always told me that I would know when I found the right person to love. I don't know if the "right" person was in front of me several times in my life or not, but I think that person could have been and I was just too busy to pay attention. For so many years, I would not allow anyone into my life, because I was selfish and I focused all my attention on my business and on my sisters and brother until he died. The company owned John Hoich. I did not own the company. I was a slave to my own success and did not reap the harvest like I should have.

I always felt it was my mission on this planet to take care of people, to help people, to serve people—all people. I sometimes come across as a flirt because I'm so nice to everyone and I'm so loving and caring and huggy to everyone. But that is simply the spirit I was born with. Some people say a person is born spiritual. Some people say a person is born gay. Some people say that a person is born with an IQ that is higher than others. I think I was born to be a loving, helping, saving, kind of person. I'm a fixer and I can solve any problem. I live for that. Also, I like to connect people from party A to party B. If I had been paid for those services all these years, I would be as rich as Warren Buffett, my acquaintance in Omaha that we all admire.

When I met Denise, I followed that same scenario. I helped her get her business on sound footing. I helped her through her divorce. I helped her with her fears and insecurities. I helped her discover the person inside who had never had an opportunity to see the light of day. That was a familiar role for me to play—and I was patient in allowing our destiny as a couple to reveal itself. Then, suddenly, that "helping" process was more or less reversed, at least in my mind. I wanted to move on in my life. I wanted a family. I wanted to get away from the dating scene. I wanted to get away from being a workaholic. This time, I wanted Denise to save *me*.

We were married on June 15, 1996, in the front yard of the home that I still reside in today. It was a beautiful garden wedding in a wedding chapel gazebo that I built for the occasion. The man I asked to give me away was ex-wrestler Karl Von Hess, the man who became my substitute father. He and his wife, Lenora—she prefered the abbreviated Le—were a big part of my life throughout my twenties, thirties and forties. (Lenora recently passed away.) When Dad died, Karl came to the funeral and told me that he had lost his son in a car accident and wanted to be there for me. I needed a dad and he needed a son, so he ended up legally adopting me, though my name was not changed. His favorite saying to me is, "Keep your nose clean— and be the captain of your ship."

After the wedding ceremony, we rode in a horse and buggy to the reception and then, for our honeymoon, we spent a wonderful two weeks in Alaska, seven days of that at sea.

They say men always chose women like their mother, but I don't see that in Denise's case. Mom was a survivor, a woman who worked twelve hours a day at the beauty shop and came home and worked another two or three hours at home before falling asleep for six hours and then starting that cycle all over again. Denise is a hard worker, but she has never had to work hard to survive, either for herself or for others. Mom was an extrovert who saw life's cup as half full. Until the day she died, she always had hope that the next morning would bring a miracle and turn her life around. Denise is an introvert who sees life's cup as half empty. She's always surprised when something nice happens in her life. Mom and Denise had different goals, different values. I'm not saying that one person is better than the other, only that I definitely didn't marry my mom.

Living together was not as big of a challenge as I had feared, even though we both were very much set in our ways. We were both so happy to be a part of a family again that we would not have recognized red flags if they had been waved in our faces. Luckily, we were in agreement that our first priority, considering our ages, was to start a family as soon as possible. A couple of months into our marriage, we found out that Denise was pregnant. I can't tell you how wonderful it made me feel about life: John Hoich the orphan was going to become John Hoich the father.

I went with Denise to the doctor's office for her eight-week checkup. I'll never forget how nervous I was seeing her in the chair as they prepared her for the ultrasound examination. Seeing an image of your baby for the first time is a big deal, I don't care who you are, and I don't mind admitting that my heart was racing. I never dreamed that John Hoich—a bastard child in the eyes of *his* dad— would ever become a real-life father.

The tension mounted as the doctor and the nurse took care of business. Denise was more relaxed about it than I was, but it was a big moment for her. We watched the screen as the doctor ran the devise over Denise's stomach, not at all sure what we were seeing. Suddenly, the mood changed drastically as the doctor removed the device from her stomach and told us that our baby was dead. Denise and I were devastated. No one had prepared us for a situation like that. We thought everything was going according to schedule. The doctor didn't know why Denise had a miscarriage. We were encouraged to try again—and we did. Denise got pregnant again, right away.

Eight weeks later, we returned to the doctor's office for the first ultrasound. I was so nervous I had to do something with my hands, so I placed them gently around Denise's head so that I could physically be a part of it. The gesture seemed to give her comfort. We could hardly breathe as we watched the doctor smear jelly on Denise's stomach and then run the ultrasound scope back and forth. All of a sudden the doctor said, "There's the baby!" That made me really excited. The baby was alive, praise God!

Then the doctor started pressing on Denise's stomach, as if something was wrong. My heart sank. "Wait a minute!" the doctor exclaimed. "What's going on here?"

Oh, no I thought *not again!*

"There's two!" said the doctor. "There's two!"

Denise replied, "Oh, *@%#!"

That was enough to get my tears of happiness flowing.

Before the babies were born, Denise had to stay in the hospital for four weeks so that she could get the rest and care that she needed. Of course, I wasn't there for her nearly enough because I was still a workaholic and still addicted to my business. That was unfair to Denise, and I apologize to her for that. I wish I had been there all day with her and fought the battle with her lying there with the babies inside her.

I stopped by to see her every evening, but I would be so tired that I would fall asleep until visiting hours were over at 10:30 AM and then I would go home. I tried to make up for my absence by doing special things for her. I sent a massage therapist to the hospital to give her a massage. I asked a woman to stop by and do her nails. And I sneaked our dog Bailey into the hospital in a duffle bag, even though it was against the rules. Our friends and my business associate must have sent one hundred flower bouquets to her hospital room. Flowers were everywhere. The room looked more like a flower shop than a hospital room.

I was at work, when the call came at eight o'clock in the morning that the babies were on their way. I stopped what I was doing and rushed to the hospital. Something inside me wanted to stop traffic and hug everyone I saw along the way. When I arrived at the hospital, I rushed into the delivery room, where Denise was being prepped for delivery.

After the epidural was done, Denise was taken to another room, where there were probably eighteen nurses and doctors in the room. I've never seen so many white coats in my life. All of a sudden, without any warning, they slapped some iodine on her stomach and performed a C-section. I fainted on the spot. When I awoke, five nurses were huddled around me, putting a cold rag on my head and helping me to my feet. "Wouldn't you know it," said Denise. "Even in here, he gets all the attention."

Jeremy Michael was delivered first and named after my brother. They wiped him off and put him into a crib. Then, all of a sudden, there was a problem with him not breathing and there was this scare that he was dead. Then I hear this whack again and this little voice, "Waaaaaaa," fills the room and I started crying.

Once Jeremy was taken care of, they dug down deep to find Justin Lee, named after me. He had fallen down into the birth canal and they had to yank him out and get him breathing on his own. Once they sucked all the stuff out of his lungs and got him crying, my tears started flowing again. Since the babies were born nine weeks early, both had low birth weights—Jeremy weighed three pounds, one ounce, and Justin weighed two pounds, twelve ounces. There are no words to express how I felt looking down at those two, lovely Mini-Me's. It was a beautiful time in my life.

Of course, the nature of the delivery meant that the babies could not go home right away.

The doctors wanted to keep them there for thirty days. I think Denise thought I wasn't there enough during that time, but I went every morning, every afternoon and every night to see the boys and, eventually, to help feed them when they came out of the incubators. We fed them with this little Barbie Doll bottle for preemies and it was quite an adventure.

As you can imagine, going home was no small matter. Sometimes I think there is a tiny rain cloud over my head that follows me wherever I go. The reason I am always going at a full run is to get out from under that cloud. As a surprise to Denise, I had the whole kitchen redone while she was in the hospital. We already had built two new rooms onto the house for Justin and Jeremy, and they were filled with gifts from our friends. The gift that I remember the most came from Joe and Ada McDermott, who gave Jeremy and Justin bedroom sets that grow from a crib all the way to a day bed and then to a single bed. I had never seen anything quite like it.

When we arrived home from the hospital, we discovered that there had been a power outage and the entire house was filled with lacquer fumes, as a result of the work I had done to surprise Denise, so we had to turn around and go stay at a friend's house for a week until the fumes dissipated. I learned right away that being a father has a lot to do with handling a seemingly endless string of emergencies.

After that, everything went smoothly. We developed a system so that whenever she breast-fed one baby, I fed the other one with breast milk we extracted with one of those pumps. At two in the morning, three in the morning, four in the morning—it was a constant thing—and nothing was harder than holding that baby after burping it, with it then spitting up all over me, so that we had to start all over again. For the first few months, Denise and I averaged about two hours of sleep a night.

Because of all the traveling I did with Denise before the children were born—throughout the United States, the Caribbean, Mexico, and a variety of Third World countries—I was able to return home with ideas on how to make our living environment more interesting and more fun for the children. I built waterfalls and made room for about thirty of my favorite animals that I brought over from the petting zoo—everything from a camel named Bumpy imported from Iraq, a Zebu bull from Brazil, and a swan named Alice, horses, donkeys, goats, sheep, pheasants, geese, a zebra, Llamas, and so on.

When I purchased the house in 1993, it was more of a dream than a reality. I transformed the house by adding elegant cherrywood paneling and granite-topped cupboards and counters. The master bedroom is massive and has a bathroom that is larger than most bedrooms and a spiral staircase that leads to a massage room on the floor below. The bedroom overlooks the swimming pool, as does the hearth room, which has a Colorado rock fireplace and a cedar cathedral ceiling.

Helping the house make that transition was a labor of love—all 8,500 square feet of it. Of course, it wasn't about ego. It wasn't about keeping up with the Joneses. It was about transforming raw clay into an environment where I could feel the most free—and safe. Elvis must have had similar feelings when he moved into Graceland after a childhood in modest public and private housing. It was a place where I could wander about the grounds with my animals. A place where no one can hurt me. A place where, like the song in the most famous rags-to-riches-story of them all, *Cinderella*, I can be whatever I want to be.

Denise and the boys were a big part of my being able to transform the house into a real-life dream, because they allowed me to share something that I had held inside myself for most of my life. More than anything I wanted the sort of family I never had growing up. A family in which bad things did not happen. A family in which everyday experiences were fun and filled with hope.

The boys were just a couple of months old that first Christmas, so they didn't understand what was going on; but the second Christmas was a different story. I'll never know how they understood at that age how to rip open a present. It was very cute. And, of course, when their first birthday rolled around, I went absolutely crazy and invited more than five hundred people to their birthday party.

We were unwrapping gifts forever. I just went obnoxious, I know. I can't do anything small. It has to be big. That's the extrovert in me. I invited everyone I knew, from close friends to acknowledged acquaintances—and, bless them, they all came. Jeremy and Justin had no idea who all those people were; neither did Denise, for that matter. Even today, I have a clear memory of the way Justin and Jeremy looked with the red and blue color of their birthday cake plastered all over their faces.

During their first few years of life, *everything* was exciting because anything new they learned was always a first. I'm proud to say that I experienced their first crawl. Then I was there for their first flop, from back to front, and then from front to back. It was amazing. I almost couldn't believe it. I was watching them in their high chairs when they discovered their fingers. They'd look at them and it was, like, "What is this? What do I do with these?" Their first haircut was incredible, and I kept their hair clippings, and, of course, when their first tooth fell out, that was unbelievably exciting.

Denise and I are convinced that they developed their own language. They said, "ooh, aah, aah, ooh," to each other, and somehow one understood what the other was saying. They had a difficult with their "J's," so for two years they called each other "Nunen" (Justin) and "Meme" (Jeremy). Everything was Nunen and Meme, and it was so cute. "Meme, leave me alone!" "Meme, no!" "Nunen, no!"

The first time they pedaled bikes with training wheels, I videotaped it and cried. Then there was the first skit that they did in preschool. The first track and field day at kindergarten. The first day we took the training wheels off of the bike. I bought them both John Deere Little Gator electric cars and it was amazing to watch them learn to turn left and then right, although it had to be explained to them ten or twenty times before they got it. By the time they started school, they were inseparable, even though they routinely told each other "I hate you—I hate you!" Today, they get up in the morning together. They have their own beds, but ninety percent of the time they sleep with each other. They do everything together. They really don't want to be with anyone else. They watch TV together. They play together. They eat together. And they pray together, because we always say our prayers at dinner and before we go to bed at night.

When it's my turn, I thank God for what He has given me and I thank the soldiers who are in far-away places fighting to keep us safe in the United States. Every day I tell them to do for others as you would have them do for you. I ask them to say it back. Sometimes I say, "Do for others . . ." and wait for them to finish the sentence.

If you think about it, all divorces begin with a single glance, a moment when emotions reach a saturation point. Midway through 2005, Denise asked me for a divorce; if I had been more obser-vant, I probably would have seen it coming in the glances I received at the dedication ceremonies. I wasn't really surprised. I was always complement-ing her and she was always tearing me down. I'd go home and she'd find fault with me instead of seeing the positive, and the fault-finding made me feel worthless, which took me back to my childhood—an unpleasant time in my life.

The Christmas before we started divorce pro-ceedings, I asked her to go with me to see a local presentation of "A Christmas Carol." Her response was, "Ah, been there, done that." Not long after that, I asked the boys if they wanted to go to the circus. Their answer sounded familiar: "Been there, done that." Well, we went to the circus anyway and had a great time, but it really irked me that they had learned that negative attitude from their mother. That's not positive thinking.

One thing that Denise and I had in common from the beginning was a mutual appreciation of all the standard holidays—Christmas, Thanksgiving, Mother's Day, Valentine's Day, Father's Day, Fourth of July. We both celebrated them to the max. Denise always made a gorgeous Thanksgiving Day dinner. In those basic areas that define family life, Denise and I were totally compatible.

Where Denise and I started to drift apart was in the area of growth and development. When Denise gets something the way she likes it, she doesn't want it changed. I'm different in that I can't imagine a situation in which I would never see the need for change or improvement. For me, life is about moving to the next level. That doesn't mean I don't see her point, because I do.

I guess I'm like a lot of men, in that while Denise and I were dating—and then later during the first few years of our marriage—I took time away from my work to be with her, mostly doing things that she wanted to do. That changed as the years went by, especially as I moved into new areas of business and found myself joining more boards and organizations, and making new business partners, some of whom were like wives in that they demanded large chunks of my time.

I've heard male friends say that their wives are jealous of the time they spend with their business associates, and I think it's because they come to see "business" as a rival to the love and affection they deserve from their husbands. Certainly, that happened with Denise. The more involved that I got with my business interests, or with the community through civic activities, the less involved Denise and I became in our marriage. I tried to make up for that by calling her four times a day to ask her what she was doing and what the kids were up to, but the more I called her, the less she called me. Finally, it got to the point that she called me at work only on special occasions, like my birthday or something. It took a long time for me to understand that, but it's pretty basic if you think about it.

To Denise, my work was the "other woman." She felt degraded if she had to call me while I was with the "other woman." Of course, my argument was that all the work that I was doing was for her and the kids—and that was the way I saw it. But I have since learned that a successful marriage is more about a husband and wife having the same vision than it is about each of them performing their separate roles to perfection. A man can be the best provider in the world, and the wife can be the best mother and homemaker in the world, but two equal, separate parts do not make a whole, or a workable marriage.

Part of my forward progress for the future involves making more time for Jeremy and Justin, and the reason for that is simple: Every day that I do not spend with them is a day lost in our relationship, and every one of those days are precious to me. To make certain that I have more time to spend with my sons, I made a decision to cut back on the thirty-one boards that I serve on. Instead of attending thirty-one board meetings and giving them each bits and pieces of my time, I whittled that list down to half a dozen charities for which I can make a significant impact.

Life isn't about the almighty dollar, or how many boards you are on, or how much money you can give to someone, or what your net worth is, or how important you want people to think you are. Life is about sustaining human relationships in such a way as to give meaning to your life. If I had spent more time with Denise, my marriage would have worked out a lot better and she might have wanted to be more involved in my life if I had given up some of the charities that consumed so much of my time.

The same advice that I have followed in building businesses—"You have to circulate to percolate"—applies to human relationships. You have to circulate within the relationship on a daily basis to keep it percolating. A relationship can't be put on ice like a rainbow trout, to be enjoyed another day.

Part II

Thoughts on Business, Service and Investing

John's First Office

How to Start Up a Grounds Maintenance Business

I f I had inherited a pair of sheers, I wonder if I would have been a hairdresser. If I had inherited a welding machine, would I be the biggest welder in America? I think that the lawn mower was simply the tool that I took, focused on, capitalized on, and took to the top, as I later did with real estate.

I think that the hardest thing about starting up a grounds maintenance business is balancing the basics—buying the right equipment, hiring the right labor, and acquiring the know-how to get the job done—with an understanding of the bidding process. If you don't bid your contracts right and correctly calculate your overhead, and if you don't determine the correct price, then it doesn't matter how much equipment you have, how much manpower you have, or how smart you

109

were in college as a horticulturist or agriculturist. The secret is to make a profitable bid that covers overhead costs such as administrative costs, payroll, repairs, and maintenance.

You have to understand what your hard costs are and understand what it costs you to be in business on an hourly basis, not by the day, week or month. Also, if you can outsource some of your business to where you are making an automatic twenty-five percent, or whatever you are trying to make, then you can accurately add that onto your billing. If you are too high because your overhead is too high, then the numbers will talk to you and let you know either that your expectations are too high, or that your prices are too low. Either way, you have to be realistic. The bottom line with grounds maintenance is to know your overhead, and adequately and correctly bill for your services. You also have to understand what the market will bear for your services or products.

Once you have that mastered, you can focus on a long-range business plan. The first step in doing that is to identify the type of customer you want to have. Small houses, medium-sized houses, large houses? Small retail businesses, small apartment buildings—or big institutions?

Having said that, I must say that you should always walk before you run. I think all new grounds maintenance businesses should start out with small houses and small businesses. There are two advantages to doing that. First, it will give you the sort of experience you need to be able to properly gauge your ability to take on larger accounts. Second, it will allow you direct access to the people who will be writing checks to you.

Knock on their door. Introduce yourself. Hopefully, you will have enough education to know what you are doing, not that I did—I didn't know *anything*! If you don't know what you are doing, at least make the customer think that you know what you are doing. Just remember it is not the grass that gives you contracts. People give you contracts, and the key to your success will ride on your ability to build and maintain relationships with people. You may know more about cutting grass than anyone in the world, but if you cannot greet your customers in a friendly, effective way, you won't get very far in the grounds maintenance business—or, for that matter, in any business.

Getting to know my customers is 90 percent of my business. I build relationships and then I build relationships with their friends, and their friend's friends. That's why I get very upset when someone is angry at me or saying something negative about me. I try to keep peace with everyone. Of course, building a relationship is just the first step. After that, you have to ask yourself: "What more can I do for that customer?" If the customer is spending money on related services such as landscaping, snow removal or sprinkler systems, you have to help the customer realize that they would be better off spending that money with you. To do that, you have to find a way to relate to them on a personal level and ask for their business.

A lot of smart people will tell you that if you have a passion for your work, you are well on your way to creating a successful business. I see their point, but I must admit that I never had a passion for lawn mowing. I hate it, actually. I suffer from hay fever and I hate grease. Along with lawns come weeds, dust, dander, sunflowers and grease. I dislike all of those things for health reasons, and grease just makes me feel like my fingers are going down a chalkboard. I hate grease, but with lawn equipment, you've got grease and there is no getting away from that.

My point is that having a passion for your work is nice, if you have it; but if you don't have it, the critical factor is whether you have a passion for success—and that's where I have been blessed many times over.

John on a Toro Lawnmower at Offutt Air Force Base

6

Dealing with the Government

I f you can put up with the government's bureaucratic hierarchy long enough to make your way through the maze of red tape, it can be a profitable and rewarding experience. It's the red tape that becomes discouraging and stressful, and is what separates the men from the boys. How many small businesses can hold out long enough to make it through the maze and then do a good, honest job?

Of course, there is so much government work out there that it can become a career in itself. Despite my frustrations with the "red tape" aspect of working for the government, I recommend it highly to anyone in the service industry. There are many government facilities throughout the world, whether it is the Army, Marines, Navy, Coast Guard, Merchant Marines, Air Force, or the Corps of Engineers; they all are in need of contractors from the private sector.

Past performance is the way of the present and the future for the government. The people in charge of those programs don't care so much how low your bid is or how high your bid is. They care about your past performance and your relationships with other vendors. If you have one bad relationship, they can overlook that. But if you have a series of bad relationships, they are going to step in and tell you that you have problems. The government is pretty fair in that way. Twice a year we get a report letting us know how well we are doing—and if we get good marks on performance, we can be confident that we will continue to receive contracts, even if we are not the low bidder, because what the government has its sights on is its main target—best value.

To provide that "best value" we have had to stay on our toes. Lawn maintenance is quite a bit different in Nebraska than it is in Mississippi. In Nebraska, we mow for basically thirty weeks a year, with our other efforts going into snow removal in the winter. In Mississippi, we mow for at least forty-four weeks out of the year, with very little, if any, consideration given to snow removal, which means that my workers there only have about a month to repair the machinery and get ready for the next season.

John and Family, 2004

Larry Wheeler (First Employee Who Became Pastor and Married
John and Denise), Sam Wheeler, and John L. Hoich
(The mower was purchased by John to help Sam start
his ground maintenance business in Missouri.)

Dr. John Allely, a
Mentor to John

John with President George H. W. Bush in 1990 at a Fund Raiser
for Hal Daub for Senate in Omaha

John and the Recipient of the John L. Hoich Paddock Road/Westside High Scholarship, Kameron Canbaz, 2005

Joe and Ada McDermott, of Loveland Lawns, and John. Together, they have had a parent/son relationship since 1974.

John L. Hoich, Tom Osborne, Warren Buffett, and Barry Switzer
at Strategic Air Command Museum, 2003

Warren Buffett and John L. Hoich, Omaha, 2003

John L. Hoich and Congressman Lee Terry
in Washington, DC, 2002

Michael Ricker
(Died January
2006) and John
in 2004. Ricker
was a world
famous pewter
sculptor. John
has collected his
pewter since
1978.

John L. Hoich, Joan and Maurice Udes (2004). Maurice purchased John's 525-acre farm, which launched his real estate career. The silver bowl is a gift from John thanking the Udes for purchasing the farm.

John L. Hoich and Chuck Lakin,
a Close Friend Since 1978 (2006)

Jim Jandrain (John's CPA), John L. Hoich, and Doug Pugh
(Real Estate Advisor) in front of John's Plane (2006)

Doug Pugh and
John L. Hoich
in Oakbrook,
IL, Closing the
Sale of John's
Shopping
Center (2006)

John L. Hoich and Doug Pugh,
Returning to Omaha on John's Plane after Closing John's
Biggest Sale Yet of the Shopping Center (2006)

John L. Hoich and
Dot Wheeler at
John's Wedding
(Another Mom to
John). Dot is now
deceased.

John L. Hoich on Mission To Haiti, 1989

John L. Hoich on Mission To Haiti, 1989

Dave Janke and John L. Hoich. Dave was the groomsman at John's wedding in 1996. Janke is now deceased.

Hoich Park Waterfall and Gardens at Hoich Residence, 2006

John L. Hoich on Mission To Haiti, 1989

John L. Hoich on Mission To Haiti, 1989

Dave Janke and John L. Hoich. Dave was the groomsman at John's wedding in 1996. Janke is now deceased.

Hoich Park Waterfall and Gardens at Hoich Residence, 2006

Hoich Residence, Omaha, Nebraska, 2006

John's Office and Stable for Animals
Behind the Hoich Residence, 2006

John with Ed Hunter, Founder of Toro Sprinkler Head and
Owner of Hunter Sprinkler equipment, 1986.
(Ed is now deceased.)

John L. Hoich, Ada and Joe McDermott, and Jerry Slusky (1996)

John is Honored at Rotary International Headquarters, 2006
On Left, Rotary International President Elect Wilfrid Wilkinson
On Right, President Bill Boyd

John with Rotary International President Bill Boyd, 2006

President George W. Bush and John in Omaha

Karl Rove and John in 2006
at an Event for Congressman Lee Terry in Omaha

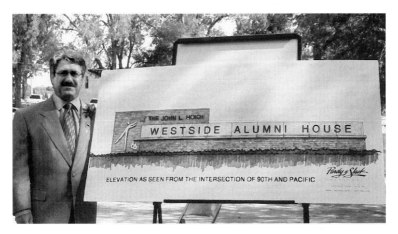

John at the Dedication of the
John L. Hoich Westside Alumni House, 2002

Jim Jandrain, John's CPA and Friend on John's Plane in 2005,
Returning from an Ethanol Meeting

John with
Joe Ricketts (Founder
and Chairman of
Ameritrade), 2006

Jim Johnson, Bob Pease (GM of Midwest Turf and Irrigation), John
L. Hoich, and Len Johnson (Owner of Midwest Turf and Irrigation).
John received an award from Toro for 25 years of customer loyalty.

Different sections of the country require different types of grasses, which mean different growing seasons and different types of equipment. If the grass gets too high, then we can be fined—and no one working on a government contract ever wants to be fined because that is a negative reflection of best value.

My worst red tape problems came about because the growth of our company, U.S. Grounds Maintenance, caused us difficulties with the Small Business Administration. Our official status as a small business was important to us because it was the basis of our government contracts.

From 1992 to 2002, everything went beautifully. During most of that time, one partner kind of sat in the background and the other partner and I pretty much ran the company, with me writing the checks and making all the deals, and with the other partner doing a stellar job supervising the employees and the equipment, like he said he would do. We made an excellent team.

Mark Morgan joined the team as general manager and eventually moved into the president's position. Mark is proof that you can start and work from the ground up and we saw it and acknowledged it and acted on it. Mark's success is a good example to both employer and employee that hard work can lead to exceptional results and promotion.

In 2002, I was in Las Vegas when I got a telephone call from my partner, who told me that we had just received a letter from the Small Business Administration that said that we no longer qualified as a small business. My first response was, "You've got to be kidding!" At that time, if we made less than five million dollars a year in the grounds maintenance business and had offices in what the government calls a "hub zone," we were qualified to receive contracts. Already, we had moved our offices for U.S. Grounds Maintenance to a blighted area. Actually, that area was sub-blighted by the City of Omaha. All this happened when we won a third five-year contract with Offutt to service 2,400 acres of grass, twenty-five miles of sidewalks and more than eight thousand trees. We used a crew of forty in the summer and a crew of less than twenty in the winter, when our primary responsibility was snow removal.

It was when we won the third contract that a competitor protested and the SBA began an investigation into whether U.S. Grounds Maintenance made more than the five million dollars a year we said it made. That investigation turned into a two-year nightmare. The gentleman from the SBA told me through emails that he thought

I was trying to be slippery and earned more than five million dollars a year through U.S. Grounds Maintenance, which really offended me because I didn't. He tried to count all my income from real estate and everything else, but that income had nothing to do with mowing lawns for the United States government.

My attorney fought the SBA ruling, and a couple of hundred thousand dollars later, we came up with a modification in the ownership structure to resolve the problem, but it meant that my partners and I had to break up our partnership. I asked one of them to stay, but he decided to stay with his friend, which meant that I had to buy them out of U.S. Grounds Maintenance for two million-plus dollars. There was a lot of stress involved, but I obtained a loan to buy their interest in the company. Breaking up the partnership was a very sad thing because we had built up the company from scratch.

Everything went fine for six months after that, but then the SBA came into the picture again, like the scary movie guy that says, "I'm back!" He told me I would have to reduce my ownership percentage of U.S. Grounds Maintenance in order to comply with government regulations. I've been around long enough to understand that the government needs a certain amount of "red tape" to function at the bureaucratic level, but this was getting ridiculous.

This time I hired a Washington attorney and packed my bags to go to the capital to do battle with the SBA on its home turf. My federal congressman introduced me to the chairman of the House Small Business Committee. The chairman had a reputation of being a champion for business, small and large, so he proved to be very helpful in getting the attention of the SBA. With the help of my congressmen and the committee chairman, I was able to attract the White House's attention long enough to explain the nightmare I had been through with the SBA's Omaha office. All I wanted was for someone in authority to hear me out and make a decision so that I could get back to work. I'm a little guy, not a great big corporation like Boeing and Northrop Grumman. Government red tape can destroy small businesses, simply by taking so long to make decisions, which is what is unfair about the process. It is the main reason why the American people are so opposed to allowing the federal government to have so much power over their lives. Too many Americans have been greeted by individuals who say, "I'm with the government, and I'm here to help you—just don't worry about the fine print." Well, it's the fine print that kills you.

The congressional help proved to be highly effective at getting the SBA to make a decision on my case so that I could return to Omaha and get back to work. The impasse was resolved by me resigning my positions as president of the company and board member, and then selling off fifty-two percent of my stock in the company, which made me a minority shareholder. According to SBA guidelines, that enabled U. S. Grounds Maintenance to qualify as a small business, while keeping me on as a consultant to ensure the company's continued success.

None of that makes sense, does it? The way the system now works, the big corporations have a two-prong strategy: To create hundreds of small businesses to slip under the SBA's radar, while at the same time using their influence to prevent existing small businesses from becoming competitive with their companies. The government expends so much effort keeping stalking horses from the big corporations out of the system that they make it difficult for genuine small businesses to prosper.

Government contracts definitely bumped my business up another level, but to stay competitive in that arena you have to, as that old watch commercial says, "take a lickin', and keep on tickin."

Government contracts are not for sissies.

John's First Farm, Purchased in 1989

Real Estate

As I said earlier, my first real estate investments were the house that I purchased and then resold and the duplex that I built as a residence, office, and rental unit. From there, I partnered with Chuck Lakin to purchase a couple of three-plex units and several single dwelling homes that we fixed up and rented out. He is a close friend and my first real partner in real estate.We sold all those properties for a profit and I bought a five-plex unit on my own and I bought a sixty-six-plex unit apartment complex with another partner. My partner and I quickly learned that neither of us had time to manage the property and that's when we hired a property management company. We remained partners for twelve years, until I sold out my interest in the apartment complex to my partner.

Throughout all those ventures, Doug Pugh and Mary Fitzpatrick continued to advise me. A lot of people look at me, I know, and think I'm just lucky—you know, always in the right place at the right time—but Doug and Mary always thought there was more to me than good luck and I have always been grateful for that.

"It's never been about luck," says Doug. "I mean, how many eighteen-year-olds own a duplex? And he nearly went broke when he was twenty-three years old. So how lucky is that? John is truly a self-taught real estate entrepreneur. I once sent him a real estate book, one that had terms in that I knew John would be encountering in his business dealings. I was afraid that he would be out of his realm with the people he was talking to–bankers, lawyers, people like that. I don't know if he read it or not, or what happened to the book, but pretty soon he was talking about stuff like that off the top of his head."

Secrets of Real Estate Success

Most people know the secret to real estate success—location, location, location. That's pretty basic, but it is still a minor ingredient in the formula for success. You've got to build the right product, whether it is a strip mall, apartments, warehouses, office buildings or homes. You've got to build in the right area—and you've got to build at the right time. And you've got to build it correctly. You've got to hire a good contractor who won't cut corners. You also have to see the unique value in your product that will allow you to advertise it as better than the next guy's so that you can sell, rent, or lease it.

One thing I've learned in real estate is that you have to pick a segment and stick with it and focus on it just like anything else. Apartments, retail strip malls, shopping centers, and land development have been my forte. You have to decide what area you want to focus on and then stay with until you've mastered it. You may never want to leave that area of real estate; but if you do, it is important that you understand the kind of real estate you want to move into so that your client or your tenant won't be smarter than you. You have to be careful not to invest in a bad deal, because that's a surefire way to sink a real estate career and your net worth.

If you plan on going into real estate, financing is one area where you cannot afford to let down your guard. For the last decade or so, we have experienced low interest rates which reduce the cost of maintaining debt in real estate. Because of that, there have been times when I obtained 80 percent loans from a local bank by putting down 20 percent, which left me with an 80 percent first mortgage.

Then, I also apply for a "gap" loan (sometimes called a "bridge" loan) to borrow the 20 percent down payment. A loan like this can usually be obtained on the basis of one's personal net worth or by putting up another asset for collateral. This gives you the money needed for whatever project you're undertaking without having to spend any of your own money. However, it leaves you responsible for a lot of debt (called contingent liability). This means that, once your project is completed (all rented, etc.) and you're ready to start another project, banks will be prohibited by law from lending you money on the new project.

At that point, you can go to an insurance company or a New York conduit loan broker on Wall Street and get a "non-recourse" loan. This means that you are not personally liable for the debt. Should you be unable to make the payments, the lender will take over the property that is the collateral, but they won't come after you for anything. Why would a lender do this? Well, they'll first investigate you and the property. They will assure themselves that you have a track record as a developer, that you have a high net worth (meaning you're less likely to default), and that the property is something they'd be satisfied with if they wound up owning it. The reason you want one of these non-recourse loans is that you will no longer have any contingent liability in the project and you can get another bank loan for another project. In fact, this is the very reason these sort of loans were created, so developers wouldn't have their hands tied. Normally, they are available at the same interest rates as regular bank loans.

When you get one of these long-term non-recourse loans, they are usually for ten years, while bank loans are usually for five years, unless you go to a full amortization (AM) loan at fifteen, twenty-five, or thirty years. An amortization loan, for those new to finance, is simply one that is paid off through regular scheduled payment over a stated period of time. Most people seem to get a 30-year AM with a 10-year balloon note, at a fixed rate for ten years. If you are 100 percent mortgaged, then none of your money is in the project and you are free to start another project. The more you keep doing that for good projects that are paying off at 10 to 20 percent return, the more deals you can put together— and that's the way successful real estate investors do it the world over.

You're using someone else's money, but if you find the right property, it is a surefire way to be successful. Of course, you can invalidate that success by paying too much for a property, or by not paying attention to it, or by not taking care of your tenants or allowing them to feel as if they are part of the team.

Everyone must be a team player, from the maintenance man to the tenants, to the insurance company, to the leasing agents. You must never forget who they are and you must remember them on their birthdays, their good days, their bad days. They are the team and you have to play right with the team and be a good team leader and a good team player or people will see right through you in no time at all—and if that ever happens you will have blackballed yourself from ever being successful in real estate.

My standards are high and it is based on hiring the best, friendliest, most positive thinking, eye-of-the-tiger leasing agents and management companies. And then I demand from my in-house Hoich Enterprises employees that they make certain that everything on the outside of the property is perfect and the sprinkler system runs well and the mowing is done well. You want people to see curb appeal. I preach it all the time.

The biggest secrets of real estate involve buying or building in the right location, paying the right price, and leasing it for as much as possible. The greatest two days of real estate success are the day you buy the property and the day you sell it, because that's when you realize the highest return on your investment that increases your net worth. At some point during that process, you have to decide whether you want to be a management and leasing company, or whether you want to hire those services out so that you don't have to worry about the day-to-day operations. Obviously, I have decided that hiring them out is the best way to go. That way, I have more time for my sons and for my other business ventures.

Real Estate

One quality I have noticed in very successful real estate investors is their ability to take a visionary approach to selling and buying property. It is easy to see the value of existing locations, anyone with half a brain can look at success and say I want a piece of that; but the challenge is in looking to the future and figuring out what properties will be premier locations five years, ten years, twenty years down the road. It takes a visionary to look at a vacant lot in the middle of nowhere and see a bustling neighborhood that will increase in value over a given number of years. That ability is what separates the big boys from the little boys. You either have IT or you don't. If you don't have IT, that doesn't mean you can't be successful in real estate; it just means that you probably should stick to proven locations and not roll the dice for a payoff that you don't see on the table.

Part III

The Principles of
Success

John, at Peace near the Water

Some Fundamental Principles

J ohn E. Everoad, a former Nebraska Attorney General, is one of the people who taught me a great deal about business, both by sharing his personal experiences and by giving me advice that has stuck with me. Before going into politics, he built a very successful company named Cummins Diesel that he sold in his late sixties for a fortune. When the new owners wouldn't let his son buy the company back, John started up a new company named Everoad Diesel and Supply. Because he was upset and wanted revenge, he tried to use his new company as a competitive weapon against his former company. He ended up losing his entire fortune.

What that taught me was that when it's time to stop, it's time to stop, and you can't let your ego make decisions for you. Besides that lesson, which he taught me unintentionally, John Everoad taught me something that has been a big part of my success. "John," he told me, "I'll tell you what to believe in—making a decision. Every single day, you've got to make decisions. Even if it's wrong, make a decision."

I can't tell you how many business executives go down in flames, simply because they are unable to make decisions at critical times. To me, that's the first requirement for success, the ability to make decisions, right or wrong. That's part of the risk for reward.

The second requirement is to do your homework before you commit your money or your time to a project. The third requirement, I believe, is: If you choose to partner, partner well and treat your partner the way you want to be treated. Fairness is not a weakness, I don't think. To me, it is the spirit that leads you through the tribulations that accompany any business deal. One way I look at it is that the American West would never have been settled and developed if the men and women who undertook that risky undertaking did not observe the three principles I just mentioned

Secrets to Building a Million-Dollar Business

The secrets to building a million-dollar business are focus, determination, persistence, consistency, dedication, and synergy. All those things are positive attitudes that help you stay focused so that you don't veer off course. The Bible says that if someone doesn't want to believe you, you should sweep the dust from your shoes, turn your face the other way, and go somewhere else. If they are not going to listen, they are not going to believe, and you've tried your best, so you need to move on.

I try to stay away from negative people as much as I can. My glass is always half full. Sure, there are days when I am upset. There are days when I get depressed. There are days when I am frustrated. But after I settle down from all those negative things, I attack the problem and fix the situation. I don't let a problem smolder. I put the fire out completely so that I can move on to the next task and continue my focus.

Negative people bring me down. If I stay around them for very long, it affects me in a negative way. If you hang with ducks, you will quack like a duck—I've said that since I was fourteen. I consistently try to get away from the bad ducks and hang around with the good ducks. Positive people inspire me. They enable me to make the best out of whatever the obstacle is. To every obstacle, there is a strategy. I really believe that. There is always a way to solve the problem, unless you listen to people who say, "You can't do that," or "It can't happen." Can't is not in my dictionary.

The one thing that I have done throughout my career that has consistently been a factor in my success has to do with my ability to duplicate myself. When I was out mowing one lawn, I had twenty-five or thirty guys out mowing twenty-five or thirty additional lawns. Microsoft founder Bill Gates has done a good job of duplicating himself. He created a unique product and then duplicated himself by instilling his vision in his employees. He sells computer software to almost every home in America because he was able, first, to duplicate himself, his way of thinking—and, second, to duplicate his product. As a result, every time you go online you touch a piece of Bill Gates.

People sometimes fail because they don't follow through in their duplication efforts. It's not enough to have a great idea. You've got to instill that idea into your employees so that when you are not standing there looking over their shoulders, they can remain true to your duplication and not veer off into areas that reflect *their* ideas.

Hundreds of people have built million-dollar businesses, and hundreds more will do it in the future—and each person has his or her own twist on success. My success is based on people skills, the ability to stay focused and a determination to keep it simple. There is no fast buck. It's done one step at a time.

Truthfully, I think that the phrase, "shoulda—coulda—woulda," is what made me millions, because instead of falling back on that phrase, I used, "dida—dida—dida." It sounds silly, I know, but it is so true. I have gone out and acquired real estate that people thought I was crazy for buying—and then laughed all the way to the bank. If you are successful, there is no shortage of people around to tell you that they could have done the same thing, would have done the same thing, or should have done the same thing. But they didn't—and I dida, dida, dida! If you make things happen for yourself, you can become a millionaire many times over. But if you just sit on the sidelines and wonder and watch, you are never going anywhere. It takes action and positive attitude.

When I think of success, I think of more than a financial balance sheet. I think of what it has taken out of me and what it will give back to me in the future. True success means that regardless of what you have put into the business, when all is said and done, you own your business and it doesn't own you. As long as you are in control of the business, whether it is as president or chairman of the board, you have to stay on top of things so that it will not slide away, or get stolen from you. It's a lot easier to lose a million dollars than it is to earn a million dollars.

WAYS TO BUILD A MILLION DOLLAR BUSINESS

- ➤ Trust in God and ask all others to pay in cash.
- ➤ Dida—dida—dida!
- ➤ Avoid negative people.
- ➤ Find a partner who will watch your back.
- ➤ Learn to promote yourself (no one else will).
- ➤ Take care of God first, family second, business third.
- ➤ Learn to just say no.
- ➤ Use the bank's money whenever possible and don't be the bank for others.
- ➤ Focus on the future, not the past.
- ➤ Give out fifty business cards a day.
- ➤ Do unto others as you would have them do unto you.
- ➤ Buy low and sell high or buy low and never sell

HOTHOUSE HOICHISMS

- ➤ To be rich is to know when you have enough.
- ➤ Pigs get fat. Hogs get slaughtered.
- ➤ Money buys experience and experience winds up with the money.

- You've got to circulate to percolate.
- 80 percent of your business comes from 20 percent of your clients.
- The root of most fear is a lack of money.
- If you hang with ducks, you'll quack like a duck. You become your environment.
- Capital greed and capital punishment have a lot in common: both can kill you.
- Store what you must. Share what you can.
- Lease what depreciates and buy what appreciates.

Surefire Ways to Sink a Business

You can get burned out on a business whether you are successful or not. If you get burned out—and you have no success to show for it—it's common sense that maybe you should consider another line of work. There are no miracle cures for a failed business. If, on the other hand, you have built a successful company, burnout is the wild pitch that can knock your company right off its feet.

I can spot a business executive who is suffering from burnout right away simply by observing his or her team. If their boss is cocky and complacent (two early signs of burnout), they seem less interested in their work. That is especially true for a business that began with a grand vision. If the person who first expressed the vision no longer believes in it, it is not reasonable to expect the employees to continue to carry the torch.

You can pay someone to do a job, or to present you with new ideas, but you can't pay them to carry on with your ideas. That's why I put such a high value on employee relations. I constantly pat my team on the back and try to keep them motivated. I want the dedication, the commitment, the consistency that made them valuable employees to stay in the minds, hearts and souls for the entire journey.

A surefire way to sink your business is to stop educating and motivating your employees to live up to your vision of the company. It's rare to see a business make a profit on automatic pilot. There has to be direction, and without it—whether you are distracted by personal problems, profoundly disinterested, or simply out playing golf all the time—it's difficult for a company to make forward progress.

Stay off the cell phone when you are at home with your family. The calls can always be returned the next day. The same thing goes for lunch or business meetings with clients. Stay off the cell phone. The callers will leave a message if you have voicemail and you can get back to them with specific answers. Give full attention to the person in front of you, whether it is your significant other or a business client.

When you are out with your significant others or business clients, don't work the room or ogle the women or look up every time the door opens. Give the person you are with your undivided attention. Don't use your guest to connect with other people. Do that on your own time. Be respectful of the person you are with.

If you become successful and build a showplace home, don't open it up to just anyone. You should maintain some degree of mystery in your life. Enjoy your possessions with your family and friends and not the whole world. Each time you flaunt your wealth to a stranger or acquaintance, you decrease its long-term value. The Indians believed that mirrors captured their souls. The same principle works when it comes to careless displays of your wealth, which can be considered a mirror of your success. Flash your wealth like a mirror and a piece of your soul will leave with each glimmer.

All of these lessons come from my personal experience. I'm still learning some of them over again. They are more difficult to master than one might think.

Pretty Woman and the 80-20 Rule

Believe it or not, I learned an important business principle from a movie named *Pretty Woman*, starring Richard Gere and Julia Roberts. Most people were probably captivated by Julia Roberts (I know I was in the beginning), but then I looked past her character to the role that Richard Gere played.

In the movie, his character bought businesses and broke them up into pieces so that more people could afford them, which meant that he made more money by selling off the pieces than he would have made selling the businesses as a whole, and that really made me think about my lawn care business. As a result of watching *Pretty Woman*, I decided to break up my business into pieces and sell them to investors. There is a saying that 80 percent of a company's business comes from 20 percent of its clients. I kept the 20 percent of my clients that were making 80 percent of my income and I sold off the 80 percent that was making 20 percent of my income.

I broke my business up into eight pieces. I sold all the residential clients as one piece; all the lawn chemical customers as one piece; all the small commercial accounts as one piece; and so on. In all, I raised more than a million dollars and still maintained control of three crucial pieces for future development.

You know, I bet other people watched *Pretty Woman* and walked away with an entirely different vision.

In business, as in life, it's important to remember the 80-20 rule. 80 percent of your business income comes from 20 percent of your clients. If you have multiple businesses, 80 percent is produced by 20 percent of the businesses. When you find yourself spread too thin, it's time to get rid of the least productive 80 percent and stick with the most productive 20 percent. I'm now at a stage in my life where I'm really putting this rule to effect. I've sold 80 percent of my businesses. I'm getting rid of 80 percent of my material possesions and keeping the 20 percent that I use 80 percent of the time. I'm even selling and donating to charity 80 percent of my collection of Ricker sculptures. All of this simplifies my life and leaves me more time to enjoy life to the fullest, to enjoy my family, and to focus on God and maintaining good health.

The Golden Rule

In 1988, I had an account to do the grounds maintenance for all the McDonald's in Omaha. It was a big deal for me. One day I got a note from them that they wouldn't need my services next year as they were going to do the grounds maintenance themselves. Shortly thereafter, I discovered that they had hired my foreman and were going to have him do the same work he had done for me. I was incensed and went to them and complained about what I thought was clearly a nasty business practice. Their response was, "It's just business." Angrily, I replied, "No, it's *not* just business!"

Ever since, whenever I'm working up a deal, I consciously remember this incident and remind myself that what we're doing is not just business, it effects people. I do my best to come up with a plan that works for all parties. Most of all, I try to live by the golden rule: "Do unto others as you would have them do unto you."

Putting the Deal Together

The deals I put together all begin in the shower, because that is just about the only time when I am alone—no emails, telephone calls, letters to read, meetings, problems to solve about the children, relationship issues. For the duration of that shower, fifteen to twenty minutes, my mind can wander without stress and be creative.

Donald Trump's deals come together in one of his towers or plazas or casinos, Johnny Lee Hoich's deals come together in the shower. That is where I figure out how to structure deals, so that when I emerge from the shower, I have a vision that I can follow. Many times, I run from the shower to the den to dry off, so that I can write down my thoughts and ideas before I forget them.

Once I have the idea behind a deal thought out, with its upside and downside, I start networking with the people who can help me cultivate the idea into a business reality. The more I circulate, the more I percolate. That's where my team enters the picture. It's their job to take my vision and run with it. You cannot be successful without a powerful team. Jesus taught us the power of a solid team when he assembled his disciples. Without his team, where would we be today?

My strength is not managing crews. I'm just not very good at that because, when I get caught up in the details of a project, it makes my head spin. The clutter of little things irritates me so much that I tend to avoid it. My accountant, Jim Jandrain, once pointed out that what I do best is finding the deal, polishing the deal, putting the parts of the deal together, matching the team with the deal, and then getting it running smoothly. It's at that point that I'm ready to move on to the next deal.

"If you looked at your entire career," says Jim, "Your most successful deals, the ones that made the most money for you, were deals in which you put something together from scratch or retrofitted a deal to be a success—and then sold it for a profit."

That makes sense, when you think about it. Maybe my business now is to go out and find deals, put them together and then sell them and put the money in a balanced stock account so that I can have a nice pie of assets. It's a good idea to have a certain amount of liquidity, some real estate, some insurance and continuing income that is diversified so that if the market falls in one area, you are stable in other areas.

One pie equals one pie. The pie has to have a little bit of everything in it to keep you well nourished. In years past, my pie was always low on liquidity because I'm always jamming and extending myself to the max. That provided me with a strong financial statement, but it left me with little or no cash flow. As a result, I was always stealing from Peter to pay Paul—and that's no way to build a solid future.

My solution was to sell off some of my assets and put the money into a managed stock account. That allowed me to focus on putting new deals together without the distractions that come from the daily operation of a business. Distractions from an old deal can kill a new deal faster than anything else I know.

If running a business is what you have your heart set on, then you should do that and do it well, without subjecting yourself to the distractions of a constant stream of new deals. If, on the other hand, what you have your heart set on is making new deals, you should pursue that as an end unto itself. Blessed are the deal makers, because they make it possible for business to flourish.

President Gerald Ford, John L. Hoich, and Dr. Edward F.
Cadman, President of Rotary International, August 16, 1985

Circulate to Perculate

A wise man knows everything;
a shrewd one, everybody.

—Anonymous

I am a compulsive networker. As silly as it sounds, I try to give out fifty business cards a day, seven days a week. I run out of cards faster than anyone I've ever known. I put my photograph on the cards so that people will remember me. Often people use the cards to call me for advice. "Can you do me a favor and explain this to me?" "Do you know where I can buy such-and-such cheap?" "Do you know where I can get a job?" Mr. Fix-It, that's me.

You've got to circulate to percolate, that's what I always say. To be successful in a service industry, you have to get your brand name before the public, one potential customer at a time, if necessary. I cannot afford to be shy and retiring. You have to ask for business. It won't seek you out. As my mom used to say, "If you don't ask, you'll never know." If

I went to a social gathering that was filled with potential clients, I can guarantee you that no one would walk up to me and say, "Hi, I'm Warren Buffett—and I'd like you to mow my lawn." It just doesn't work that way. Back in those early days, if I didn't ask people if they wanted their lawn mowed, I wouldn't have built a business.

Before I was married and while I was too busy to date anyone, if I needed an escort to a special function, I'd usually ask Mary Fitzpatrick. Doug didn't mind. I know I drove Mary nuts at some of those functions. My standard introduction at that time was, "Hi, I'm John Hoich—and I mow lawns." I would give people a business card and then ask, "Can I mow your lawn?" It was a pretty straightforward approach to business, but sometimes I would come across an existing customer, which was fine as long as they were satisfied with their service. If they weren't satisfied, I might hear something like, "John, you're already doing my lawn. In fact, I was going to call you. My wife is really mad because you mowed down the petunias."

When things like that happened, I always wrote down the customer's name on a matchbook or a scrape of paper and promised to remedy the problem. Then I moved on to the next person and said, "Hi, I'm John Hoich—and I mow lawns." Later, I learned how to work the crowd a little better at social functions, but back then I always took the direct approach—and, if Mary was standing next to me—poor Mary!—she always looked so embarrassed.

"Mary would return to Kansas City and say, 'John drives me nuts!'" recalls Doug.

> Once he went up to Warren Buffett, handed him a card, and said, "Mr. Buffett, my name's John Hoich. I mow lawns. I'd like to mow your lawn." And he would follow up on it. I don't know if he ever mowed Warren Buffett's lawn, but he certainly had no reservations about asking. If he met the president, I am sure he would say, "Hi, I'm John Hoich. Who's doing the White House lawn?" John is so tenacious. He's always up at dawn and working all the time—always hustling for business.

Doug and Mary were also very good about offering me advice. One day she said, "John, no more matchbooks. No more pieces of paper. No more cards. Either you get organized or you're going to be poor the rest of your life. You get organized. You need an office manager." And she was right, too.

I am also the novelties guy of the century. I've been giving out paperclip holders and letter openers for thirty-one years. If you give someone a key chain, they will put it in their pocket or purse and never see it. Paperclip holders and letter openers tend to stay on top of desks and that means that your logo and photograph are in plain sight where they will be viewed over and over again. Not only do you influence clients that way, you also attract the attention of their friends and business associates who come into their office and see your logo and photograph.

Not all my networking is one-on-one. I have twenty-seven years perfect attendance at the Suburban Rotary Club. To a lot of young people, organizations like Rotary seem outdated, like something out of ancient history, but I saw it as a refuge, a place of safety where I could make new friends and share common goals. I did not join Rotary so that I would become more successful in business, but that was one of the benefits. There are very few businesses or professions in which hermits can thrive. To be a successful business person, you must interact in the community in which you live. Rotary showed me how to do that and I consider organizations like Rotary to be essential ingredients for success in life.

Publicity can be just as helpful. In fact publicity was a big aid in getting me started. One week after Mom died, the *Omaha World-Herald* published a story about me, under a headline that read:

PARENTLESS FAMILY IS LED BY YOUTH.

The story explained that our family was broken up and sent to three different foster homes, and that our sister, Susan, was at the Youth Development Center in Geneva, Nebraska. The point of the story was that everyone now expected me to be the family leader. Not only does the Lord work in mysterious ways sometimes, he apparently has a direct line to the *Omaha World-Herald*. That publicity opened a lot of doors for me.

My senior year at Westside High School, I spent a lot of time as a volunteer on behalf of educating teens about alcoholism—and I spent considerable time in Mayor Zorinsky's office, asking to help with one thing or another. Mainly, I was learning about politics and public service and their linkage with the business world. It was Mayor Zorinsky who encouraged me to start up my own business, specifically an employment agency that would provide part-time jobs to teens.

I went out and knocked on the doors of three hundred businesses in the Westside area and asked them what jobs they had available—and they told me. I explained that I was looking for jobs for kids from age twelve to nineteen. Believe it or not, I found jobs for three hundred students, simply by knocking on doors and appealing to people's sense of community. For that achievement, the Douglas County Board gave me the Youth of the Year Award. That silver plaque and silver medallion, which was presented to me by P. J. Morgan, who later became mayor of Omaha, was my springboard for doing even bigger and better things. After he handed me the medallion, Mr. Morgan asked me if I was a Republican or a Democrat. I said, "What are you, Mr. Morgan?"

"Republican," he answered.

"Me too!"

I don't know if it was Mayor Zorinsky's influence or not, but my senior year I ran for the Omaha school board. My platform called for alcohol programs in every high school that would teach students about the hazards of alcohol and show them how drugs like alcohol can affect everyone in the family. I lost the election, but I certainly gave it the all-American try. I guess the thought of having a high school student on the board with all those adults was more than voters could process at that time. Plus, I've noticed that it makes a lot of adults uncomfortable if you refer to their martinis and beers and fine wines as drugs. They really don't want to hear that.

The experience taught me a valuable lesson about doing business, a lesson that I transferred to my lawn care business. Publicity is a key to getting new business. It makes sense if you think about it. If a potential customer has a choice between hiring an anonymous person to cut their grass, or someone they have read about who is trying to help not only his own family but other students who need money, they are almost always going to go for the situation in which they get "two for the price of one." They get their grass cut *and* they get to help people who really need help.

Jerry Slusky, John's Partner in Slusky/Hoich Real Estate

10

Partners, to Have or Have not?

From the very beginnings of human history, people have usually functioned more effectively in groups than all by themselves. It was true for cave men and it's still true today. In business, having a partner or partners can be the key to success—if the partnership is appropriate, compatible, and useful. On the other hand, a bad partnership can be devastating.

There are two good reasons for forming a partnership—to gain experience, or to gain operating capital. One of my favorite sayings is "money buys experience, and experience winds up with money."

One person that I consider an ideal partner is Jerry Slusky.

I formed a partnership with Jerry Slusky and Steve Durham. In 1992, we purchased a 144-unit apartment complex named Pacific West Apartments, which was really the launching pad to my first big real estate ventures. Steve ended up selling out to me and moving to Dallas, Texas, to pursue other interests. But Jerry hung in there with me and we ended up building a strong partnership that continues to this day. I jokingly tell him that instead of "Starsky & Hutch," we became "Slusky & Hoich."

Jerry is a handsome, sixty-something, Texas-born, Jewish man with balding red hair that I think the world of. His family used to own a famous amusement park in Omaha called Playland Speedway. He was graduated from the University of Nebraska in 1967 and then went on to get a law degree from Creighton University. As a lawyer, he specialized in real estate development, tax planning, and general corporate law. In 2003, he was voted among the best lawyers in the United States by Best Lawyers in America, and in 2004, *Omaha Magazine* recognized him as one of "Omaha's Best Real Estate Attorneys."

When Jerry and I started working together, I had a stronger net worth than he did because he had recently gone through some obstacles, yet we worked well together as a team. My financial statement may have been better at the time, but he has a level of genius that I have never had. So, in the beginning, I was contributing the ability to borrow money, and he contributed the deals and the expertise on financing them. Once Jerry's financial statement got stronger, we entered into those deals as equals, with both of us understanding the financing and the structure of the deals.

"John's got the best eye of anyone I've ever seen—and he's got the gift of gab, which allows him to move around Omaha society and find out information that few people can get," says Jerry. "He's a great person to partner with because I respect his judgment and trust him. After that, it's a situation where I bring the legal and development expertise, and John brings the deal . . . well, not all the time, but certainly the help in shaping the deal. Together, we are a pretty powerful combination."

Jerry and I once went to Florida together to work on a deal, just the two of us. It was part vacation and part work. He's a big napper and I'm not, and I think it disturbed him that I don't take naps. Maybe I'm overloading my system. I hope not. He once told me, "John, I've never even seen you yawn." It's true. I think I'm just too driven to slow down for mundane detours like yawning and napping. If I took a nap, it would scare the hell out of me because I would wonder what I missed while I was asleep.

Jerry and I talk to each other a couple of times a day on the telephone, and we exchange emails more often than that, but we don't do things together with our families because his children are grown and have children of their own, and my sons are still at the cowboy and Indian stage of social development. Even so, we get together often on weekends and in the evenings to work on new projects, despite his busy law practice and my busy lawn-maintenance business.

About his relationship with me, Jerry says: "John just won't let go. I don't know of another person in my life who will find a way to get the job done. Just about the time that most of us will be sinking or saying that they can't get the job done, John moves into an extra gear that most of us don't have. He won't take no for an answer. It is a tremendous character trait that I see in very few others. That unwillingness to admit defeat, I think, can be traced back to his childhood, when he went through so many hard times with his sisters and brother. I think John is determined not to let that happen again, and I think that drives him every day."

I don't think I have met anyone with as big a heart. He is so caring about people—kids, people who do not have as much as he does, charity causes—he just goes out of his way. That must come of him not having nurturing parents and the attention that other children received. I think he craves that and gives it back.

—*Jerry Slusky*

Along with everything else they did, Doug Pugh and Mary Fitzpatrick also taught me the benefits of partnering, especially when venturing into a new field like real estate. By partnering with someone who has expertise in an area you want to explore, you not only benefit from their practical experience, you share the risks involved in a new venture.

"If John enters into a partnership, it's always with a sense of fairness," says Doug Pugh.

> He enters into it with the idea of being fair to his partner, which is sort of an anomaly in real estate, trust me. Everybody's trying to slip a nickel out here and there. John wants people to like him. We're working on a deal now, where the guy is [difficult]. When all is said and done, if John buys him out, John will walk up to him and he will shake his hand and say, "Joe Blow, I want you to know there's no hard feelings, and I hope we can be friends from now on." I would bet you a hundred dollars that something of that nature would be said at the closing table. He will express a desire to be friends—and he will mean it. If it were me, or probably eighty percent of the people who would be in a deal like that, fifty percent would get up and punch the guy out. Twenty percent would just get up and say, "kiss my fanny," while

one percent—John— would walk away and say, "I hope we can be friends."

As for me, I don't believe in having more than one partner in a business. I learned that from my mistakes in the Special Mowing, Inc. partnership. Two people can effectively run a business. Three or more gets too complicated and stifles productivity. As the old saying goes: "two's company, three's a crowd."

A very important rule to remember is to consider the feelings of your partner, whether the partnership is personal, romantic or business-related. Rule number one—and there are no other rules in this category—is to acknowledge that he or she is your partner. Don't say "I"—say "We." Don't hide your partner or pretend that he does not exist. Make certain that the world understands his relationship with you.

If you have a partner, kill him with kindness and let him know when you have made mistakes. If your mistake involves him, ask for forgiveness and make certain you don't cross that line again. If your partner is a grudge-holder and cannot forgive your mistakes, then move on with your life. If you discover that your partner is a nasty person, then buy him out or sell out to him—and find a new partner.

I was recently involved in a nasty partnership, and it's no fun, because no matter what you try to do to make it work, your partner will continue to find fault with you. When a nasty person is a nasty person, he is just nasty and you spend all your time feeling negative. It's better to show him to the door.

Top: John and His Twin Sons, Jeremy and Justin, at the John L. Hoich Westside Alumni House

Bottom: John L. Hoich, Governor Dave Heineman, and Congressman Lee Terry at the Ribbon-Cutting Ceremony for the Stephen Center, John L. Hoich Center for Recovery

Getting Involved in Your Community

I f you want to be successful in a community, you have to participate in that community. I have twenty-five years perfect attendance at Rotary. For the past thirty-plus years, I have joined every activity offered by the Metropolitan Builders Association. I have served as a member of the local Chamber of Commerce. I have participated in dozens of charities. It is important to be active in your community. At the same time, you must be careful not to overdo it. If you overextend yourself in areas of public service, you invariably pay a price for that in your personal relationships, especially in your marriage.

Somehow, I intuitively recognized the importance of community involvement even when I was in high school where I was involved in Alateen and created that teen employment service—and I even ran for office on the school board during my senior year.

That same year, I got involved in a congressional campaign, when U.S. Rep. Lee Terry's father, also named Lee Terry, ran for Congress. I don't recall why I got involved, but the elder Terry had worked as a television reporter and had a passion for issues that affected the disabled and I think that must have been the hook that grabbed me. He didn't win the election, but his son and I became lifelong friends. Says Congressman Lee Terry: "John became an instant member of our family. He was several years older than I was and I looked up to him as a big brother. In fact, even today I call him brother. He has the most amazing drive to succeed. He's bent on proving to himself, I think, that he can rise above the bad breaks that were given to him in childhood. He's got the biggest heart in the world and he won't say no to anybody."

In the late 1980s and the 1990s, as I mentioned, we created the petting zoo that has benefited thousands of children.

In the early-to-mid- 2000s, I participated in a lot of events that involved my family. In 2001, the *Omaha World Herald* awarded us their annual Community Service Award, part of the newspaper's salute to families. I was honored to receive the award because it seemed to confirm my own feelings about the importance of family.

The following year, my high school alma mater, Westside High School, purchased a four-story building for an alumni center and named it the John L. Hoich Westside Alumni House. Previously, I had been named to the Westside Hall of Fame, one of only six people in the school's history. It was quite an honor. Not only does the alumni center bear my name, it contains a reflection room devoted to my accomplishments.

The lower level is used for an alumni center, where former students can come and look up information on themselves or look back through fifty years of student life and find addresses and telephone numbers for former friends. The next floor houses the reflection room. My first contribution to the room was the Sears Craftsman lawn mower that I used to start my lawn maintenance business at age sixteen. There will be space for memorabilia associated with my paper routes, the jobs I held at restaurants and the gas station, and my various investments that took place under the Hoich Enterprises umbrella. One of the features of the room that I am especially excited about is a tree that has leaves of copper that bear the photographs and names of the students that are provided with scholarships through the foundation. I like to call them John's Kids.

The third floor is used for the early childhood development program. At the dedication ceremony for the alumni center, I presented the foundation with a check for $200,000 to support the program and to support the early childhood development program run by the district, which provides scholarships and grants to students and teachers.

The writer Thomas Wolfe said you can't go home again, and you can't in the sense of reliving your life, but you can go home again on occasions such as this, when the purpose is to change the lives of youngsters just starting out in life, some of whom may have had childhoods as dreadful as my own. As a young adult, my dream always was to go back to my childhood and rearrange it so that I could step through a magical door into a new life. That's impossible, of course, but each time I have reached out and helped someone in need, it has that same effect: Perhaps it is too late for me to go home again and

walk through a different door, but it not too late
for me to help others open more promising
doors for themselves.

The Westside dedication was a big day for
me, not just because of the honor—Congressman Lee Terry was there, along with Omaha City
Council President Chuck Sigerson, and 2001
Heisman Trophy winner from Nebraska, Eric
Crouch, whom I am proud to say I helped mentor along the way—but because I was able to
share it with Denise and the boys. The ceremonies are a blur to me today, a mix of band music,
sunshine and friendly faces in the audience,
which is why I am glad that I put together a
photo album to document the occasion.

Today, when I look at the photo album, I can
still remember the sights and sounds of that
day, but I also can see something that I did not
see at the time. Denise was at my side the entire
time, smiling and being her usual gracious self
to the guests, but when I look at the photographs today I see moments of strain and stress
on her face, at those times when she thought no
one was looking. This gets back to the fact that
she is an introvert and I am an extrovert. She
doesn't like crowds or loud noise or situations in
which everyone is looking at her. I, on the other

hand, revel in those situations because they are like sunshine to me.

Charities are an important part of community service, and I strongly believe that it's important to contribute to worthwhile charities. However, one of the things I've learned the hard way is that charity work can quickly eat up your time and resources without accomplishing much. Instead of giving to 853 charities, most of which are of questionable value, and serving on dozens of boards, I'd recommend that you pick four or five charities that have a reputation for effectiveness and devote all of your time, energy, and money that you can set aside for charity work to just those four or five. In the end, your business life and family life will suffer less and you'll have accomplished more.

Community service can be as rewarding to the philanthropist as to the community. I've personally received such a reward from a project that is especially dear to me and combines an old dream, a resolution of part of my family history, and a need of the community. This project is part of The Stephen Center, which specializes in treating mental health and substance abuse. They are creating a new center called the John L. Hoich Center for Recovery. This new center will help recovering drug and alcohol addicts, which has long been a dream of mine.

The fall of my junior year at Westside High School, after attending three sessions of the Nebraska School of Alcoholic Studies, I conducted a course on alcoholism and shared my experiences with my classmates. Part of my presentation was a film that showed the various ways that alcoholism affects families.

Because my course was such a novelty, the student newspaper published an article about it in which I expressed my opinion that the first step in controlling alcoholism was to admit that you have a problem. I told the newspaper that I was "starting a mission for the world. I want people to realize that alcohol is a serious drug—worse than even hard drugs and nicotine."

At that point in my life, what I wanted more than anything else was not a successful lawn-care business, but to attend Valley Hope Alcoholism Training Center in Norton, Kansas, where I hoped to become a certified alcoholism counselor. That never happened because life has a way of grabbing you up out of your dreams and giving you a good shaking. My reality was that I had obligations to my brother and sisters that were more pressing—and more important—than any dreams I had for my future.

The Hoich Center is being built on the very spot where the old First and Last Chance bar used to stand. This was the bar that my Uncle George and my dad owned and operated. This was the very bar from which my father came home drunk every night and beat me, my mother, and my sisters. It gives me tremendous satisfaction to know that this location is no longer such a bar; it is now a place of hope, of a new beginning, a true second chance for alcoholics, addicts, and their families.

It's true that community service is good for business—the contacts you make and the publicity you receive can open many doors. But beyond that, it is just right. If you've enjoyed business success, it is at least partially because you have received support from your commu-

nity—the people who have become your customers. It's only fair that you return the favor by
working to improve the quality of life for the
community as a whole.

John with His Twin Sons, Jeremy and Justin,
Each with His First Lawnmower

Winning Personal Traits

The contents of this chapter actually should not need to be said. Sadly, too many people make success impossible simply because of inappropriate action or poor mental attitude.

First and foremost, "just say no!"

Alcohol is a drug and there is no addiction worse than alcoholism. It doesn't receive the focus it should, I think, because so many parents use alcohol and pretend that it is not a dangerous drug. I do know that many people respond to the kind of childhood that I had by turning to alcohol or other drugs. That way never leads to success.

In many respects, human behavior is easier to understand than business principles. In business, if you fill a need at the right price in the right location, success is likely but not guaranteed because intangibles such as weather, politics, and competition can upset the best-laid business plan. Business is always a roll of the dice. In human relationships, if you fail to fill a basic need, if you suppress needed emotions, the results are more predictable: negative behavior is learned to replace the needs that never were met. The trick is to find a nondestructive way to cope with such trauma.

One of the basic human needs we all have is the need to be loved. I was loved by my mom and by my brother and sisters, but never by my father. A lack of love in that area left a hole in my soul. Just as Michael had holes in his heart, I have holes in my soul. From a very young age, I have tried to fill those holes by working hard and proving myself as a lovable human being. I have also tried to fill those holes with what psychologists call obsessive-compulsive behavior.

Since I was a kid, I have felt compelled to touch everything twice. In business, if I start something I have to complete it. I cannot start something unless I can finish it. If I am supposed to lock a door, I check it twice. If I am supposed to turn out lights, I check twice to make certain that

I have. Since I was a kid, I have had this habit of cleaning out a drawer in my house every Sunday. Every drawer in my home is spotless. Once I go through the drawers, I put the items in a big box and then I give those items away to people who need them. My motto is: store what you must, share what you can.

When I turned forty, I developed a new ritual that replaced the touching twice that is an outgrowth of my obsessive-compulsive behavior. I cannot get out of the shower until I drip a drop of water from my nose into the center hole of the drain. I have to turn the water on and off until I get that drop of water into that hole. That is not as debilitating as it seems because the more time I spend in the shower, the more successful I become, and that is because the shower is where I make all of my business decisions.

I think more clearly in the shower. I can think and see visions of what something would look like, or what something would be like if I did this or did that. If I have to talk to someone, I first have that conversation in the shower—how I'm going to say it and so on. I can see cause-effect principles more clearly in the shower. My thoughts are more innovative when I am in the shower.

Over the years, I have filled the holes in my soul with behavior that has predictable outcomes, at least for me. My shower rituals are harmless and they provide me with something to hold onto to when I am out in the world navigating through treacherous waters. I am the way I am because I never had the love of a father. Little boys who have loving fathers in their lives don't develop obsessive-compulsive behavior. Little boys who grow up without their biological fathers develop obsessive-compulsive behavior, if they are lucky. If they are not lucky, they develop more destructive behavior and end up in prison or in mental institutions. Did you know that most of the males in juvenile detention centers are fatherless sons?

Another personal trait that is most useful in business is a healthy balance between trust and suspicion. I've always been a very trusting and forgiving person. Sometimes this has helped me, but more often, it has been a negative in my life. We all naturally want to trust people, but the simple fact is that people will often let you down.

Only God can be counted on unequivocally. A good example of this was my partnership in Special Mowing, Inc. I trusted them, but twice they put a knife in my back. I should have figured out the first time that I could never trust them again. This is why one of my favorite sayings is "Trust in God, ask all others to pay cash."

Throughout this book, I've talked about the need to avoid negativity and foster positive attitudes. I cannot stress enough that it's nearly impossible to succeed with a negative attitude. I take this step even to the extent of trying to avoid negative people so that they won't bring me down with them.

One of the important aspects of having a positive attitude is to focus on the future. I know that in many ways, it is my past that drives me, but it is my past that also causes me to look toward the future.

Unless you're incredibly lucky or a trust fund baby, you're not going to build a highly successful business overnight. If you think only about today, you are most likely to remain where you are today forever. When you look at the world, you not only need to see it as it is today, but also as it can be tomorrow.

I'll never forget something Denise said in an interview with *Omaha Magazine*, when Jeremy and Justin were three years old. "I believe in living in the moment," she said. "I don't dwell on the past, and I try not to worry about the future. I believe I'm exactly where I'm supposed to be in life, and I let the Lord take it from there."

Those comments struck a chord with me because it made me realize that I live mostly in the future and the reason for that is a past that drives me to keep moving so that my past never again becomes part of my future. Unlike Denise, I'm not where I am supposed to be.

For many years, that focus on the future helped me grow my business. However, I'm just beginning to learn, finally, after all these years, that I'm headed toward the second half of my life. I am now ready to learn and accept a new way of living. The first step to doing that is to really appreciate who I am and to understand that I am okay as I am. My life coach, Susan Koenig, has really helped me understand who I am. Now I'm beginning to see that I didn't have to do all the attention-getting behavior that I did earlier in my life. Now I realize that true success is finding out how to be content with who I am; it is not dependent on having someone in my life provide me with contentment. If I can't be content with myself, how can I be content in a relationship? It has taken me a long time to understand that. It has been a lifetime journey.

I want to enjoy life more now, whether that means hiking through the trails of my resort, or fishing in the lake with Jeremy and Justin. I'm ready to take off my tool belt and start learning how to enjoy my success.

There was a time when growing my business meant adding new customers, but the nature of my business has changed so drastically in recent years that is no longer the case. Today, growing my business means *adding* new types of business and *subtracting* old customers. I expanded by purchasing a 24-million-gallon ethanol plant in Rosholt, South Dakota; a packing house in Wellington, Kansas; the High Tech Weight Loss Clinic; Greek Island Restaurant, and Silver Crest, an assisted living facility in Ames, Iowa, to name a few ventures. In 2003, I moved the Hoich Enterprises corporate headquarters to a location that provided me with a focal point for all my ventures in business and real estate.

As I look back, my whole life has been about business. Every day was work, work, work. All the time I was planting seeds from the ground up, building relationships, meeting people. Someone once asked me: "Do you have to know everyone everywhere you go?" My answer was, "yes." I meet people and they never forget me and I never forget them. Each time I meet a person, I plant a seed. Those seeds grow into mowing contracts, real estate ventures, and business opportunities. If I made money off them, I also made money for charities off them, because I have always linked charity and business. My mom always said, "When they quit talking about you is when you've got to worry." I like to keep them talking.

In 2005, I did something I never thought I would do. I sold my thirty-one-year-old lawn service business, the one that I founded with my mom's Sears Craftsman lawn mower. But I didn't just sell it to anyone. I sold it to three of my employees. The new company, which is named Liberty Grounds Maintenance, is headed up by my old friend Kirby Clark, the same Kirby Clark who was with me the day Mom died. I've known him since kindergarten and I have complete faith in him to carry on the tradition I began.

I kept one crew to maintain the lawns of my real estate investments, plus my own home, but the major accounts—Omaha Steaks International, Oriental Trading, Mercedes Benz, Connectivity Solutions, and Wear Properties, whose account I have had since day one—were all transferred to Liberty Grounds Maintenance. Kirby will be very successful with the business because he won't have the overhead I had in the beginning.

What selling the business did for me was to eliminate fifteen work hours a week, and that is time that I was be able to give to my sons, Jeremy and Justin, and to devote to new business endeavors, such as American First Communities. Five years ago, I came up with the idea of buying the military housing at Offutt Air Force Base. Why not? The new trend in the military is privatization of services, including privatization of housing.

At that point, all I had was an idea, so I approached a potential partner, a successful businesswoman I met in the Young President's Organization. Working as equal partners, we put together a proposal for Offutt that had the Air Force deed to American First Communities 2,400 housing units on base, many of them constructed in the 1950s and 1960s, for one dollar, in exchange for which we agreed to invest more than a quarter of a million dollars into renovating appproximately 800 existing homes and constructing approximately 1600 new homes over a fifty-year period.

Just think: I began my career mowing grass at Offutt, the home of the Strategic Air Command, and today I am half owner of 2400 military homes on the base. If that's not a true reflection of the American Dream, then I have misread the requirements of achieving American Dream status. Besides that, I have a fifty-year mowing contract with the air base that will enable Jeremy and Justin to have substantial income long after I am gone. Of course, I will only be ninety-seven when the mowing contract expires, so I may just bid on it again.

There are many ways to become a successful business entrepreneur, but the key to holding onto that success, as the song says, is to know when to hold 'em and when to fold 'em. Director Woody Allen once played a role in which his character compared a romantic relationship to a shark, the bottom line being that both have to continue moving forward to stay alive. Business is a lot like that. To be successful, you have to keep moving forward—and that's what I always have tried to do.

Julie and Joe M. Smith, John L. Hoich, Joe McDermott, and David Janke with Twelve Sisters of the Good Shepherd "Omaha" (John did free lawn care for them for ten years.)

13

Religion and Business, They Do Mix

In my opinion, there is room for God in big business. There is room for God in little business. There is room for God everywhere. Whether you are a leader or a follower, there is room for God in your life. I believe in Christ Lord Jesus, the Savior. I believe that he got me through a lot of tribulations in my life. That's why I always say that happiness is taking care of God first, family second, and business third.

As long as my friends believe in God, whether they are Muslim, Jewish, Christian, whatever, then I am okay with them. I don't think that I could have a close friend who is agnostic, since to be that is to be a believer in nothing. I don't care if a person believes that trees are God, as long as he believes there is power higher than himself. When it comes to friends, you have to ask yourself: If a person believes in nothing, how can he believe in you?

God does not always get in someone's face to tell them what to do. Sometimes He stands back and gives them choices that allow them to take one direction or another. I don't know if He has a name for that, but we mortals usually refer to it as a test of character. To be honest, I don't know if I had character when I was sixteen and seventeen—I don't even know if I have character today, because that's for others to determine—but I do know that the path that God laid out for me was well lighted and intolerant of man-made detours.

A couple of years before Mom died, she and I left the Catholic religion, accepted Christ into our lives, and joined a non-denominational Christian church. That's when I really started trying to be a Christian. The impetus from all this came from Patty Schroeder, who was a true friend of Mom. She is a woman of great faith and a true believer in the Lord. She invited Mom and me to a revival meeting one night and that's when we both accepted Christ.

One of the most influential men in my life was Pastor John Walker at Glad Tidings Church. He became an inspirational person to me because of his ability to talk about God and the love of Christ that lives inside each person. He was the person who brought me into Suburban Rotary as the youngest member in Omaha history. What was so cool about Pastor Walker was that he placed happy face stickers on everyone he met. He'd put those stickers on their suits, their shirts, or even their heads. He'd slap that sticker in place and say, "Be happy!" He died of cancer at the age of sixty-two, but his influence on me and countless others has not died.

Sure, you can be successful without recognizing a higher power or a God. But, the truth depends on what's inside your heart. We're here such a short time and have such a short visit on earth, that if some human beings want to take all the credit and not give it to their God, or their higher power, or the Lord Jesus Christ; after their time on earth is over, they will sure be lonely, because they ain't goin' nowhere. If they aren't going anywhere, then what was it all for? How great was it? Was it all that wonderful?

John and His First Horse

14

Surviving Success

It's easy to spot beginner millionaires. They go out and buy an airplane that's too big. They buy too many fancy cars. They buy lake homes and desert properties in Las Vegas or California or Florida. They buy expensive toys they will never use because they are still workaholics. They become successful without ever learning how to manage their success. Most people figure it out eventually, but many do not. They crash and burn and walk away from their businesses in a daze, as if they had just survived an airplane crash.

Surviving success is an art unto itself. It has everything to do with learning to delegate authority and trusting the people you have put in place. If you don't set boundaries in your personal life, it is difficult to set boundaries for your company. Nothing is more demoralizing to employees than seeing their boss make a fool of himself by going on personal spending sprees that ignore the conservative business principles that he has instilled into his employees. Any employer that tells his employees, "Do as I say, not as I do," is strolling on the deck of a sinking ship.

Another thing to keep in mind is that before you were successful, no one paid you much attention. Success draws attention. Now that you are a success, you must be careful about the people you associate with. You cannot afford, literally, to fall in with the wrong crowd. You never asked to be a role model, but it goes with the territory. Your future income may well be determined by the presence or absence of rumors about your personal life. The more money you earn, the more boundaries you need to set.

If by failing to set boundaries, you lose your integrity, your soul and your spirit, what have you really accomplished with your success? Money? The almighty dollar? Nobody gives a damn how much money you have. No one cares. People are either jealous or they crab about you. Very few people will love you unconditionally because you have a few dollars in the bank. It took me a while to learn this, but at the end of the day, I am still just John Hoich—and people either like me, or they don't.

Postscript

I had two purposes in writing this book. One was to put some closure to my past. I hope that by putting it all on paper, I'll finally be free to face the future without fearing that the past will catch up to me.

I really believe that this is happening; but even if so, it is still a meager accomplishment.

What I most want to happen is for one of you readers who may think that you have too much going against you, that you don't have enough resources or enough experience, that there's no way to escape from whatever cruel lot life has dealt you, that you may realize from these pages that your situation is not hopeless. When I started, all I had was an old lawn mower. I believe that if I had had some other piece of equipment, I still could have done what I did—just in another field. If all I had was a pair of scissors, maybe I would have made clothes, or whatever. The point is that you start with whatever you have, no matter how little. I hope that you will realize that determination, focus, positive think-

ing and actions, cooperation, and the willingness to make decisions can lead you to enjoy a
successful and happy life.

Keep your priorities straight: God, family and
then business. I'm still practicing at what I
preach. I hope what I've preached and said to you
will help you find success and happiness.

Index

Index

One to Keep

Other Books by Lexi Blake

Evidence of Desire, Coming January 8, 2019

Masters Of Ménage (by Shayla Black and Lexi Blake)
Their Virgin Captive
Their Virgin's Secret
Their Virgin Concubine
Their Virgin Princess
Their Virgin Hostage
Their Virgin Secretary
Their Virgin Mistress

The Perfect Gentlemen (by Shayla Black and Lexi Blake)
Scandal Never Sleeps
Seduction in Session
Big Easy Temptation
Smoke and Sin
At the Pleasure of the President, Coming Fall 2018

URBAN FANTASY

Thieves
Steal the Light
Steal the Day
Steal the Moon
Steal the Sun
Steal the Night
Ripper
Addict
Sleeper
Outcast, Coming 2018

LEXI BLAKE WRITING AS SOPHIE OAK
Small Town Siren
Siren in the City
Away From Me
Three to Ride
Siren Enslaved
Two to Love
Siren Beloved
One to Keep, Coming August 7, 2018
Siren in Waiting, Coming September 25, 2018
Lost in Bliss, Coming September 25, 2018
Found in Bliss, Coming Fall 2018
Siren in Bloom, Coming Fall 2018
Pure Bliss, Coming Winter 2018

One to Keep

Nights in Bliss, Colorado Book 3

Lexi Blake
writing as

Sophie Oak

One to Keep
Nights in Bliss, Colorado Book 3

Published by DLZ Entertainment LLC

Copyright 2018 DLZ Entertainment LLC
Edited by Chloe Vale
ISBN: 978-1-937608-89-7

Sign up for Lexi Blake's newsletter
and be entered to win a $25 gift certificate
to the bookseller of your choice.

Join us for news, fun, and exclusive content
including free short stories.

Go to www.LexiBlake.net to subscribe.

There's a new contest every month!

Dedication

For Rich – I wouldn't know anything about love and romance without you. It might not be like a romance novel, but every day with you ends in a happy ever after as long as we're together.

2018 Dedication

Stefan Talbot was the character who taught me that POV truly matters and that I can't always please every single reader. He was the first character I'd built up a lot of hype around and some readers felt like I let them down. He wasn't what they'd expected. He wasn't the perfect Dom they'd dreamed of. Turns out he was vulnerable and unsure at times. He was scared and didn't always make the right choices. I got some bad reviews. It crushed me at first, the idea that I'd gotten it wrong. Years later, I'm good with it. What I realized from Stef was we have to be who we are—even if we look perfect on the outside, we're human. I'm human and that's a good thing. So this book is dedicated to the people who love me, the real me, the one who makes mistakes and can be arrogant at times and hideously vulnerable and unsure at others, the me who seeks to be better and inevitably fails. This book is dedicated to the ones who pick me up and make it easy for me to try again. You know who you are.

You are my world.

Chapter One

"Let's go, Waters." A surprisingly deep voice made Jennifer Waters start. "You have a visitor."

She brought her head up, her heart pounding, and looked at the guard. She'd kept her head down because it seemed the safest way to survive the whole jailhouse experience. It had been all right when her cellmates had been a couple of prostitutes. Annie and Roxie had been sweet, if totally underdressed for the February weather. Unfortunately, Annie had turned out to be Andy and Roxie really had a set tucked away in his miniskirt. They'd been taken to the men's holding cell, and now Jen was left with two drunks and a woman who had already threatened to kill her because she didn't like brunettes.

All in all, a visitor seemed like a good thing.

She rose from her seat in the corner and followed the bulky guard. It was quiet this early in the morning, but the hum of paranoia seemed loud in her ears. That was what happened when one minute you were an up-and-coming artist and the next the police were hauling you away.

It had been a rough twenty-four hours.

"In there." The guard opened the door to one of the interview rooms, and Jen walked in.

It was a small, dank room. The fluorescent lights gave everything a slightly green cast. There was a metal table bolted to the floor and two chairs. Whoever designed the sets for those procedural TV shows

had obviously spent some time in lockup.

An expensive-looking briefcase sat on the table, and a man paced by the barred window. He turned immediately when the door opened.

"Thank god. I thought they were never going to bring you out. I've been here for three hours." The man looked to be in his late twenties, maybe early thirties. He was strikingly handsome, with dark hair and green eyes. He wore a dark suit and a snowy white shirt. An emerald silk tie matched his eyes.

"Are you the public defender?" She'd been waiting for way more than a few hours. It was reassuring to see someone who didn't have a gun strapped to his waist.

The door closed behind her. It locked with a telling thud. Everywhere she'd been for the last twenty-four hours had a locked door. She sat down, her legs shaking.

"Not exactly, but I am your lawyer," he said, sinking into the seat across from her. "My name is Finn Taylor. Do you know why you were arrested?"

She knew why. The police had been over it about a thousand times. She knew the whole story, but it didn't make any sense to her. "I've been accused of theft. They think I stole a painting."

A painting worth roughly a half a million dollars, to be exact. She didn't think she would ever forget that moment when her boss, Jean Claude Renard, led the police back to the office of the prestigious art gallery where she'd been working for the last five months. Boss? Jean Claude had been much more than her boss. He'd been an experiment to see if she could ever get over…

She took a deep breath. She wasn't going to think about him. She was going to do what she'd been doing her whole life, focus on the here and now. Thinking about Stefan Talbot and everything she'd left behind in Bliss would only make the situation worse.

"Yes." Finn Taylor's voice brought her back to reality. "You've been accused of grand larceny. Renard is accusing you of stealing a painting from the gallery. It was a painting by Picasso."

"Yes, I know it well. It was one of his smaller canvases. It was brought in for repair. The owner had a fire in his home, and there was some smoke damage. Jean Claude is a renowned restorer." It was one of the reasons she'd been excited to work for him. She'd been in the

same room with several masterpieces, so close she could see the brushstrokes. The first few months with him had been a series of wonders. The last had been a complete nightmare.

The lawyer's eyebrows quirked up as he flicked open his pen. A perfect white notepad lay in front of him. "Any chance that you know where it is or who might have taken it?"

Tears filled her eyes. His words reminded her how utterly helpless she was. "No. I walked in yesterday morning, and it was gone. I know that painting was in the restoration room the night before. Jean Claude had been working on it. It was almost done."

"And you have access to that room."

She forced herself to nod. She'd been over this with the police. "Yes, I know the code to the room. Jean Claude lets me work in there. It's a large studio. There's more than enough space for two easels. I work in there almost every day. The light is perfect."

She'd been planning to work yesterday when all hell had broken loose. She'd gotten off the train at her stop in Deep Ellum and made her way to the gallery, feeling light for the first time in a long while. She'd known how to fix her painting. Renard had told her he might be able to find a buyer for her newest work. That was exciting news. Still, she had some work to do on it. It was good, but it wasn't perfect. She hadn't gotten the colors right. She'd stared at that painting for days while the oils dried. Even after they had dried, she'd stared at the painting. After the gallery show the night before, she'd known what it needed. Despite the late hour, she'd stayed and worked. This painting, unlike the first, would be perfect. It was similar to the one Jean Claude had liked, but this one would be better. This would be the piece that broke her out as an artist. She'd been thinking of how her last three works had sold quickly. She'd been smiling when she entered the gallery because she'd felt like an up-and-coming artist.

She'd never felt quite as alone as she had when they put her in the back of that police car. Her only thought had been to call the one man she'd promised she would never call again. Even now she longed for his authoritative presence.

"When was the last time you saw the Picasso?"

She sniffled and straightened her back. She was alone in this, and she needed to be strong. "It was there the morning of the gallery

show. I assumed he put it in the safe. He wouldn't leave it lying around with all those guests in the building. After the gallery show, I stayed late to supervise the cleanup. I went into the restoration room because I wanted to work for a while. Jean Claude said he might be able to sell another painting for me, and I needed the money. I wanted to work fast, though. He said he had someone coming in this morning to look at the work. I thought if I could get it right, maybe the buyer would be impressed. I didn't want him to see the first one. It's fine, but the colors weren't right, you see. There was too much red. I needed something soothing. Green. I mixed a lovely green. It had some blue tones. Emotional but muted."

"Okay, the day before the Picasso was still there. It went into the safe, and you didn't see it again." Finn ignored her arty comments, but she was used to that. He was a lawyer, after all. He probably didn't care much about the feelings colors invoked. He was all business. "You didn't see the painting after the show?"

"No, I didn't. And I had no idea it was missing. I didn't get to the gallery until after ten in the morning. I worked late the night before, and then I had to take the first canvas home because Jean Claude hates it when I have two canvases in the restoration room. I wanted the new painting to be waiting for the buyer right there in the middle of the room, as though it had a bow on it. The trains had stopped running. I had to walk home lugging that canvas. I can be forgiven for sleeping in a bit, right? When I walked in yesterday morning the whole gallery was chaotic. Jean Claude was screaming. The receptionist was crying. He immediately started yelling at me. He says I was the last one to use the code."

Finn's lips turned down, and he made a few notes as he spoke. "Yes, that's what the security company is saying. They claim they can produce records that show when you entered and when you left. We can't tell when the safe was last opened. It's manual. Is it true that the code you used on the door was unique to you?"

There was the rub, and Jen knew it. "Yes. When I was hired I was interviewed by the security company, and I selected a password. All employees select a code."

"And no one else knows this code?"

"No. Well, I suppose the security company knows it. And Jean

Claude gave me the combo to the safe. He didn't like hauling stuff around himself."

Finn's pen flew across the paper.

"Is that important? I mean, do you think someone from the security firm stole the painting? Or another employee?"

A light shrug. "Well, it gives us a place to start. The problem is the security camera in that room was out. The last footage the company has is of you handling the camera."

She felt her whole body flush. "I was told to turn it off."

"By whom?"

"Jean Claude. He didn't want the thing beeping while the gallery show was going on. I told him no one could hear it, but he gets touchy when we have a show going. It's best to placate him. I forgot to turn it back on."

"He claims he never told you to do that."

Yep, that was what the police had said. Her stomach turned. Why was he lying? The implications scared the crap out of her. Was she being set up? If she was then she had no idea how she would fight it. She had a little money saved up from the sale of her work, but it wouldn't pay a lawyer for long. Who were they going to believe? A respected businessman or an artist who came from the wrong side of the tracks?

"I didn't do it," she whispered.

His hand came out and covered hers. "I know you didn't."

That was not the answer she'd been expecting. It made her wary. She pulled her hands back. Too many people lately had seemed nice and turned out to be so very cruel. It was a lesson she should have learned early in life. Hell, she had learned it and learned it well. Her time in Bliss had made her forget how fucked up the real world could be.

"And how do you know that?" She sounded rude even to her own ears.

The handsome lawyer didn't seem to take offense. He smiled, a boyish look on his face. "I have it on the best authority I know. My partner is good friends with someone who firmly believes in your innocence. As my partner also happens to be my Dom, I never argue with him. It tends to get me spanked."

He said it with the glow of a man who was well loved, but the word *Dom* made her heart plunge. It reminded her of everything she'd lost and everything she'd walked away from.

"Who do you work for?"

"My partner is named Julian Lodge. He's good friends with—"

"Stefan Talbot." The name came out of her mouth with a thud. Of all the people in the world she didn't want to know about her current situation, he was number one. Her shame washed over her like a scalding bath. She'd always meant to go back to Bliss someday. She'd dreamed of confronting the man she'd loved, but in her dreams she always returned as a successful, wealthy artist. In her fantasies, she had a man on her arm so Stef wouldn't think she'd spent years pining over him. Never once did she think he'd have to bail her out of jail.

"How did he know?" She hadn't called or talked to anyone in Bliss since the morning she left. It had been hard, but it was the only way to go. She'd cut her ties and moved on like her mother had taught her. Keep moving. It was the only way to live. Staying too long in Bliss had tripped her up. It had caused her to do the stupidest thing of all—fall in love.

For the first time, Finn looked slightly uncomfortable. "I think it's best that you take that up with Mr. Talbot."

"Just tell me. I can handle it." It was a lie, but one that came easily to her. She'd spent a good portion of her life handling things she shouldn't have.

"Uhm, I believe Mr. Talbot hired a private investigator to find you. Once Mr. Taggart tracked you to Dallas, the firm he owns kept tabs on you. Julian has been getting regular reports from McKay-Taggart. When he was told you had been arrested, he immediately called Mr. Talbot and got in contact with the district attorney. Your arraignment has been scheduled. Mr. Lodge will pay your bail, and you'll be released to his custody."

"Doesn't a judge have to decide that?"

A smirk crossed the lawyer's face. "Mr. Lodge can be persuasive when he wants to be. Trust me, I'll have you out of here in a few hours. I'll take the lead on your case, but I'll consult with the best criminal defense attorneys. I already have McKay-Taggart researching Renard. If he's behind this, we'll string his ass up. I

promise, it's going to be okay."

"Why would he lie? Jean Claude is lying."

"My guess? He knows more than he's telling us. That painting is incredibly expensive. Maybe he's selling it on the black market."

Jen shook her head. "Why that one? We had a Dutch master in the studio last month. It was worth millions. Before that he worked on restoring a Renaissance painting that's considered priceless. It doesn't make any sense. He can't get more than a half a million for that one on the black market, if he can sell it at all."

"A half a million is more than enough to tempt a lot of people. It's a lot of motive."

"He's independently wealthy." At least, as far as Jen knew he was. His house was in the best part of Dallas. He drove a Jag.

"I'll have someone look into his finances." He glanced down at his watch. "It shouldn't be long now. When we get the judge to release you, I'll personally take you to your place so you can pick up some things."

"Why do I need to pick up my things?"

The door to the office opened, and Jen looked up in shock.

"Don't worry about your things. You won't be going back to your apartment, Jennifer." Stefan Talbot stood in the doorway. He was lean and tall. His suit was immaculate, but his black hair fell over his eyes. The slight messiness did nothing to distract from his overwhelming presence.

She got to her shaky feet and kind of wished she was back in the cell. The bars would stop her from doing something stupid. The need to throw herself in his arms was almost overwhelming. He was solid and seemed like the safest thing she'd seen in forever. It was an illusion. Stef was dangerous. He'd already broken her heart once. Damn if she was going to give him a second shot at it. Before she could manage to speak, he was walking into the room, making a straight line toward her.

"Everything's been arranged, Finn. The paperwork is done. Julian can work miracles when he wants to. I can't tell you how much I appreciate this. We'll be in close contact as this matter moves forward. I've left notes with your secretary on how I want to proceed legally. I assume you'll work with the investigators on the case. The

17

first thing I want is every bit of information you can dig up on that fucker Renard."

"Excellent." Finn Taylor was the only one in the room who looked satisfied. He stood and collected his things. "I already have a team working on Renard. We'll know something soon, Sir."

That *Sir* grated on Jen's nerves. So did the deferential way Finn Taylor nodded at Stef. It was more than the polite acknowledgement of a lawyer to his client. Finn wasn't being polite to his client. He was honoring a Dom.

"Your work is impeccable, Finn. You honor your Master. Tell Julian I'll be in touch with him." He turned back to Jen. "Let's move, Jennifer. I have a plane ready. We need to be at Love Field in an hour. I have an officer waiting to process you out."

Jen's head whirled. "Plane?"

"Yes, plane. We're going back to Bliss."

"Bullshit."

Cool, gray eyes slitted, and she could practically feel the will rolling off him. Stef was tense, and she knew it was a bad idea to push him, but she couldn't help it.

"I'm serious, Stef. I'm not going anywhere with you." She couldn't go back to Bliss. Panic threatened to swamp her. He was here. He was right here in front of her, and her heart didn't give a damn that he was a bastard. For the first time in months, she felt desire for something besides her art. She couldn't, wouldn't, go down that path again.

He got into her space, a move he'd perfected seemingly long before he met her. She held her ground. Even though he didn't touch her physically, he seemed to surround her. Suddenly her whole world was Stef, his gray eyes, the heat of his body, his masculine, clean scent. He filled her every sense.

"I'm not going home with you." She forced herself to say the words.

His lips hitched up. "At least you admit Bliss is your home."

That wasn't what she'd meant. Bliss, Colorado, had felt like home when she'd been there, but she knew beyond a shadow of a doubt that Bliss wasn't big enough for the two of them. "It's your home. Hell, Stef, it's your little kingdom, and you like to play the

king, don't you?"

"Yes, because everyone does what I say." Stef's low growl made her breath speed up. "Everyone in Bliss bows down to me. Have you been gone for so long that you forget Max regularly kicks my ass? And Nell and Henry are currently protesting my gardening practices."

He was too close for comfort. She gave in and took a step back. She could see plainly that he was satisfied with her discomfort. "Don't try to play the poor rich boy with me. You're a puppet master. You like to pull the strings and see how people dance. Well, I'm not in your kingdom anymore, and there's no way you can get me there again. So you can take your money and go back to Colorado."

It was stupid. Even as she said the words, she wanted to take them back. She'd spent the last twenty-four hours terrified in a jail cell. She would have to be the stupidest woman in the world to turn him down, but she'd never thought around Stef. Since the moment she'd met him, she'd been a quivering mass of emotion and desire every time he entered a room.

"Stubborn thing. I'll make it easy on you." His hands caught hers, and before she could think she felt cold metal surrounding her wrists. He flicked the cuffs on with the cool precision of a man who often cuffed the women in his life.

"What are you doing?" She stared at her hands. At least this time they were in front of her. She preferred it that way. Damn, her life had taken a wrong turn when she could compare and contrast her experiences with men who handcuffed her.

"Taking you home, Jennifer. Whether you like it or not."

He leaned down and picked her up. She was in his arms, nestled close to his chest. She looked up at the square, inflexible line of his jaw. His arms tightened around her, and she was caged more closely than she'd been in the holding cell. She had the suspicion that this time Stef would be harder to escape from than before. He kicked open the door and started down the hall.

Yep, like it or not, she was going back to Bliss.

Chapter Two

Stefan Talbot kicked open the door to the interrogation room and strode down the hall. Jen's slender body finally relaxed in his arms as she seemed to figure out he wasn't letting her go. He stared straight ahead, unwilling to look down at her. If he looked at her he might falter, and he couldn't risk it. Six months had gone by, and all he'd had was a bunch of photos taken by some private investigator named Karina. He'd stared at them every day. It made him feel like a complete pervert every time he looked at them. Luckily, he was comfortable with his perversity since he couldn't seem to help himself.

Trouble. She'd always been trouble. When he'd met her two years before, his first thought was to run for the hills. No. That hadn't been his first thought at all. His first thought had been to snap a collar on her and chain her to his side. He'd decided to run for the hills when he'd come to his senses.

"Why are you doing this?" Her voice was quiet, almost as though she was asking herself the question, or didn't really want to know the answer.

He stopped right there in the middle of the bustling hall and finally looked down at her face. Golden-brown hair and large green

eyes stared up at him. Her skin was like porcelain, but there was a smattering of freckles that crossed her nose and made him want to run his lips across her face to kiss each and every one.

Why? Why did it have to be this woman? Why did she have to be so fucking young?

"Because you need me." He kept his answer short. If he didn't, he would end up a blathering idiot.

There was a sheen of tears in her eyes that told Stef he'd fucked up. He always managed to with her. He was a Dom of the first order, known for taking care of his subs, but he fumbled the minute she batted those eyes at him. There was nothing to do about it now. He simply continued down the hall. He would fix her when they got back to Bliss.

Now that he thought about it, he should have expected this greeting. The entire plane trip here, he'd had all sorts of fantasies about being her hero. In his fantasies, she'd cried prettily and thrown herself into his arms. He'd gotten her out of this current scrape and then protected her. He'd set her up in a nice studio in Bliss, and she'd be waiting for him when she was old enough to know what she wanted.

Twenty-three. She was fucking twenty-three years old. He was a thirty-two-year-old man in love with a girl barely out of college. She had no idea who she was, and she'd proven it by running away. She was just a kid, and he'd done all sorts of nasty, dirty, glorious things to her.

Maybe he wasn't so comfortable with his perversity.

He turned down the main hall. Standing off to one side was a man he'd been told was named Ian Taggart. He was large and seemed to speak Sarcasm, but he owned the company Julian had hired to watch over Jen. Next to him was a quiet man dressed in jeans and a T-shirt. The one time he'd heard the guy speak it had been in a lyrical Irish accent.

Nate Wright, his old friend and the current sheriff of Bliss, Colorado, stood talking to the district attorney and the chief of police. Lucky for him both men belonged to a private BDSM club and both wanted to be in the debt of insanely wealthy men. They had streamlined the process of getting Jennifer out on bond, going so far

as to wake a judge to do the paperwork. It wasn't exactly procedure, but otherwise, Jen would still have hours in a cell, and he couldn't even consider that.

"Damn, I hope I can keep the press off this." The chief shook his head as he signed the paperwork releasing Jennifer Waters to the custody of Stef and Sheriff Wright. He looked over at Taggart. "Will you monitor the situation?"

The blond guy nodded. "We're already on it, Chief. I've sent you the file we have on Waters. I've had Karina Mills and Liam, here, tailing her. She's as boring as a chick who talks to herself can be."

"I do not," she said, her eyes wide.

The Irishman sighed. "You absolutely do. You had an entire conversation on the train two days ago about the color blue. You didn't even notice that the man next to you thought you were talking to him. He was hitting on you, by the way. I don't think you noticed that either."

"I hope you made sure he stayed away from her," Stef said, knowing it was a stupid thing to get upset about.

"I was being paid to follow her, not monitor her sex life," Liam replied. "Not that she has one. She did pick up a vibrator the other day. It's all in my report."

"Spies are…spying on me?" Jen asked.

"You know you love it." Taggart glanced down at Jen, his eyes seeming to stick on the cuffs. "Julian said you were good. Way to learn, Talbot. She got away once. She won't get away if you cuff her to something that doesn't move. I've found headboards are perfect."

He did not need advice from the peanut gallery. He turned to the DA. "We've tried to keep everything quiet."

The DA seemed much more comfortable than the chief. "The girl's never been in trouble before. It's unusual, but we're releasing her to law enforcement custody. The people who own the painting are fine with letting her go for now. You have to talk to them because they could still press charges. Besides, I don't know if I buy Renard's story. He's a shady fellow. If she stole the painting, then where is it? We've searched her place."

Jen's head came off his shoulder again. "You did?"

Nate never looked up from the paperwork he was now signing.

"They didn't find anything beyond your own paintings, and this afternoon the whole thing is being packed up and moved to Bliss. Stef packed your work himself this morning while we were waiting on the judge."

"I'll make sure all of your canvases get back home." He hadn't been able to get her latest painting out, but it appeared she had recently finished it, possibly the night before her arrest. The oil was still wet. Renard, the fucker, had refused to release it, and no amount of intimidation had worked on him. At least the work in her apartment was properly packed and readied for transit. Perhaps he would set Mr. Sarcasm on Renard personally. The big guy wasn't merely obnoxious. He also was thoroughly intimidating. If he couldn't money whip the man, maybe Taggart could actually whip him.

Jen's lips turned down, and she held her hands up for all to see. "And do you intend to keep me cuffed during my stay?"

He'd love to. He'd love to bind her arms and legs and keep her tied to his bed exactly as had been suggested. He'd let her out to paint. It was important, and she was far too talented to ignore, but other than that, she would be constantly spread for his pleasure. He shifted uncomfortably. His cock was hard as a rock.

Nate's eyes went straight to the handcuffs around Jen's wrists. "Was that necessary, Stef?"

"She was being uncooperative."

"And he was being an asshole," Jen shot back.

At least she was getting her spirit back. It made him happy that she was starting to fight again. He'd watched her in the interview room while she spoke to Finn Taylor, and everything about her had seemed dimmer than normal. Her eyes had been dull and downcast, her shoulders slumped. Now there was fire in them again, and it gave him hope.

"No surprise there. He's been a complete asshole for six months now," Nate complained. He settled his hat on his head and looked every inch the small-town sheriff he was. "He's giving Max a run for his money. I swear if I catch the two of them pounding on each other again, I'm going to put them both in lockup."

Stef set her on her feet and hoped he didn't have to chase her down. She immediately walked to Nate, holding out her cuffed hands

in greeting.

"It's good to see you, Sheriff. How are Callie and Zane?" Jen's face shone as she looked up at the sheriff.

She hadn't smiled once at him.

"They're fine. Zane opened a bar, and now he's got Callie hopping. I had to hire a new admin because Callie's having so much fun learning to bartend," Nate explained. His face went a little bit hard. "She's looking forward to seeing you again, Jen. She missed you."

Jen flushed. Her skin was so pale he never had trouble reading her.

"I missed her, too."

"A letter would have been nice. It would have let her know you were alive." Nate turned his stony face to Stef. "We should get going if we're going to make the plane."

Jen's smile fell, and Stef kind of wanted to put a fist through his friend's face. He knew how Nate felt about Jennifer. Nate had made it entirely plain to him during the trip to Dallas. He was angry because his wife, Callie, had been hurt by Jen's sudden disappearance. Callie's other husband, Zane, was a bit more forgiving. Zane understood the need to run. If Zane would have been a lick of help, Stef would have brought him instead of Nate. Unfortunately, Nate was the sheriff of Bliss, and there was no substitute in this case.

"Come on." Stef tried to soften the gruff command by placing a hand on her back.

She stepped away. "You're sure I can't stay here? My trial is going to be here. That lawyer person said I could stay with him. And apparently there's a bunch of spies following me around. I can't go anywhere."

His heart plunged. She would rather stay with a complete stranger than come home. Maybe he should let her. Julian Lodge would make sure she was safe. McKay-Taggart would work on the case from the investigative end while Finn handled the legalities. Perhaps he should simply bow out. He never meant to come after her anyway. He should step back and allow her to live her own life.

"You're coming with me or you can go back to jail." So much for stepping back. He couldn't. And Julian lived in one of the most

notorious BDSM clubs in the world. No way was he going to allow Jennifer to live there. She'd be collared in a heartbeat. She'd belong to someone else. He couldn't handle the thought. He turned to Finn and the security guys. He wasn't going to call them spies. They were more like protectors. "We'll contact you when we get back home. I hope you'll have something for me."

"See? Puppet master Stef is in the house. Fine. I'll go back because Bliss is way better than the Dallas County Jail, but don't think I'll trade favors for my freedom." She turned and walked out the door, her back regally straight, as though she were a queen leaving her castle.

"See, that's what I meant about cuffing her to something that doesn't move," Taggart was saying. "Just cuffing her hands together kind of misses the point."

He ignored the security guy, preferring to stride after Jen since she really was getting away.

"I wouldn't dream of it, love." Stef shed his own jacket because the queen was going to be awfully cold. He caught up with her and settled the jacket around her shoulders. He thought briefly about uncuffing her but decided he didn't want to get slapped. He led her to the driveway. "Wear it."

She smiled up at him, but there was no warmth in it. "Of course. I wouldn't dream of refusing Master Stefan. Besides, I like the fact that you're cold."

"How could he possibly be cold?" Nate asked with a smirk. "He's been running ever since the investigators called him yesterday morning. I don't think his heart's settled down once since he got that call. He had everyone in Bliss on their toes five minutes later."

Stef sent Nate his best "shut the fuck up" look.

Jen turned to Nate as the limo pulled up. "I wish I could have seen that. Tell me something, how is she? Is Callie happy? Has Rachel had her baby yet? Did Stella find someone to replace me? I mean, I know she did, but I just…I missed everyone. More than I realized."

The driver popped out and opened the door. He got in and turned back to help Jen.

Nate softened slightly as he settled into the seat across from

them. He looked slightly out of place in the elegant limo. Sometimes it was hard for Stef to remember Nate came from money. "Callie's doing great. She and Zane are having the time of their life driving me crazy. I wouldn't have it any other way. Rachel is due in a couple of weeks. Stef brought in a doctor. We have a nice clinic now."

Thanks to him. "Well, I had to or Max and Rye were going to drive me crazy. Why Rachel ever let them read those *What to Expect* books, I have no idea. They've been paranoid. And Max has become quite the medical expert. He's diagnosed Rachel with everything from GERD to preeclampsia. I expect Ebola is next on his list of things his pregnant wife is dying from. I had to bring in Dr. Burke to save poor Rachel from Max keeping her on bed rest."

Jen laughed. It was practically music in Stef's mind. "I can't believe I missed that. Has Mel made sure the baby is safe from alien probes?"

"Naturally," Nate replied. "He's consulted with Dr. Burke about making the birth completely alien free. The doc is a tolerant man. He's also good with electronics. He's modified the Detector 5000 to warn us if an alien invades Rachel's womb."

"Excellent." Jen turned her face to the window as they drove toward the airport.

He watched her carefully. He wondered if she was sad to leave Dallas. He'd been inside her tiny apartment on Good Latimer. It was a studio space, but it looked like an art bomb had gone off inside. There had been canvases and three different easels, each set up to catch a different type of light. Everywhere he'd looked there were signs of her creativity. Sketchbooks were littered through the place as though she wanted one anywhere she sat in case an idea hit her.

The limo fell silent as Nate played around on his cell. He was probably texting Callie or Zane, who would immediately call Stella, and the grapevine would be in full bloom. In roughly five minutes, everyone in Bliss would know he was bringing Jen home. They turned up Mockingbird, and Stef thought about his own work. He'd only managed two canvases while she'd been gone, each a portrait of a slender brunette with flashing green eyes.

How was he going to keep his hands off her?

Minutes later, the limo rolled to a stop right on the tarmac.

"Wow, a private jet?" Her eyes were wide as she looked at his father's corporate jet.

He helped her out of the limo.

Nate was shaking his head. "The rich are different, girl."

Such a hypocrite. "You flew in corporate jets most of your life, asshole."

Nate winked and tipped his Stetson. "I don't know what you're talking about. I'm just a country sheriff." He disappeared up the steps.

Jen turned and stared at him for a moment. She bit at her bottom lip, tugging it into her mouth. "Stef, this is a bad idea. We don't work. You know we don't."

He stood there, unable to confirm or deny the allegation. He didn't want to do either because that would mean making a decision, and he wasn't ready for that.

She came in close and went up on her toes. "But I want you to know that I'm grateful you came for me. Though I wish you hadn't brought in the European spies. Still, it's the nicest thing anyone ever did."

She kissed his cheek, her lips warm on his cold skin. Then she turned and managed the stairs into the jet.

He reached for the keys to the handcuffs as he followed her. He had no intention of leaving her that way. She wouldn't go back to Bliss in cuffs, although no one would question it there. Bliss was different from Dallas. It was why he'd dug it at a young age. He turned and looked at the city he was born in. It wasn't home anymore and hadn't been for a long time. It was simply a place where his father summoned him from time to time. It was a prison to do time in until he could get back to his real life.

The pilot was waiting at the top of the steps.

"Mr. Talbot, if you'll take your seat, we'll be ready to go in a few moments now that all four passengers are aboard. Mindy will be our flight attendant. I believe she's already getting your father his drink. Please let her know if you need anything at all. We'll set down in Alamosa at roughly noon Mountain Time."

Stef felt his whole body start to sink into the floor. He ducked into the jet, his mind racing.

Please, no. Let it be a case of mistaken identity. Please, let

27

it be some executive who's catching a ride. Not my father.

He couldn't handle his uptight father right now. He didn't need another lecture on fulfilling his family duties. He didn't have Callie with him to act as a buffer. *Crap.* He didn't have Callie anymore. The ramifications hit him suddenly. Callie was married. She probably wouldn't be able to play the role of his longtime girlfriend to keep his father off his back.

Or would she? Stef *had* bankrolled Zane's bar. Hell, he was the whole reason those three had gotten together in the first place. They owed him. It wasn't like he was taking her away. He would merely borrow her from time to time to placate his father. That shouldn't bother anyone. Callie had been doing it for years. His father believed he'd stayed in Bliss because he was deeply in love with Callie Sheppard. He would probably be upset to find out she was now Callie Hollister-Wright.

But it would be okay, because it wasn't his elegant father, who had a perpetual stick up his aristocratic ass. The pilot was misinformed.

"Hello, son."

His father sat across from Nate, a broad smile on his face. He wore a sweater and jeans instead of his usual three-piece suit. Sebastian Talbot looked older, softer than Stef had ever seen him. He wore his hair short, and it was gray. His father had always had a stylist darken his hair.

"Dad."

Jennifer's whole face was lit with glee. She held her hands out. No one could possibly miss those shiny cuffs. Nate was back to texting furiously. For a badass ex-DEA agent, he'd become a terrible gossip.

"I was telling your father all about how you kidnapped me and how you're a righteous pervert," Jen explained.

His dad shook a finger at him. "And I told her that wasn't how I'd raised you."

"You didn't raise me." It was true. His father had left him behind in Bliss to be raised by a nanny. Although now that he thought about it, he'd really been raised by Bliss. Mrs. Harper had let him spend night after night at her house. Callie's mom had taken him shopping

and taught him to drive. And Stella, well, Stella had been his mom in every way that counted.

Sebastian shrugged. "Well, I'm sure I left a note for your nanny. One always believes that not allowing your child to turn into a righteous pervert is implied. It can be hard to find good help."

"What are you doing here, Dad?" Stef uncuffed Jen and gently showed her to a seat.

His father leaned forward, his face serious. "I've come with a request, son."

"And you couldn't e-mail me? My cell works. How did you even know I would be here?"

"I had to approve the request for the jet." Familiar gray eyes assessed Stef. "I knew this might be the only time I got to see you. You've been busy the last few times I asked you to come back to Dallas."

"I have several projects due." It was true. He had a couple of commissioned works he needed to finish. He didn't bother to mention he hadn't worked on them because he couldn't get Jennifer out of his brain. "I apologize, but I couldn't get away. Now, please hurry and tell me what you want. The plane is about to take off."

"I've got cancer, Stefan. Prostate cancer. I've been in chemo and radiation, and I'm in remission now, but it could come back. I've come to beg you to marry Callie. I want to see you settled and happy before anything happens to me."

Nate stopped texting, his phone falling to the floor and his mouth hanging open. "What did he say?"

Stef felt his world spin. His father had cancer. His father had gone through therapy, and he hadn't been there. Of course, his father hadn't asked him to be there, hadn't even told him he was sick, but it didn't matter. Guilt gnawed at his gut.

He had another problem. *Shit*. His father wanted him to marry Callie. Nate and Zane might have a problem with that.

"And I'm not getting off the plane, son," his father said, settling back in his seat. "I'm coming to Bliss with you and I'm not leaving until I get what I want."

The plane started to taxi down the runway. Stef felt like he was trapped inside a coffin. Everything was coming unraveled. His well-

ordered world was coming back to bite him in the ass. His father had been sick and could be again. Nate glared at him, obviously waiting for an answer. His father, who had lost his damn mind, leaned over and patted his hand.

Jen let loose with a long, robust laugh. "God, I missed Bliss."

Stef felt his stomach turn as the plane took off. He gave Nate a shake of his head. Nate frowned, and Stef was grateful when he sat back, willing to leave this argument for a more private time. He looked out the window and watched Dallas fall away as the jet climbed. His mind wandered back to that night with Jen. That was when it had all started to whirl out of control.

If only he could change it all.

Chapter Three

Six months before

Stef walked into the Bliss County Sheriff's Office with blood on his hands. He gripped the shotgun he held like an old friend. Despite the fact that the threat seemed to be over, he couldn't come down. He felt the adrenaline racing through his system. It made him ragged and jittery.

"Hey, Stef, you got the keys?" Max, one of his best friends, ran to catch up to him. They had driven back together, he, Max, and Max's twin, Rye. Each had been silent in the car, as though they all had to take in what had happened.

Stef reached into his pocket and pulled out the keys Nate had given to him before he'd been loaded into the ambulance to go to the hospital. Stef had replayed the whole scene in his head a hundred times. A pair of rogue DEA agents had taken Callie hostage and offered to trade her for Zane, who had information that would lead them to millions of dollars' worth of drug money. No one had been willing to give up Zane except Zane. Nate had set up a plan to take out the agents. It had gone well until one of the bastards had captured Nate. Stef had thought he held the ace when he caught the man's

partner and offered an exchange. The bastard had simply shot his partner between the eyes and held on to Nate.

He'd had a hand on the man when he died. Leander. He thought that was the man's name. It was all a jumble, but the blood was clear. It clung to his hands. The image was burned in his brain. The DEA agents were dead. Mel and Nate had been shot. Callie was worse for the wear. His sweet, pacifist friend had been forced to kill a man to save her loves, Nate and Zane.

Everyone he loved was alive, but he was still shaking inside.

"Max! Where is Rye? Oh, god, where's Rye?" Rachel's shout broke through his dark thoughts, the panic in her voice ringing through the stationhouse.

Rye pushed him aside as he ran toward his brother and their wife. "I'm fine, baby. I'm fine. We're all fine."

Stef stood in the doorway, watching as Max opened the cell he'd placed his pregnant wife in to ensure her safety. He himself had shoved Jennifer in with Rachel. She had no place walking into an ambush with a shotgun, and he didn't trust her not to follow him. She was as stubborn as the day was long, and she loved Callie.

Max and Rye surrounded their wife. They hugged her and kissed her, whispering words of comfort to her. Their hands found her belly and rested on the child growing there.

"Where are the sheriff and Zane and Callie?" Laura Niles stood tall on her formidable heels as he stared at the cell. Jennifer was inside, watching him with hooded eyes. He could still remember the way she'd cursed him as he locked her inside.

He spoke to Laura, but he couldn't take his eyes off Jennifer. "Hospital. Mel's with them. No one is critical. Nate was shot, but it was in his shoulder. He doesn't want anyone visiting until tomorrow."

Stella patted his back as she walked past. "I'll head down anyway. Someone will have to sit with Mel. And maybe translate for him. He has a theory about the aliens taking over pharmaceutical companies. It could go really poorly for those doctors. I don't know why they call drugs those silly names."

Laura hurried after Stella. "I'll keep you company, Stella."

Marie and Teeny had been left behind, too. They were one of Bliss's oldest couples and ran the Trading Post together. Nate's

deputy, Logan, called them both Mom. After Max assured them Logan was all right and was simply handling the paperwork with the feds, they decided to stay on and man the station so the men could get some rest.

Rest. He wasn't sure he'd be able to do that. A weird, angry energy thrummed through his veins. He wanted to hit something—or fuck someone. Not someone. Jennifer. Sinking himself into Jennifer's soft body would take away the pain.

He shook off the thought. He couldn't use her like that. It would mean something to her. Hell, it would mean something to him, and neither one of them was ready for that. She was too damn young, far too impetuous. Tonight had certainly proven that.

"Come on, Jennifer. I'll take you home." He owed her that, at least. She was so beautiful, even with mascara staining her cheeks. She took a hand wipe from Teeny and washed off her face. He would have to stay away from her. He couldn't ask Max or Rye to take her home. He had to do it himself, but he needed to keep his distance or he would make a mistake they would both regret. He could feel it.

"Fuck you, Stef." She shoved her way past him.

Volcanic rage threatened to overtake him. It wasn't about her, but she was going to take the brunt unless she stopped pushing him. Hell, she'd been pushing him for a year and a half, ever since she waltzed into Bliss and declared she'd come to learn from him. She'd wanted him to teach her his techniques.

Stef didn't teach. Not art at least. Now the finer points of Dominance and submission, that was another story. The Dom in him responded to her lack of respect. He followed her as she strode out of the building.

The early autumn air was already taking on a distinct chill at night, but it did nothing to cool Stef's blood. Watching her walk away spurred his instincts to track her down. She strode quickly, as though she knew the danger she was in. He followed, blood pounding through his system. His thinking brain kept reasoning that he would simply follow her and make sure she got home all right.

But that dark, dirty part of him knew what this was—a hunt that would end with him taking her down.

He quickly opened the door to his Land Rover, stashed the

shotgun, and resumed his pursuit. Her shoes clicked on the sidewalk as she passed the town hall and rushed across the street. He knew exactly where she was going. Her tiny apartment was over the diner. Stella had rented the little studio to her when she'd taken the waitressing job there. She turned the corner of the alley that led into the parking lot, and he jogged to catch up. He wouldn't let her close the door on him.

She stopped at the bottom of the stairs and turned. Her slender body fairly vibrated with rage. "What are you doing?"

That was an awfully good question, and he didn't have much of an answer. He came up with the safest one he could find. "Protecting you."

She rolled those green eyes. In the moonlight her skin looked luminous. "From what? Max said all the bad guys are dead."

He groped for an answer to that. "The bikers are still around. Until they know the hit is off Zane, they'll still look for him."

She walked straight up to him and shoved a finger into his chest. "Then go keep Zane safe. I don't need your protection. I don't want it, and I don't want you."

"Liar." She'd always wanted him. She'd thrown herself at him. He hadn't thought it was a good idea to catch her.

She shook her head. "Nope. After the stunt you pulled tonight, I have zero desire to have anything to do with you. As a matter of fact, I should thank your perverted ass. Thank you, Stef. Thank you for finally showing me what an asshole you are. It totally frees me up to find someone who can get it up around me."

He actually saw red. It swam in front of his eyes like a mist, clouding everything, making the world seem a little unreal.

She obviously didn't notice because she kept talking. "I think that tomorrow I'm going to do what Callie didn't manage to do. I'm going to find myself some hot tourist and fuck the hell out of him. I've wasted a year and a half hoping you would actually see me. That's not going to happen because you can't fuck a woman who doesn't kiss your feet. Can you, King Stefan?"

He tried to breathe deeply. "Stop. Jennifer, if you stop now, I might be able to walk away."

"If there's one thing I am sure of it's your ability to walk away

from me." She turned on her heels. "Go back to your palace. I'm done with you."

He reached out and grabbed her, hauling her back by her wrist. She stumbled, but he caught her.

"What are you doing?" She yelled the question as she tried to get her balance back.

He was done talking. Talking didn't mean anything to her. He'd tried to explain. He'd tried to stay away. He'd tried to be her friend. She wouldn't stop pushing. He planted his shoulder in her midsection and had her in a fireman's hold before she could move.

Her hands beat on his back. He welcomed the sensation.

"Put me down, you jackass!"

He climbed the stairs toward her apartment with no thought but getting her inside and showing her just how fast he could get it up around her. He could handle the accusation that he was an asshole. That was a simple, documented fact. But he was always hard around her. Fuck, half the time he couldn't breathe when she was around. And he knew he couldn't think. How could he be expected to when all the blood in his body shifted to his cock the minute she walked in a room?

He reached out for the door. It opened without the need of a key.

"Damn it, Jennifer. Anyone could walk in here."

"Yeah, I'm getting that now." She pounded on his back. She tried kicking her legs, but he had a good hold on those. "Let me down."

He set her on her feet and shut the door. He had her in a neat cage now. She wouldn't be able to get away from him. She stumbled, trying to put some distance between them.

"Get out."

He looked around and quickly found what he needed. She had a pile of folded laundry in a hamper on a table in the small kitchen area. Delicates. He selected a tiny pink thong. It would look lovely between the cheeks of her ass. He had another use in mind.

"OMG, you are such a perv," she ranted on. "You're going to steal my panties? You ignore me for over a year, and then you steal my undies?"

"We can do this the easy way or the hard way." He heard his Dom voice turn on. It was low and seemed to come from a place deep

inside his chest. It felt good to lose control, like a drug running through his system, lighting up his every nerve.

She finally stopped, and her eyes widened. "What are you talking about?"

Good girl. She was finally getting it. That little hint of fear in her eyes hardened his already rock-hard cock to painful proportions. If he didn't get out of his pants soon, they might split on him. "Give me your hands so I can tie you up."

There it was, that hitch in her breath that had nothing to do with fear. Despite it, she shook her head. "No. No, Stef. That's a bad idea."

"Yes," he agreed. "But it's going to happen. Easy way or hard way, Jennifer. It's your choice."

Her throat moved up and down as she swallowed. Her eyes darted around the room, and her chest heaved. She closed her eyes for a moment, and when she opened them the fear was gone, replaced with a glint of challenge. "Oh, I think it's going to be very hard, Master Stefan."

He'd always known she would be fun to play with, but he wasn't playing now. This was serious. "Safe word. Pick one now."

She didn't prevaricate or pretend to misunderstand. She spat out her chosen word as though she'd always had it in her back pocket, just waiting to use. "Impressionist."

"Excellent." What he was about to do to her was so far away from gauzy and slightly surreal. It would be rough and hard. "You can run, if you like."

"Fuck you, Stef." She turned and ran for her bathroom.

He was on her before she'd gotten three steps. He grabbed her around the waist and eased her to the floor. Using his weight to pin her down, he bound her hands in the silky thong and flipped her over.

"God, you're good at that." There was no mistaking the admiration in her tone. It was another thing he loved about her. Her perversion seemed to match his own. If only he could trust her to know her own heart at such a young age.

He put a hand on her lips. "No. No talking."

"That might be hard for me."

"Then let me make it easy." He got off her and quickly swung her up. He sat on her lumpy couch and had her over his lap in a second.

He pulled at the denim of her miniskirt, tugging the hem up toward her waist to reveal her ass. She wore a pair of cotton panties. They were easy to rip off her.

"Damn it, Stef. I just bought those."

He brought his hand down on the fleshy part of her ass. "No cussing."

She gasped and went still under him. "You spanked me."

He brought his hand down again, loving the way her ass got pink. "Yes, love, what did you expect?" Another slap, right on the pretty crease of her ass. Jen might be slender, but she had a perfectly plump ass. Made to take a spanking. Made to fuck. "And I'll do this every time you disobey me."

"Every time," she agreed with a husky moan.

His hand came down again. "That's one for cussing. And one for questioning me."

"I didn't question you."

Smack. "And another for arguing. And ten for giving me hell all night long."

He spanked her, sparing her not at all. His hand came down in short arcs, delivering his punishment all over her cheeks. He could feel her crying, but not once did she ask him to stop or scream out her safe word. She simply held on to his legs as though seeking more connection. They were partners in play and pleasure. When he was done he admired his work. Her ass was hot pink, and he could smell her arousal. He slipped a finger between her cheeks and let it slide toward her pussy. She was coated in cream.

He set her on her feet and unbound her hands. Her face was as red as her cheeks. "Clothes off, Jennifer. Unless you want me to rip them off the way I did those panties. Take them off and then sit in my lap."

She was still for a moment. "You hurt me."

"No. I tortured you a little. If I had hurt you, you would have said your safe word. You would have fought me." He held his hand up, showing her the juice glistening on his fingers. He brought them to his mouth and sucked them inside, tasting her for the first time. He sucked every ounce of her tangy cream off his fingers. "That pussy of yours is throbbing, isn't it? Do you know how delicious you taste? Do

37

you know what a meal I could make of you?"

"You'll be the death of me, Stef."

Her hands went to the hem of her shirt. She pulled it over her head and tossed it aside. They would go over proper procedure later, but for now he wanted her against him more than he wanted to follow protocol. She wasn't wearing a bra. He stared at her perfectly formed breasts. They were small, but adorable. They would fit in the palm of his hand. Her nipples were brown and pink and tight with arousal. She shimmied out of her skirt and placed herself on his lap. Her arms went around his neck.

"You're beautiful, love." He pushed her hair back. Why had he waited? It felt so right to have her in his arms. His anxiety had fled, leaving only a sense of joyous anticipation. Jennifer was naked, her breath warm against his neck. This was where he needed to be.

"I feel beautiful when you look at me like that." She cuddled close, all of her previous worry seemingly gone.

"Give me your mouth."

She turned her face up obediently. Stef brought his lips down on hers and kissed her the way he'd wanted to from the moment he'd met her. He devoured her. His mouth ate at hers hungrily, tongue invading the moment she opened her lips. He swept in and they tangled together in a lustful dance. He wanted her like he hadn't wanted anyone before. All the gorgeous submissives he'd claimed before couldn't hold a candle to the way she moved him.

Before he knew it he was on top of her, spreading her legs and making a place for himself at her silky pussy. He didn't hold his weight off her. All he wanted was to sink into her and lose himself.

He let his hands find her breasts, and his mouth followed close behind. He popped a pink nipple in his mouth and sucked, delighting in the way she groaned and moved beneath him. His hips pumped against hers.

"Stef." She moaned his name again and again.

"Do you want me, love?" He needed to hear her say it.

"So much." Her eyes pleaded with him.

His hands went to the fly of his pants. He knew he should get off her. He should take control—of her, of himself. He tore open his pants and shoved them and his boxers down. His cock sprang free.

"Wow," Jen said in a breathy voice that did amazing things for his ego. Her small hand came out and touched him. He stared at the sight. He'd always been fascinated with her hands. He loved how they moved across a canvas as she stroked a painting to life. Now they ran across his cock, making him feel more alive than he had in years.

"Stef, I'm on the pill. I'm clean."

It was all he needed. He'd had a physical and hadn't ever had sex without a condom before. He wanted her with nothing in between them. He pushed her hands away and lined his cock up with her soaked pussy. He pulled her legs around his hips to open her up and started to push his way in.

Tight. She was incredibly tight around him. She was a vise on his cock. He had to move carefully, advancing and retreating in a maddening dance. He wanted to shove himself in balls deep, but he wouldn't hurt her for the world.

"It feels so good." Her nails found the bare skin of his ass and sank in, urging him on.

"It feels right." He shoved against her and sighed as he finally was as deep as he could go. Every inch of his cock was surrounded by hot, delicious pussy. He held himself steady, allowing her to accept him. The muscles of her pussy quivered around his dick.

Jen's throaty plea cut through the silence. "If you don't move soon, I'm going to die."

He was more than willing to give her what she wanted. Stef pulled out until the head of his cock rested in her pussy and then slammed back in. And he was off. All thoughts besides fucking her were blasted from his brain. She was everything in that moment. He was surrounded with her. The touch of her skin. The smell of their fucking. The sound of her breath as she pushed against him, fighting for her orgasm. It was primal and out of control and perfect. She was everything he'd ever wanted. His perfect mate.

"Oh, Stef. Stef. It feels...I..." She stopped trying to talk. Every muscle in her body seemed to tighten, and she cried out. Her legs clamped down on his hips; her pelvis thrusting.

He followed her. He let himself go, pounding away at her until his balls drew up, and it was impossible to stave off the inevitable. He came in long, glorious jets. He pumped into her, delivering every

ounce he had in his body.

He fell forward, shocked at how his heart was still pounding. This was supposed to be his quiet time, but he wasn't satisfied. He wanted something more, something he'd never had before.

"I love you." Her words were whispered as her fingers sank into his hair. He felt her lips on his head.

Still, he wanted more. There was something else he was missing, something that would complete the scene they had just played out. His heart stopped as he realized what he wanted. The words were right there on his lips, practically dripping from his tongue. Foreign words. *I love you.* He'd never said them before. He needed to say them to her.

He held back and let himself rest on her breasts. Eventually her breathing slowed and steadied into the rhythm of sleep. She rested, her arms wrapped around him.

He lay there, unwilling to wake her, but his mind raced all night.

What the hell had he done?

In the morning he was waiting for her. He'd untangled himself and gotten dressed again. He'd sat at her tiny table and scolded himself in every way imaginable. She wasn't ready for a relationship. She was too young for him. He wanted too much from her. He didn't have the right to demand that she settle down, and he wouldn't, couldn't, settle for less from her.

He'd played out the scenarios in his head. He'd thought about simply starting a D/s relationship. That would be the easiest way to keep her close. They could have their own separate lives and come together for play. It was the way he'd handled his relationships for a long time.

He'd watched her sleep, and he knew he wouldn't be able to keep it there. He would have her moved into the estate and under his thumb before she knew what was happening. It was his nature.

He could see clearly the way it would go. They would be happy for a while, but then she would need more. She would grow and change and leave him behind. It would be exactly like…

He didn't want to think about his father right now. This was

about Stef and Jennifer. His own parents were simply an object lesson as to why an older man should not marry a much younger woman.

Jennifer stirred, twisting as though seeking something in her sleep. She didn't find it, and she went up on one elbow to look around the room. There was slight panic in her eyes, and then she softened as she saw him.

"Hey, good morning," she said in a sleepy voice that went straight to his cock.

He wanted to strip down and climb back on the couch with her. He would push her legs apart again and be where he always wanted to be—inside her.

"We need to talk," he forced himself to say. If he gave in now, it would be disastrous for both of them. She had a whole career ahead of her. She didn't need a man in her life who would try to take over.

She sat up, clutching the quilt he'd pulled over her. "Do we have to? I liked it better when we didn't talk."

He did, too, but this was morning, and they had to face reality. "Jennifer, last night was a mistake."

Her eyes slid away from his. "You bastard."

He didn't argue. He was a bastard. He'd taken her last night when he'd known it was wrong. "It was a mistake, and I take full responsibility. It wasn't your fault. I took advantage of you."

Now she looked at him, tears shining in her eyes. "Because I wasn't here at all, was I? Because I didn't make a choice? What the hell am I to you?"

"You're a friend," he said gently.

"No, I am not. People trust their friends. You said once that I knew nothing of trust, but you're the one who doesn't trust me. You think I'm a child, but I'm not. I know what I want, Stef. I want you." She leaned toward him, holding her hand out. "Last night wasn't a mistake. This morning is. Can't you see that?"

It was hard to look at her, to see that expectation on her face. "Jennifer, I remember being twenty-three. It's not the easiest time of your life. There are lots of things that you think you want, but you simply don't have the experience to know."

Now she stood, her expression turning to anger in a heartbeat. "Fuck you, Stef. Get out of my house. I'm not some child, but you're

never going to see it. You're never going to see me as anything but some airhead kid."

Well, she was acting like one. He knew better than to say that out loud. "I'd prefer to talk about this reasonably."

"Screw reason. I'm done reasoning with you. I've begged and pleaded and made a fool of myself. Well, I'm done with all of that. And I'm done with you, so feel free to leave."

"Last night you loved me, and this morning you're through." Everything she said made his point clearer.

She shrugged. "Well, I guess you were right about me then. Get out!"

He left, the door slamming behind him and the worst feeling in the pit of his stomach telling him that he'd fucked everything up. He'd intended to be gentle, to talk it out. As he walked away, he thought he heard her cry. He knocked on the door, but it was locked this time. He stood there, hand on the door, and wished he could go back in and hold her.

He left a few moments later, but that afternoon he was back like a moth to the flame. He came with flowers he'd bought at the Trading Post and plans to, at least, talk this out. He couldn't stand the thought of her feeling down. Maybe, he thought, maybe, they could try.

Her apartment was empty of anything that was personal. Only the furniture remained. She'd packed up and left in a matter of hours.

He walked out, tossing the flowers in the trash. It was better this way, he told himself. It was better that she left now, rather than later.

Chapter Four

Stef was jarred awake as the chair he sat in was kicked hard. He sat up straight, forcing himself to come out of the dream he'd been having. It was a familiar dream, one he had every night. He'd made love to Jennifer again. He'd chased her down and taken her. He'd made her his. She'd been soft and utterly submissive by the time he'd gotten her underneath him. It had been perfect in his dream because this time he'd said the words he wanted to say. This time he'd made it right, and she hadn't left him.

When his vision cleared he saw the reason he couldn't say those three words. His father was asleep in the chair across from him, his eyes closed and a blanket around his body. He was older, more fragile than Stef had ever seen him. His father was a rock. His father was a workaholic who never seemed to have an emotion, much less show one.

Except that one day. The day his mother had left them alone. He remembered little beyond shouting and his mother's pronouncement that no amount of money made up for being tied to a husband and a kid. But he remembered his father's knees hitting the floor. He could still feel the way his father had clung to him as he cried. The next day, Sebastian Talbot had been back to smooth, CEO perfection as if

nothing had happened. He'd divorced his young bride and never mentioned her name again. It had been years before Stef had heard anything about her, and then it had been a single e-mail explaining she'd remarried and requested contact. He'd been twenty. He'd deleted it and blocked her from his e-mail.

Stef let his eyes slide to Jen's sleeping form. She was even younger than his mother had been when she married his father.

"You want to explain to me why your father thinks you're going to marry my wife?" Nate's low growl brought Stef out of his revelry. He'd whispered the question, but it jarred Sebastian awake.

"What?" His father sat straight up and glanced around. There seemed to be a moment's panic, as though he didn't remember where he was, but then a smile lit his face. He stretched and moved aside the blanket the flight attendant had settled on him while he was sleeping. "Sorry. I must have fallen asleep. I tire easily these days. I'm afraid I was dreaming. How far are we from Bliss?"

Nate backed off. "Another twenty minutes, Mr. Talbot."

Sebastian shook his head. "No, no, Nathan. That won't do. Please call me Sebastian. Half the time Stefan does. I can't wait to see Bliss again."

The panic was back. His father was coming home. "Dad, this is insane. You don't vacation. The whole time I was growing up, you rarely left the office."

His father turned and looked out the window. He took in the gorgeous mountain views. "That's not true, son. I spent two whole years in Bliss running the company from the estate. It worked well then. Given today's technology it would be even easier now. Don't worry. I won't be a pest. I'll stay in the guesthouse."

"No!" Both he and Nate shouted the denial.

"The guesthouse is drafty," Nate managed to sputter. "It's cold right now. You've been in Texas for a long time. Colorado winters are hard."

Stef was glad Nate was such a quick thinker. He nodded. "Yes, the guesthouse needs some renovations."

The guesthouse was perfectly comfy. It was also filled with sex toys. Often it was where he kept his subs when they came for training. Of course, for the last six months the place had been empty, except

44

when Max and Rye had brought their wife there to play. Stef hadn't brought in a sub since that night with Jennifer. It seemed wrong somehow.

Sebastian shrugged as he got out of his seat. His father had lost a lot of weight. He seemed small and frail. "Well, there are six bedrooms. I'm sure we'll all manage. I promise you'll barely know I'm there."

He walked toward the back of the plane and disappeared into the bathroom.

Jen's eyes came open. She looked sleepy and soft. A secret smile curled those plump lips of hers up. "Liars. What's up, Stef? Don't want your dad to find your stash of butt plugs?"

He shuddered to think about it. There were far more exotic toys than anal plugs in the guesthouse. "I'm more worried about what he would say about the St. Andrew's Cross. He also might think the new violet wand I bought is a massager. Really, it's best he doesn't go into the guesthouse. For all our sakes."

"He might know you better than you think," Jen said, pulling a blanket around her.

He pulled his blanket off his body and handed it to her. She didn't argue, simply tucked it around her and settled back down.

"I don't think he knows you at all." Nate's face was flushed, his jaw perfectly square. "Especially since he thinks you're sleeping with my wife."

Jen grinned at the sheriff. "Didn't you know, Nate? Callie's been his beard for years. Ever since they were teens."

"She is not my beard. For god's sake, Jennifer." She was making far more of this than was true. He and Callie had a simple agreement. She pretended to be his girlfriend, and he did stuff for her. They took care of each other. He turned to Nate, hoping he could make the man understand. "On several occasions Callie accompanied me to Dallas. My father would summon me from time to time, and Callie went with me. He never made me stay for long. Maybe his conscience got to him, I don't know."

"Maybe he wanted to see his son," Jen offered.

"I doubt it. I found it awkward and unsettling to have to go to my father's place. I did not consider it home. It's strange. I was born in

Dallas, raised there for years, but even at the age of eight, I knew Bliss was my home. I fought him when he decided to move back to Dallas, and he left me there with two nannies and a staff of ten. He summoned me home twice a year, but ignored me when I was there. He had meetings, you see. What he truly wanted to do was lecture me. When I was seventeen he asked whether I had a girlfriend. I told him no and was immediately presented with several applicants for the position. I doubt it had much to do with my happiness. He simply wanted me to marry the right sort of girl."

Jen's eyebrow arched. "Callie must have come as a surprise."

"Callie's the right sort of girl. Callie's the perfect girl." Nate was unwavering in support of his oft-naked wife.

Stef smiled, happy Callie had finally found the right man. Well, the right man and Zane. He loved Callie Sheppard, though not in the way his father thought. She was the sister he'd never had. Callie was a brilliant combination of quirky and strong. She was like the town where she'd been born. And she was completely the wrong sort of woman for a man concerned with high society to marry. She spent far too much time at naturist camps to be comfy with jet-setters.

Yet his father had taken to Callie right away. He'd been utterly charmed by her. Every time Stef had brought her to Dallas, his father had taken them out, and not once had he tried to change her or talked to Stef about her beyond how sweet she was. Every time his father called, he asked about Callie.

"Okay, I get why you used her as your fake girlfriend when you were younger, but you're thirty-two now and she's taken," Nate said, sounding more reasonable. "Don't you think it's time you came clean?"

"How many phone calls from your father have you ducked lately, Wright?" He knew where to shove the knife in. Nate was completely estranged from his father, but the man kept calling. He seemed to think Nate should loan him money.

Nate sighed and sat back. "Family. What are you going to do?"

He knew exactly what he was going to do. "I'm going to let it ride. My dad wants me to be happy with Callie? Fine. I'll tell him I'm going to ask her to marry me soon, and we'll leave it at that. He's been sick. This is a phase. Trust me, the first emergency at Talbot

Industries, and his CEO hat will be right back on. He'll go back to Dallas, and I'll get a Christmas card from his secretary."

"Are you forgetting that I'm Callie's husband? Well, I'm one of her husbands. We're not looking for a fourth, Stef."

It was time to bring out his big guns. "And who facilitated your marriage? Who introduced you in the first place? Who gave you a job and a place to stash the big guy when he was post-traumatically stressed out?"

Nate's jaw became a hard line.

Jen nodded at Nate. "See, King Stefan. Like I said. The king giveth and then expects payback when you least expect it. First, it's a simple 'hey, come get Jen out of jail with me,' and now you have to give him access to your wife."

Her teasing made him want to spank her. He didn't need that mental image now. "I'm not demanding to sleep with Callie. I'm merely borrowing her in an attempt to misrepresent my love life to my father."

Nate sat back, but suddenly a smile spread across his face. It made Stef unaccountably nervous. "You're right. I owe you. You know what? Callie is meeting us at the airport. I'm sure she'll be thrilled to see your father again. Don't worry about a thing. I'll step back and let you have your little ruse."

"Thank you." It solved one of his problems.

Jen was gaping at Nate. "You are so mean, Sheriff."

"I am entirely reasonable." Nate smirked, and Stef wondered if he was missing something.

Before he could process the problem, the plane began a turn.

The flight attendant walked in and announced it was time to buckle up. Sebastian came out and began talking about his plans for his stay in Bliss.

Stef wanted the whole thing to be over.

* * * *

Alexei Markov stared down at the man currently being worked over by his partner, Ivan. Jean Claude Renard had started out like they all did, with threats and promises of retribution because he was such

an important person. And like almost all the rest, he was a sniveling mass of begging, pleading flesh after a couple of minutes with Ivan. Despite his deep loathing of the man, Alexei had to admit that Ivan was a master at what he did.

"It was here, I tell you. I hid the damn thing like I promised." He managed to get the words out of his swollen lips. "Somehow she must have figured it out."

Ivan hit him again. Alexei could have told Renard that it didn't matter what he said. Ivan would use him like a punching bag because he was a sadistic son of a bitch. Of course, a certain streak of sadism was always required when one became a mob enforcer.

Sadism, or a well-defined and patient sense of revenge.

He couldn't help Renard even if he wanted to, and he didn't. If he did, he put everything he'd worked years for at risk. He was so close to getting in the same room with Pushkin that he could taste it. Then he would be free.

He'd worked too long and hard, and his cousin Nikolai had placed himself in too much danger, to waste it all on a bastard like Renard.

Ivan stared down at his victim. "My boss would like his package. He paid for it, and he would like it now. I have to be on plane to Moscow in four hours. We can use that time to bundle up the package, or I can simply beat on you until we board. It is up to you. It make no difference to me."

Ivan's English was decent, though he sounded like it pained him to speak anything but Russian. Alexei was well aware his could use a bit of work. His cousin made fun of him, but then he wasn't trained in espionage the way Nick and his sweet sister Katja had been. They'd been raised in different parts of the country, but when they were young, he'd been close to his cousins. It had only been after his brother died that Alexei had lost touch with them. After he'd heard the news of Katja's death, he'd reached out to Nick. They'd both lost all their immediate family and they'd become allies in their quests for revenge. Nick had been the one to suggest that he watch American television and become accustomed to their ways so that Pushkin would send him to the country. If he survived his meeting with Pushkin, he would find a way to build a new life in this country. He

would be free here.

Well, he would be an illegal immigrant on the run from both the Russian police and the mob, but at least he wouldn't have to listen to Ivan anymore. Ivan was a brute. Having to share a room with him for the last year had been trying to say the least. The man did not understand that the world had made great strides in personal hygiene products. He seemed to think smelling like a bear made him more intimidating.

Alexei tapped a foot on the floor. He was tired of being a lackey. He needed to be back in Russia, doing whatever it took to get close to the man who had killed his brother. "Or he could give back money to Pushkin. With twenty-percent increase for all our trouble."

Ivan snorted. Alexei knew that no amount of money would satisfy Pushkin, but it would buy this idiot an hour or two to come to his senses. He wasn't sure why Renard had decided to renege on his deal with the head of one of Russia's most notorious crime syndicates, but he seemed a reasonable man. Most people wanted to live. Alexei did some quick calculations. If he got Renard to come to his senses and give up the package by five, he could be home in roughly twenty-four hours. He could deliver the package himself. Pushkin was being strangely paranoid about this one painting. He wanted to meet with Ivan and Alexei himself to take the package into custody. But first he had to convince Renard to give up the painting.

A wet cough came out of Renard's chest. "Sure. I can do that. But I'm going to need some time to get the money."

Alexei felt his eyebrows rise. "I was told Pushkin sent you two million four days ago."

Another cough and a shudder. "I spent it. I owed some people, some people from Colombia. Please. You can't tell Pushkin I lost the painting. He'll kill me. He might kill you, too. God, how did this go so wrong? I need a little time. I can find it. She must have taken it with her last night."

"He's a very international idiot," Ivan said in Russian. "He's paying off the Colombians? How many dangerous groups can one man get involved with?"

Alexei shook his head. Renard was going downhill fast. It was obvious the man had spent Pushkin's money on cocaine. "Please,

show some respect, Ivan. We are in his country. We should kill him in his own language."

Renard let out a pitiful cry.

Ivan backhanded the art dealer. "Fine. I will speak in the English. But Alexei, you are too soft on these people."

As Ivan continued to pound on the gallery owner who'd been foolish enough to make a deal with the Russian mob and then renege on it, Alexei looked around the small room. The gallery outside had been stark and modern, but this was a work space. It was much more intimate, with small details that let a person know something about the occupants. Before he'd been too preoccupied with wailing from pain, Renard had explained that this was his restoration room. Apparently he was not an artist himself, but he cleaned up works that had been damaged. It was in this manner that he had acquired the painting Pushkin desired.

Alexei bent over and picked up the canvas that had been destroyed by Ivan when they first entered the room. Renard had tried to play a game with them. He'd told them to pack up the painting and leave as though they were mere messenger boys without a brain in their heads. Alexei knew better. Pushkin had sent them a copy of the photo of the painting they were supposed to bring back. He'd pulled up the photo on his cell phone, unwilling to take the man's word for it. Between the man's sweaty, nervous demeanor and Alexei's excellent eye, he'd quickly discerned that the man was attempting to fool them. The painting looked similar, but it wasn't close to the same to his eyes. There was something about the colors. He'd seen it right away.

Renard had explained, through his cries of pain, that he had hidden the Picasso for safekeeping and easy transport. Now he could not find it.

It had been a foolish play on Renard's part.

Ivan had torn apart this work to prove what Alexei suspected. Ivan had cursed because the paint was still wet. Apparently, Renard had hidden the Picasso behind another painting and switched them, hoping no one would notice until he was long gone. Alexei stared at the canvas Ivan had pried off the frame.

It was odd. Mostly it was a collection of colors, and yet he could

feel the emotion from the canvas. It was all blues and greens and the slightest hint of purple. There was the faintest impression of a male figure. Despite the fact that he'd grown up poor, his father had taken him to galleries, had taught him and his brother to appreciate art.

"Who is artist?" He would bet it was a female. Something about the softness of the work spoke of femininity.

Ivan let the gallery owner drop to the floor. "What do you care? This is not the painting that the boss desires. Are you sure it is painting at all? It looks like someone tosses paint can at a canvas."

Philistine. Ivan wasn't smart enough to know his art. Alexei shrugged. "I am curious."

Ivan kicked at Renard, his booted foot connecting viciously with the man's gut. "Tell my friend, who is artist. He wants to know."

Renard turned his bloodshot eyes up and looked at Alexei. "She's an employee."

So it *was* a woman. "She is sad. This is sad painting. I like it. It say things to me."

"It speak to you, Alexei. That is the right phrase. Don't lecture me until you get your English right. You are correct about one thing. We have to be able to speak to the people we are killing or they will not know why they are dead."

At those words, Renard began to scream. His high-pitched wails ate at Alexei's nerves. He looked at Ivan and spoke in Russian.

"That was not helpful."

Ivan shrugged. Renard tried to crawl away, but Ivan's boot came down on his back. "Better he knows what is coming for him. He does not have the painting. He would have given it up by now."

Most people would have given it up by now. Ivan was an expert at pain delivery. So Renard didn't have the painting, and apparently the money had gone straight up his nose. If he didn't have the painting, Alexei needed to figure out who did. It would do him no good to return to Russia with nothing to show for his efforts. He needed that painting.

"Would police have painting?" he asked, hoping that the answer was no. He knew why Renard had brought in the police. The idiot wanted to keep his business, and the best way to do it was to pin the crime on someone else. But he prayed the man had been smart enough

not to allow the prize to become evidence.

"No, it was a different painting, I tell you," Renard managed. "I hid it behind a different painting. I don't know. All of her stuff looks alike to me. I prefer realism. Her stuff is mostly swirly colors meant to express emotion. I've been staring at her work for months, and I don't get it. Sold a couple for her. Always the same buyer. He pays top dollar."

Ivan frowned as he looked down. "Perhaps I hit him too hard."

"You think?" Alexei shook his head. Ivan always hit them too hard. It made it difficult to interrogate a victim when his teeth were stuck halfway down his throat. He started to point at Ivan and noticed that his fingers had a fine coating of blue paint on them. "This artist, she works in here? What if she took the painting you need and begins new one?"

Renard's eyes flared. "That's what I've been trying to tell you. She has to have the painting. I tried to get into her place, but the police were there, and then some other people were there early this morning. I haven't been able to get in."

If it was true, Alexei might still salvage this mission. "This artist, she live close to here?"

Renard sagged, apparently pleased to have a few more moments of life left. His eyes were sparked with wild hope. "Yes, Jennifer lives on Good Latimer. I'll take you there. That has to be where the painting is. I know it. She took it. She didn't know what she had. We might have to wait until the place is empty."

Ivan smiled. "I will take care of anyone in our way."

But forty minutes later, Ivan neatly and efficiently took care of the only person in their way. Ivan slit Renard's throat. It was quiet, and they weren't worried about clean. The shag carpet beneath their feet was old but quickly soaked up the blood.

There wasn't a single painting in the apartment Renard had led them to. Alexei looked around. It was obvious to him that an artist lived here. There were easels and unframed, unpainted canvases. There were half-used tools and oil paints all over the kitchen table. There were brushes in a can in the bathroom. The whole bathroom smelled of chemicals.

"The boss is not going to like this." Now that the mark was dead,

Ivan shifted back to Russian.

Alexei followed suit. "He will be angry."

Ivan started looking through the artist's kitchen. "I need to find a good butcher knife. Pushkin will want us to at least bring back the head. I hate these international jobs, Alexei. It's gotten hard to get a decapitated head through an American airport. How much cash do you have? We will need to bribe someone."

He felt his deep groan rumble from his chest. This was a nightmare. "Pushkin will be even angrier we spent his cash on bribes, which is why we should attempt to offer him an alternative."

"And what is that?"

He glanced around the room. It was obvious the woman had left in a hurry. This woman either knew where the painting was or knew who took it. He needed to find this woman, this Jennifer. There was an old-school answering machine blinking by the phone. Curious, he pushed the button. A cheery female voice came on.

"This is Jen. I'm not here, or I'm off in la-la land, so leave me a message." There was a long beep and then another soft, feminine voice.

"Jen, it's Callie. I can't tell you how happy I am Stef tracked you down, though I'm sorry about the whole jail thing. Nate is coming to get you. You might not even get this message, but if you do, know that Zane and I will be waiting at the airport in Alamosa. I can't wait to see you. Bliss isn't the same without you."

"What is this Bliss?" Ivan asked.

Alexei looked around. "It is a place, I think. This Alamosa is where the artist has gone, and I think she took her canvases with her. Perhaps it is as Renard said and she doesn't know."

"Or maybe she does and I have more work to do." Ivan sounded like a man anticipating a treat.

Alexei stared down at the only framed picture in the whole house. It was of two young women and an older female. There was a tall brunette with lovely, slender features. He would bet she was the artist. There was a shorter but equally pretty woman with dark hair. The older woman was a blonde. She wore a shirt with dangling fringe, and a red cowboy hat sat atop her puffy hair.

He read the marking on the shirt the slender brunette wore.

53

Stella's Café – Bliss, Colorado

If he was the smart man who managed to track down the painting Pushkin wanted, the boss would have to thank him personally. That would be the moment that Alexei avenged his brother.

"Call Pushkin. Tell him we are going to Colorado."

Chapter Five

J en shivered as the door to the jet was opened and the arctic February air hit her. She pulled Stefan's coat around her. She turned to look at him. He was wearing a dress shirt and slacks. He must have been freezing, but the minute she began to shrug out of his coat he sent her a look colder than the wind outside. Jen stuck her tongue out at him and buttoned up the coat.

"Very mature, Jennifer," Stef murmured as he gestured for her to go first.

She felt her spirit sag. That was the crux of their problems. He thought she was too young for him. It wasn't like he was some old guy. He wasn't even ten years older than she was. It also wasn't like she'd asked him for marriage. She'd been in love with him. That didn't necessarily lead to marriage. She'd seen her mother fall in and out of love many times. She'd never pushed Stef for anything more than friendship and some sex. He seemed to think she was too young even for that.

Jen stood at the top of the stairs and looked down. One lone figure stood on the tarmac holding a handmade sign that said *Welcome Back, Felon.*

Callie Sheppard grinned as she held her sign up, and Jen felt tears

fill her eyes.

"She missed you," Nate said from behind her.

For the first time she thought about what she'd done when she'd snuck away from Bliss. She had meant to leave behind Stef and all their problems, but she'd done more than that. She'd left Callie and Stella and Rachel and Laura. She'd walked out on Mel and the Harper twins, and Zane and Nate. Tears flowed freely now as she took her wobbly first step down the staircase. She'd left the only place that had ever felt like home because she'd been too embarrassed to see Stef again.

Maybe he was right. Maybe she was too young. And maybe, just maybe, it was time to grow up.

Jen took hold of herself and rushed down the steps. She didn't stop until she threw her arms around Callie.

"Hey!" Callie dropped her sign. Her arms quickly enveloped Jen. "Hey, it's okay, sweetie. It's going to be okay. Don't you worry about a thing. You're home now."

Jen felt Callie smooth down the back of her hair, and she cried. She didn't care that everyone was watching. Now that she was standing here, she knew Callie was right. Everything would be fine because she was home. Bliss was home.

"I'm sorry," she managed after a moment. "I should never have left the way I did."

"It's okay," Callie said softly. "You're back now. That's what matters."

And that was Callie in a nutshell. Callie would never hold it against her. She would never withhold her affection. Jen could have been gone for ten years and Callie would have stood there waiting for her. Callie's heart was a mighty thing.

She felt another hand on her back, and she looked up at the sheriff. Nate Wright's eyes were far softer now, and he nodded down at her.

"Callie's right. It's going to be okay. We won't let you go back to jail. Stef is already working on getting the charges dropped. Let's hop in the car and get out of this weather."

Callie had changed that man. He'd been closed off and unwilling to love. Callie's heart had been enough.

Could she do that for Stef if she was brave? If she was as strong as Callie, could she change both their lives?

Jen took a step back, and Callie went on her toes trying to press her lips against her husband's. Nate's gloved hand came out to stop her. Callie's lips made a little *O*.

"No can do, baby." Nate shook his head as he stared down at her.

Callie pouted. Her hands went to her hips. She was drowning in a parka, her small, curvy body completely covered by her coat. "What did I do?"

"It wasn't you. It was Stef," Jen supplied, saving Nate the trouble. "He needs his fake girlfriend again, and he doesn't care that she's already double married."

Callie's brown eyes widened. "What are you talking about? Oh my, Sebastian! And Stef! Why didn't you call? And what are you doing without a coat?"

Callie stalked toward the plane where the Talbot men were disembarking. Jen stared at Nate. He had some explaining to do because she'd already figured out what all that texting had been about. Nate hadn't smiled and accepted his fate. He'd been planning something with Zane.

"Okay, where's the big guy? I know you two have something awful cooked up for Stef." There was no way Nathan Wright allowed his wife to be used in some cover-up.

A little smirk crossed Nate's face. "I have no idea what you're talking about, darlin'. I'm just helping out an old friend. I am a very patient and tolerant man."

"Since when?" The only person less patient than Nathan Wright was Max Harper. Nate was a notorious hard-ass, and the last thing Jen would expect him to do would be to allow his wife to pose as another man's girlfriend.

One shoulder came up negligently. "You know this whole threesome thing works on several levels for us. It takes two men to keep Callie out of trouble, but more than that, I can always count on Zane to do the right thing."

Jen listened to Nate talk, but her eyes were on Stef and Callie. She felt a sick pit of jealousy form in her gut as Stef wrapped his arms around Callie. She knew that it was all for show. She could see Stef

whispering to her, probably begging her to play along, but it still hurt. Callie was good enough to show off. Callie was sweet enough to bring home with him. She doubted Stef had told anyone about the night they had shared. Callie might be a fake girlfriend, but Jen doubted it hurt worse than being the dirty little secret.

Stef was talking to his father, his arm firmly around Callie's waist as she twisted her head around slightly. Her brown eyes were questioning as she looked back at Nate. The sheriff merely gave her a hearty thumbs-up, and she shrugged and turned back around to talk to Sebastian Talbot.

It was at that moment that Jen noticed big, gorgeous Zane walking down the tarmac, two Styrofoam mugs of coffee in his hands. Zane Hollister was roughly six and a half feet tall—a massive, glorious beast of a man. His beautiful face bore some scars from his time as a DEA agent, but he was heavenly-looking to Jen. She'd always wanted to paint him. It would be a challenge to get his spirit right. He was an intoxicating mix of rough man and vulnerable boy. But now he looked like an angry bull. He stopped in the middle of the tarmac, and his mouth dropped open. Jen followed his line of sight back to where Stef was leaning over, placing a light kiss on Callie's lips.

Nate sighed, satisfaction plain in his stance. "You see, I can be the good guy in this situation. I can say, sure, use my wife the way you have for years. Don't worry about me. I don't mind. I can say all of that because I know that Zane will do the right thing."

Apparently, in Nate's mind, the right thing was to toss down his coffees and run toward the man horning in on his wife. Stef turned around in time to get tackled. Jen rushed toward the fight.

"Zane, you get off of him right now!" Callie shouted at her husband.

"You fucking overgrown ape, stop hitting me!" Stef tried to push Zane off.

"You get off my son, sir!" Sebastian's back stiffened, and he looked at Callie. "Call the police, dear."

"The sheriff is standing right over there laughing his ass off, Mr. Talbot." Jen looked down at Stef, who was trying to give as good as he got. For a rich boy, he knew how to fight dirty.

"Zane Hollister, stop beating up my best friend." Callie's booted foot stomped in the snow.

Zane got Stef in a chokehold. "Not on your life, babe. He kissed you. We took sacred vows to never allow another man to get close enough to kiss you. Right, Nate?"

Nate was all smiles now. "That's right, buddy. You do what you have to do."

"Asshole," Stef managed to wheeze out. He pulled his elbow out and caught Zane squarely in the gut. "I won't forget this when your next contract is up. Don't think I won't talk to the mayor about finding a new sheriff."

Nathan Wright was totally not intimidated by his threat. "Good luck with that, Stef. No one wants the job except Nell. She's threatened to run against me. Other than that, you got nothing."

Callie pulled at her dark-haired husband. "Zane, you get off him right this instant. I'm invoking the note clause in our marriage contract."

Zane popped up in an instant, his face a storm of pent-up rage. "Fine. I'll go bring the car around, but his ass is walking, and if you ever touch my wife with your lips again in a non-brotherly fashion, I'll kick your ass even harder."

Zane stomped away, leaving Callie shaking her head as she lent Stef a hand.

Jen brushed the snow off his back. "Note clause?"

Nate frowned. "Yeah, every time we do something she doesn't like she points to the note we wrote when we left her all those years ago. She saved it. She framed it and put it on the wall by the door, and she's threatened grave bodily harm if we take it down. She uses it like a sledgehammer filled with guilt."

"I merely remind the boys of the poor choices they once made." Callie turned to Stef. "Are you all right?"

"I'm fine." His gray eyes narrowed as he looked at Nate. "You planned that."

"I have no control over Zane's actions, man." Nate turned and followed his partner.

"So, Callie isn't your girlfriend anymore?" Sebastian was looking between them all as though desperately trying to figure out what was

going on.

"I was never really his girlfriend, Sebastian," Callie said, her voice a sad sigh. "I'm sorry I misled you. Stef has always been more of a brother to me than anything else."

Sebastian glanced over to where Nate and Zane had gone. "And now that…large, rather brutish fellow is your husband?"

"His name is Zane." She sighed again, this one a dreamy sound. "Stef introduced us. He introduced me to Nate, too. They are the best husbands a girl could have. Don't let their rough exteriors fool you. They're sweeties. I should probably go and make sure they don't leave Stef behind. It's a long way to Bliss."

Sebastian's eyes stared at a place right below Stef's face. "So you hid this from me? Callie got married, and you never mentioned it?"

"I didn't think you would ever find out," Stef admitted. His whole body was shaking. It appeared the adrenaline from the fight was gone and he felt the cold again.

Jen got close, and he shoved his arms under hers, wrapping himself under the coat she was wearing and rubbing his body against hers. "Hey!"

"It's my damn coat. You can share." His beautiful face was stark, and his lips were turning a nice shade of blue.

Damn him. She couldn't resist that slightly quivering lip. She pushed her body against his, sharing her warmth. But she wasn't going to lie down and give it up for him. She'd done that and it hadn't worked. She wrapped her arms around Stef but turned to Sebastian. "He's been lying to you because he didn't want you to find out the truth."

Stef's father's face fell, and a chalky whiteness took over his skin. "Stefan, you have to know that you're my son no matter what. I'll still love you."

"I never knew you loved me in the first place," Stef managed to chatter.

A slight flush permeated Sebastian's skin. "Of course, I do. You're my son. Just because you're…well, nothing changes that." There was a long pause. "Is it, well, is it one of those boys?"

Stef shivered in her arms, and he planted his face in her shoulder. "What is he talking about, and can you make him stop?"

She had an idea, and it made her giggle. "Which boys are you talking about, Mr. Talbot?"

He pulled his wool pea coat around his slender frame. "Those Harper boys he was always around. I suppose I always knew deep down. He talked about them all the time. I couldn't get him away from those two. I thought it was about Callie, but now I can see the truth. I don't see why he wouldn't admit it. I've never been one to hold a person's sexuality against them. Talbot Industries offers life partners insurance and benefits. Why would my own son lie? Unless…oh, no, it's that Max fellow, isn't it? Oh, my son, you can do better than him."

Stef's head came up, and he stared down at Jen. His eyes closed briefly as though in terrible pain, and then those gorgeous gray orbs were piercing into her. "Does he think what I think he thinks?"

A bit of glee lit her heart. "I think he thinks you love Max."

Stef turned to his father, his face turning red despite the cold. "Damn it, Dad! I am not Max's lover. Max is married."

Sebastian sighed, his relief a palpable thing. "Okay. I can handle Rye. He's a nice young lad."

"I'm not with Rye, either! He's married, too. I am straight."

Jen tried to contain her giggle, but it was hard when his whole body was quivering and he seemed to be trying to crawl into her. He looked like a little boy arguing with his dad. She'd never seen Stef look so open. "I can vouch for the straight part, Mr. Talbot. I know for a fact that Stef Talbot is one hundred percent capable of sleeping with a girl. He simply needs to tie her up and spank her a little bit first."

"Jennifer!"

She shrugged. "Do you deny it?"

"TMI, Jennifer. TMI." He frowned down at her before burying his face in her hair. His breath was warm against her ear. "You're under my authority now, love. I have the papers to prove it. I've been indulgent to this point, but now you're racking up the punishment time."

Now she didn't need the coat. Her whole body flushed with the memory of what it felt like to be punished by Master Stefan. Then he shivered again, and the moment was lost.

"Where the hell is Zane with the car?" Stef asked.

Sebastian's mouth was open as he watched his son. "Perhaps I should have come much sooner. We're going to have to talk about this, Stefan. I didn't raise you to spank people."

Stef groaned in her ear and burrowed further, as though he could escape into her skin.

When Zane pulled the SUV around, Stef pushed her into the back, making sure she was in between him and his father. The two men stared at each other over her head the whole hundred miles from Alamosa to Bliss.

* * * *

Two hours later, Stef was back in fighting form, and Jen sort of wished they could go back to that delicious moment when he needed her body heat and her support. The minute Zane turned into the Talbot estate's drive, he'd sat up and held himself away from her. He'd gone from needy little boy to the distant Dom she'd tried so hard to get to know. He'd neatly and efficiently packed everyone into separate rooms as he and Nate filled Zane in on what was going on with her.

She figured she should have been in on that meeting, but apparently her voice wasn't required. She heard them in the study talking to someone over the conference phone. It sounded like Finn Taylor explaining what legal maneuvers he was planning and the other guy, the security dude, providing sarcastic commentary. Jen simply let Callie lead her to a big, brightly decorated room that contained all the stuff Stef had packed up from her apartment. There was a suitcase of her clothes and some of her sketchbooks.

"He was upset when you left," Callie said as she opened the drapes and let in some of the most beautiful light Jen had ever seen.

That light was soft and seemed to caress everything it touched. She'd forgotten how much she loved the light here.

"Really? Because the way we left things, I thought he would be thrilled." Jen didn't like to think about the morning she'd left. Sometimes she couldn't help it and it played over and over in her mind like a bad movie. Of course at night when she was asleep, she dreamed about making love with Stef. She couldn't help it. In her

dreams he took her over and over. He spanked her to warm her up and then made love to her like a starving man.

Callie blinked behind her glasses. "I don't know what happened between the two of you. I only know he was upset. I know Stef. He was far too quiet, and he retreated into his studio for two weeks after you left. He barely said a word to anyone."

She couldn't imagine Stef being upset. He'd told her it had been a mistake. She'd actually thought she'd done him a favor and saved him the embarrassment of having to see his "mistake" around town. "He was probably feeling guilty. And annoyed. I guess I didn't react the way he thought I would."

"I don't think so," Callie said. "But I'm not going to be able to convince you."

There was a brief knock on the door that saved her from Callie's further explanations. Jen opened the door expecting to see Stef. She was surprised at the large, lovely man inhabiting her doorway. His hair was cut startlingly short, but Jen could see it was reddish. His face was an intriguing mixture of craggy lines and lovely features.

"Hello. Did Stef send me a toy?" She wasn't going to let anyone see how much being here again upset her. Not upset, actually, but she was definitely in midst of all the feels.

He frowned, his brows making a neat V in his forehead. "No. I'm a doctor." He looked past her to Callie. "Is this one of those patients, Callie?"

Callie laughed. "No, Caleb. She's just extremely sarcastic. Jen, this is Dr. Caleb Burke. He's the new town doctor. Stef brought him in for Rachel's birth."

He was carrying a large, battered leather bag. The man strode into the room like he owned the place. He set his bag down and shrugged out of the thick parka he was wearing. The doc worked out. That much was plain.

"Don't forget all the people who get shot around here. For such a small town, you deal with a lot of trauma. I wasn't here for the last two shootouts, but I have an emergency plan for the next one."

Jen had seen the effects of the last emergency that happened in Bliss. Mel and Nate had gone to the hospital. Before that, both Max and Rye had been injured when they faced down a man stalking

Rachel. "Hopefully we've seen the last violence for a while."

The doc slapped his hands together. "Nope. Place like this is a magnet. Bad things will always happen, and I'm going to be ready for it."

Callie nodded and gave the doc a smile. It was the same smile she gave Mel when placating him. Bliss was a magnet for sure. "Caleb is a great believer in preparedness. He made the whole town act out a scenario where the town was taken over by armed gunmen. Nell and Henry decided to protest and…"

"Nell and Henry got shot. Protesting won't stop an armed gunman," Caleb insisted. "Kevlar. That's what you need, and a damn fine plan of action."

Caleb Burke had his hands on his lean hips, looking down at Jen like a drill sergeant with a new recruit.

Jen turned to Callie. "Tell me Nell and Henry are still in one piece."

Callie waved off the concern. "He used paint guns. It was fine. Henry was surprisingly mouthy for a dead guy. The big problem was that Mel was late, and Caleb used green paint."

There was no question in her mind where this story was going. "Aliens have green blood."

"Yup. Mel freaked out. Guess you weren't so prepared for that, were you, Doc?" Callie asked with a smile.

Caleb had the good grace to look slightly apologetic. "It wasn't bad. I took out Mel with a tranq gun. I've got a couple stashed around town. He was perfectly fine. Now, let's get on with it. If you'll take off your clothes, we can get started."

Jen took a small step back because the man didn't look like he was joking. "Excuse me?"

"Stef brought in the doc to give you a physical," Callie explained. "He's worried someone broke you in prison. He's got a shrink coming in next week to help you with the trauma."

Had Stef lost his damn mind? "I was only in jail for a day. I didn't even get moved to actual prison. It was city lockup. What does he think happened to me?"

Caleb coughed a little, his eyes avoiding hers suddenly. "Well, any number of things can happen to an incarcerated person.

Dehydration, injuries due to violent acts, staph infections." He leaned in, his voice going low. "Sexual injuries. You don't have to be afraid or embarrassed. I've seen it all."

"OMG, I was in lockup for twenty-four hours in the Dallas County Jail, not lost in some war-torn tropical jungle. I'm fine. They gave me water. I didn't even have time to acquire a girlfriend. Tell Stef to stuff it." She turned to Callie. "I am hungry, though. They tried to give me bologna."

Callie shuddered as she grabbed their coats. "We should go to Stella's for lunch, then."

"Hey, I have a job to do here." Caleb got between her and the door.

Callie patted his chest. "I wouldn't, Caleb, sweetie. She's like Rachel."

Caleb paled slightly and backed down. "Okay, then. Um, well, if you need anything or, you know, start to remember stuff like torture, call me. You know, post-traumatic stress can hit you when you least expect it."

"He's insane," Jen stated as they walked out the door.

Callie pointed toward the snowmobiles on the lawn. "You expected different? He was the best we could get. He's a damn fine surgeon, and he's feeling his way as a general practitioner. He used to work at a big hospital in Chicago, but something happened and, well, let's just say Caleb knows where of he speaks when he talks about post-traumatic stress disorder. You should see him get together with Mel. Caleb is sure Mel is repressing trauma that happened while in the military, and Mel is certain Caleb's been probed."

"Nice," she said, hopping on the back of the snowmobile.

"They've gotten to be really good friends." Callie gunned the engine and headed toward Stella's.

Chapter Six

"What the hell do you mean he's dead?" Stef heard himself shouting, but he couldn't help it.

"Generally dead means ceasing to exist," the security expert said over the line. "Let me tell you, that is the case here. Dude lost most of his blood. I don't think that's coming out of the carpet. Your girl is going to lose her deposit, if you know what I mean."

"I don't care about that. What happened?" He took a deep breath to quell his rising panic.

Finn Taylor's voice was perfectly smooth over the speaker. "The police were called out to Ms. Waters' complex when the movers Stef sent got there to finish cleaning out her apartment. The police entered and found a Caucasian male aged thirty-five with his throat slit from ear to ear in the living room."

"I got there in time to see the body," Taggart said with what felt like glee. "One of the detectives who worked the case used to be in my unit. He gave me a heads-up. Dude was almost decapitated."

"Detective Brighton remembered Renard from the day before and recognized Jennifer's name," Finn explained. "The receptionist at the art gallery made the official identification. Jean Claude Renard is dead."

Stef felt his stomach churn. This was trouble. It had started out as

bad trouble, but this was much worse than he expected.

Nate sat back in his chair, crossing one booted foot over his knee. He looked every inch the lawman he was. "Do the police have any idea what Renard was doing in Jennifer's apartment? We locked up after we left. Did he have a key?"

God, he didn't want to think about that fucker having a key to her apartment and what that would mean. Had she turned to him? Had he been kind to her in the beginning and she'd found solace in his bed?

It was a good thing he was dead because Stef was thinking about killing him again. Decapitation was too kind for that fucker.

"He didn't have a key. Someone kicked that door in," Taggart said. "And I'm not so sure the crime didn't have two scenes. Renard was fucked up but the only blood in the apartment seems to have come from the death incident. As beat to hell as this guy was, there should have been blood splatter."

There was a sigh over the line. "I agree with Big Tag, but we need to wait until we get the full police report. This crime is so fresh I have little information about it. The only reason I know what I know is my partner's extremely good relationship with the chief of police."

Stef snorted. That was a delicate way of putting it. Julian Lodge probably had more dirt on the chief of police than he could imagine. Owning Dallas's most exclusive sex club put Lodge in a position of power. None of which would help Jen if Stef himself couldn't keep her safe.

"Do the police know the time of death?" Zane sat in the office with Stef and Nate, their previous fight forgotten after Stef had promised to keep his lips far from Callie. Though the big guy annoyed Stef on occasion, he was a close friend. Despite his current profession of bar owner, Stef knew he'd been a damn good cop at one point in time.

There was the sound of papers shuffling before Taggart came back on line. "Yes, they estimate that Renard was killed at approximately ten o'clock this morning."

Stef didn't like that timing. "So as our plane was taking off for Colorado, Renard was getting offed by someone."

There was a new voice added to the crowd. "The wounds, were there any hesitation marks?"

Stef looked up to see Caleb Burke in the doorway. The former trauma surgeon was staring at the speaker as though it was a person he was talking to.

"Um, I don't know. Give me a second." Taylor's side of the conversation was put on hold.

"You think it's a pro?" Zane asked, looking at the doc.

Caleb's head jerked slightly in the affirmative. Stef was getting used to the doctor's somewhat odd mannerisms. He was an excellent doctor, if a bit too thorough for some of his patients' tastes.

"What makes you think that?" Stef asked, dreading the answer. Somewhere in the back of his mind he'd been praying this was all a huge mistake. He'd hoped that Renard had damaged the painting and was too much of a coward to own up to it. It wouldn't be the first time a wealthy man set up one of his employees to take the fall. Stef could solve that problem. He would throw money at McKay-Taggart until they dug up enough crap on Renard to get him to back his ass down. This was something different.

"It takes a lot of strength to slit a throat," Caleb said, his voice hard and distant. "It's not like cutting a piece of cake. There's skin and muscle and sinew. To do it right and kill instantly, you have to cut to the bone. It takes power and practice to really learn how to slit a throat."

"Whoever is talking is absolutely right," Taggart assured them. "This wasn't someone who got lucky and hit his jugular. Whoever did this knew what they were doing and has likely done it before."

"So we're not talking about some random robber or an angry girlfriend?" Stef asked.

Nate shook his head. "Nope. The doc and Taggart are right. Whoever did this wanted it to be quiet and quick. He knew there wasn't anyone in the apartment, and he wasn't worried about someone walking in. Shit, our prints are all over the place. You'll need to come with me. Logan can print you. Mine are in the database. They'll need to eliminate us."

There was a little hiss as the speaker came back on. "Okay, I talked to the officer in charge. There's good news and there's bad news."

"Give me the bad news." He was a "glass is half empty" kind of

guy.

"The police searched Renard's apartment and didn't find the painting," Finn explained. "They also didn't find it at Jennifer's house when they executed the search warrant yesterday."

Well, that was too much to hope for. "And the good?"

Taggart sighed over the line. "That is good news. Though not for me. I was going to squeeze Talbot for bodyguard services. I need to get Adam out of Texas. He's annoying the shit out of me. According to this report, it looks like Renard was involved with some industrious people from Colombia."

Caleb's hands slapped together. "That would explain it. Those Colombians like their guns, but they know how to slit a throat."

Stef found himself looking to Nate and Zane for confirmation. They both nodded in agreement.

"That's excellent news," Nate said.

Zane sat back. "Takes a load off my mind."

The other three men seemed satisfied by the news that Jen was involved with someone who had a Colombian drug lord after him. "And this is good why?"

There was a deep chuckle from the Dallas end of the phone and then Taggart was speaking. "Because it means it's over, Talbot. The police here are theorizing that Renard stole the painting himself to pay for his coke habit. They found a kilo in his apartment. Apparently, his supplier thought he was scamming and took care of the situation. The police believe that he tried to convince them Ms. Waters had the painting, and they killed him when they couldn't find it. That painting is probably on its way to Bogotá as we speak."

"This is a good thing," Finn assured him.

Stef felt an enormous weight lift off his shoulders. "And the charges against her?"

"Well, I might have a solution to that as well," Finn said smoothly. "Renard was never the one who pressed charges. He convinced the owner of the painting that Jennifer had taken it. Given the evidence he managed to manufacture, it isn't any wonder the owner believed him. I happen to know this couple, and they are big collectors of contemporary art. I think a simple explanation, a donation to the college where they endow a chair, and a Talbot

original might go a long way to getting them to drop the charges. I think the charges will be dropped anyway, but this would speed up the process."

"Done." He didn't hesitate for a second. The faster he got Jennifer out of this mess, the faster they could move on with their lives. "Set up the deal. Let me know when it's done."

After a moment of wrap-up, Stef shut the connection down. He breathed a huge sigh of relief. She was safe. The charges would be dropped.

There wasn't any reason she shouldn't go back to Dallas.

The rolling sensation in his gut was back.

"Poor guy. He's got it bad," Zane said to his partner, a smirk on his face.

Caleb looked between the two men. "Stef has a thing for the brunette? Is that why he wanted me to give her the full *treatment*?"

They were worse than gossipy old women. "I asked you to check out Jennifer because she's been through a traumatic experience. She was in prison, for god's sake."

Nate snickered. "Yep, he's got it bad."

Stef chose to ignore him. "Is she all right? I know you couldn't have gotten the blood tests back yet, but does she seem to be okay?"

"Oh, she wouldn't let me touch her. I think she's fine." Caleb leaned against the wall, a frown on his face.

"I don't pay you to think. I pay you to know."

Caleb shook his head. "Yeah, you don't pay me all that much, anyway. Look, the girl didn't want to get examined. She wanted some lunch. It's a good sign that she has a healthy appetite. I wouldn't worry about it. If she starts showing signs of stress, give me a call."

He shook it off. He had to pick his battles. At least she was safe under his roof. Though not for long if she found out she wasn't under investigation. "Gentlemen, I hope you can keep this conversation between the four of us. Nothing has been settled yet. Until the charges are dropped, Jennifer is still technically under my custody."

"He's afraid she'll bolt," Zane said.

He wished he'd punched the asshole harder. "Are you going to keep quiet or not?"

"Sure," the big guy replied. "It would make Callie sad if she left.

I'll keep my mouth shut."

"I'll be quiet as the grave," Nate offered.

They all looked back at the doctor. "I don't care enough to say anything."

"Excellent." The day was looking up. She was here. She was safe. He had to figure out what the hell that meant, but he had time to do it now. Of course, Jen wasn't his only problem. His second problem walked through the door. His father wore a worried expression, his hands full of objects Stef immediately recognized. Yeah, he'd hoped to avoid that.

His father held up a plastic item. "Stefan, I went out to inspect the guesthouse. It's not drafty at all, but there is a problem. What on earth have you gotten yourself into? I don't know what half these things are. Are you aware that you have a large cross attached to the wall out there? What are all those hooks for?"

He felt his head start to pound.

His father dropped the plethora of sex toys he held in his hands onto the desk. "Is this some strange art thing?" He picked up a large plastic plug. "It's not your best work, son."

"Sir, that's an anal plug," the doctor in the room offered in the same no-nonsense tone he used to explain chicken pox to worried mothers. "It's a sex toy, and a rather large one. You might want to start with something a little smaller. And you should make sure you have plenty of lubricant on hand before you use that."

His father went white. Nate and Zane laughed like loons.

Stef let his head hit the desk and prayed the room would open up and swallow him whole.

* * * *

"So, are you fellas here for the Winter Festival?"

Alexei looked at the innkeeper. He was a balding, middle-aged man who wore a small badge that proclaimed him to be named Gene. He seemed to be the owner of the Bliss Movie Motel. It was on the outskirts of a sleepy little mountain town. What he'd seen so far was lovely. Still, he wasn't here to take in the scenery. He was here to get the painting and then use it to get close to Pushkin. Then he would

most likely be dead. No, he shouldn't waste his time on scenery no matter how lovely it was.

Ivan shoved an elbow in his side and spoke to him in Russian. "He called this winter. That is amusing."

Gene smiled at them, his face completely open. "Wow. Now that is cool. Where are you fellas from? You gotta tell me." He pointed to a globe behind the desk. It was covered in pushpins. "See, I have this globe so I can keep track of all the places the people who stay with us come from. It's a small world, when you think about it."

Ivan snorted. Alexei knew he would see this Gene's globe as childish. And yet Alexei found himself staring at it. The world represented as something he could spin around, play with, learn from. All of those brightly colored pins represented another person who had come to this town from far-off places. Places he would never see.

And his brother hadn't seen them either, would never see them because Pushkin killed him. That was what mattered.

"We are be coming from Belarus," he heard himself saying.

"That is neat. I love hearing different accents," Gene commented as he pulled out a purple pin and stuck it in Belarus. "We don't get many people from your part of the world. What's it like there?"

"It stink of fish," Ivan said, giving Alexei a dirty stare. Ivan hated Belarus. It was precisely why Alexei had chosen it.

"Oh. Well that's nice if you like fish." Gene looked from man to man, his eyes narrowing as though he was finally understanding something was off.

Alexei couldn't have that happen. He gave the man a broad smile. "Forgive my brother. He is, how you say, a pooper on parties. We are happy to be in this country. So beautiful." He leaned in and gestured back toward Ivan the Sour. "His last girlfriend leave him for fisherman. He has the women's troubles. You must to forgive him."

Ivan growled behind him but played along.

Gene was back to smiling. He laughed loudly. "I understand that, but, son, it's woman trouble. He's got woman trouble. The other way makes it sound likes he's menstruating."

Alexei nodded, though he had no idea what menstruating meant. He would have to look it up. If it meant Ivan was difficult and cranky, then it was a proper word to describe him. "So what is this Winter

Festival?"

Gene slid a pair of keys across the table. "Oh, it's one of the best times of the year. It's a week of skiing and snowboarding, and there's a supper at the end of the week and a drawing with all kinds of stuff you can win. The Rep Theater is doing a revue with singing. It's a lot of fun. It's why you're darn lucky I had a room left. Things fill up quick around this time of year. Here's a schedule of events. Don't miss the ice sculpting. We have a guy who carves these gorgeous sculptures with a chain saw. And he's real careful, too. After he lost his pinky last year, he's much more careful."

"This sounds fun." It sounded like an excellent cover. With all the citizens of the town mixing with a bunch of tourists, they wouldn't stand out. Perhaps he could get what he needed without killing the girl. The last thing he wanted was more blood on his hands.

Gene pushed a packet toward him. "Here's a map of the town. And a welcome package. It's got some fudge from the Trading Post and a menu from Stella's and a coupon for Trio. Oh, and don't forget, every night I'm running some great movies. The drive-in is normally closed this time of year, but I run some movies for the festival. Folks like to huddle under blankets and watch the show. It's real fun. All you have to do is open your window and you can see the screen. Tune the radio to the setting in the instructions for the sound. And the first bag of popcorn's on me."

Ivan huffed and picked up the keys. Alexei said good-bye to Gene and followed him outside. The snow was falling lightly, giving the entire world a gauzy feel. Mountains surrounded the valley on three sides. Somehow the sky seemed bigger here than it did at home. He stared at the mountains in the distance.

"This is not winter," Ivan complained in Russian. "This is a light spring breeze where I come from."

Since Ivan came from a dunghill close to the Arctic Circle, he was probably right.

"Why are we checking into this place?" Ivan asked. "We should walk back in there, put a gun to the innkeeper's head, and make him tell us where this girl is."

"And then?"

Ivan shot him a look that made Alexei know his intelligence was

in question. "And then we kill the innkeeper and kill the girl and get the painting."

"And the American police will let us stroll out?" Alexei tried to reason with him. Ivan was a barbarian. He was pure muscle with not a thought beyond killing and taking whatever prize he was supposed to get. "This is not Russia. You can't go around killing people and expect the cops to look the other way."

Ivan followed him when he started walking toward the room. "I don't see why not. Do police in America not appreciate money? We pay them and they look the other way."

Alexei found the room and shoved the key in. "I don't think it will work here. The media is different. No one will care if we kill Renard. He was a pathetic drug addict. If we kill this Gene person, someone will care. If we kill the girl, someone will care. We must be careful. These Americans are addicted to justice. Have you not watched their television?"

Ivan sniffed. "No. I am not as interested in what goes on with all those housewives as you are. I say no one will care if I kill all of those people. I will probably get a medal." Ivan dropped his bag beside the bed. He tossed his body down. "I will take this side. Wake me when it is time to kill someone."

He was asleep, snoring like a bear, almost instantly. It was a skill of his. He could sleep anywhere.

Alexei, on the other hand, barely slept at all. The minute he dropped off he saw his brother's bloody face. He saw how still his brother's body was. It was hard now to remember that his brother had always laughed and smiled. His brother had been the one to tell him stories about what their lives would be like when they finally got to America. They would find good jobs and good women. He'd been nine and not terribly interested in the women, but he wanted to play for an American hockey team. That had been his dream.

It had shattered in an instant when one of Pushkin's thugs decided to make an example of his beloved older brother. He'd found a new dream that day. He would grow strong and kill the man responsible for his brother's death. He'd managed to quietly kill the thug who had pulled the trigger, but Pushkin was the one he wanted.

And he would have him.

Alexei walked back outside and retrieved his cell phone because he wouldn't miss a chance to check in.

Despite the insane time difference, his cousin immediately picked up.

"This is Nick." Nikolai Markovic's accent was upper class, showing off his education. One did not go to work for the SVR without a proper education. Of course, the SVR was nothing but a fancy name for what it really was—KGB. Not that Nick worked for them now. Now his cousin was busy doing exactly what he was doing. It seemed revenge was the family business.

He spoke in Russian, the language he knew so well. "It's Alexei. There was a change in plans. I've had to re-route to Colorado."

A chuckle came over the line. "Colorado? That is interesting. I was in Denver once. It's not so far from Seattle."

It was a long way from Seattle from what Alexei knew, but his cousin's heart was in that city. Not that he would admit it. Nick had fallen in love with a woman named Hayley. He'd walked away from her when he realized he could take down the men who'd murdered his sister. He was with a woman he'd known for years, from his time in the KGB, but his true love had been left behind.

"Yes, I'm sure we're close. Do you want me to look in on Hayley?" The minute he said her name, he winced, knowing Nick would feel that word deep in his soul.

"No. She's fine. She's in college, where she should be. What do you need from me, cos?" The question came out in a polite blank tone, no emotion at all.

Anything he said from here should be professional. After all, they had jobs to do. "I need all the information you can find on a woman named Jennifer Waters. She was arrested for stealing the painting. I'm still not sure she knows what she's done, but I need intelligence on her. She was released from jail quickly once a man named Stefan Talbot became involved."

There was the sound of keys clicking that made Alexei think Nick was sitting in front of a computer. "I know the name Talbot. I think he's associated with the art world. Give me a second."

"Stefan Talbot?" An upper-crust British accent came over the line. Desiree. She was Nick's...lover? Partner? He wasn't sure

exactly what the gorgeous ex-MI6 agent was to his cousin. "He's an artist. He's also wretchedly wealthy."

"Yes," Nick said. "That's what I'm getting as well. If he's involved, you need to be careful, Alexei. He lives in a small town, but he's a world-renowned artist. This needs to be handled with some delicacy."

He didn't want to hear that. He wasn't exactly partnered with a man known for his delicate hand. "I'm with Ivan."

"Fuck." Nick cursed a bit more and then a long sigh came over the line. "Is there any way I can talk you out of this? The last place I want you to be is stuck in some small-town jail."

"Killing Talbot will land you in a federal jail," Desiree said. "We might be able to break you out, but it would take some time. And honestly, I don't want to have that blood on my hands. No one cares if we kill mafiosos and spies. They'll care when we have to kill prison guards."

Nick's partner was often the voice of cold reason. He was on his own. He'd always known that. "Don't worry about that. I don't intend to get thrown in prison. I'm going to find the painting and then I'll take down Pushkin and this can be over. I'll join you and we'll clear all the debts owed to our family."

And then they would die because it appeared his family was cursed.

"I'll look into it. But be careful. I've been following Pushkin's movements and listening in on some of his lieutenants. I think you're right and this is important to him. Something feels off about this. I know the painting would be important, but this feels like something more," Nick said.

He agreed. Even if the painting was worth a couple of million, Pushkin was pushing hard on this. The fact that the American authorities could get involved should have given his boss pause. Pushkin was nothing if not cautious. "I will be careful, but I cannot stop. I'm far too close."

A long sigh came over the line. "Des, I need to speak to Alexei in private." There was a muffled sound, as though Nick had put his hand over the phone. It was a moment before he returned and then his cousin sounded haggard. "I'm sorry for the delay. Des is unhappy

with me at the moment. She thinks I'm distracted."

He understood what that meant. Desiree thought Alexei was a distraction. "I won't bother you again. You've done much for me. Perhaps if we both come out on the other side of this, we can get together for a drink."

"You won't come out of this, Alexei. I know you. If you keep to this path, you'll die."

"You're one to talk."

"Yes, I am," Nick replied simply. "I'm a hypocrite, but I also have backup and you don't. Come home and when I can, I will help you."

He was too close to the prize. "I can't."

"You don't have to give up your whole life," Nick said, his voice low over the line. "I gave up mine. Listen to me. I wish I could go back to Hayley, but there's too much blood on my hands. Don't make the same mistake."

He wouldn't even know what to do with his life if he did go home. He was in far too deep. "I'll call you when I get back. Stay safe."

"Good-bye, cousin. I'll send you a report soon. Watch your back." The line went dead.

Alexei shoved the phone in his pocket and dragged cold air into his lungs. The conversation with Nikolai had put him in a strange mood. He should have stayed in his room until the job was done, but he was restless. He found himself walking, studying this odd world.

Damn, but his brother would have been fascinated by this place. He would have talked all afternoon with the Gene person, asking him questions about the town and the people Gene had met. Mikhail had never met a stranger.

Alexei found his feet moving toward the front office. It wouldn't hurt to talk to the man. He could find out more about the town. He was supposed to be a tourist. He would be a friendly tourist. Friendly tourists talked to people. His stomach growled. Maybe he would go to the diner after he talked to Gene. It could be reconnaissance, a way to bide his time until Nick came through with his report.

Yes, it couldn't hurt to explore this place a bit. Getting to know these people wouldn't change anything.

Chapter Seven

Jen pushed through the glass door of Stella's diner and was welcomed by a nice blast of heat. She shook off the cold, dragging the parka over her shoulders and hanging it up on one of the hooks on the wall. A sense of nostalgia nearly overwhelmed her. She'd worked in this little diner for a year and a half. Though she'd had a ton of jobs before she'd waitressed at Stella's, this was where she had been the happiest. Stella had been the best boss, always willing to work out a scheduling conflict or just to listen to her employees. Stella had given her a job and a home. Jen was shocked at the way tears filled her eyes.

Why the hell had she left?

Two arms wrapped around her, enfolding her in a sympathetic embrace. Callie was always quick with a hug, always seemed to know when she needed one and never held back. "Oh, sweetie, it's all right."

"I left her." Jen's heart clenched. She bit back a sob. She was in the middle of the diner. It was after the lunch rush, but the place was still packed. And she didn't care. "She gave me a job and took care of me, and I didn't even say good-bye."

A throaty voice broke through Jen's misery. "Well, I figured Stef did something to make you run, baby girl. Although I do wish you

would have written to let me know you were okay."

Jen turned to see Stella Benoit standing at the counter. She was a forty-something bottle blonde who wore far too much makeup. She was entirely beautiful to Jen's mind. Stella had given her so much more than a job. She'd given her a home and a place where she could be who she wanted to be.

"I'm sorry." It was the only thing Jen could think to say.

Stella's eternal helmet of blonde hair nodded. "All right then, sweetie. You come and sit down. I'll get you a nice cup of coffee. You want some food?"

"I would love a burger. I haven't had a decent burger since I left." A huge weight lifted off her shoulders. Stella wasn't tossing her out. She had Callie at her side. She might be able to come home after all.

Suddenly Dallas seemed so far away. The fight she'd had with Stef had been a silly reason to have left her home. She'd done what she'd been taught to do. She left when the going got a little rough. It was what her mother always did. Every time her artist mother had broken up with a boyfriend or gotten into financial trouble, she would move on to the next city. It would be better in Denver or Cleveland or Miami, she would say.

Life would never be better than she'd had it in Bliss. Bliss was the end of the road for her. She could run as far as she liked, but this was her home.

"You have to stop, or you're going to make me cry." Callie reached out, her hands brushing along Jen's cheeks as she slid into the booth across from her.

"I'm happy to be back. I didn't think I'd be this emotional." A great sense of calm came over her. She took a deep breath, enjoying the familiar smells of frying burgers, the piney scent of the cleaner Stella used on the floor, and slightly mangy dog. She felt a smile cross her face as she looked down at an old friend. "Hey, Quigley."

The enormous dog shoved his head under her hand, his not-so-subtle request for attention. Jen obliged and looked up at his owner.

Rachel Harper stood by the dog she'd taken on when she'd married the Harper twins. Rachel was a lovely woman in her early thirties with strawberry blonde hair, pretty green eyes, and a wry

smile that let the world know she didn't take it too seriously. Jen's eyes caught on the biggest change since the last time she'd seen Rachel. She appeared to have swallowed a beach ball.

"Don't even say it." Rachel stopped her with a shake of her head. "Damn, you're exactly what I need, another skinny thing in town. Scoot, Callie."

Callie snorted sweetly as she made room for Rachel and her soon-to-be-born kiddo. "Yeah, 'cause you're not glowing and gorgeous."

"It's hard to feel that way when I waddle like a penguin." Rachel snapped her fingers gently at the dog. "Q, take a load off."

The big mutt lay down on the floor by her feet, his head settling onto his enormous paws, and an audible sigh came from his chest as if he'd been waiting for this moment.

"Is there a reason Q is following you around?" Callie asked.

Rachel's eyes rolled, but there was an indulgent smile on her face. "Max. He's making me and Rye crazy. He's got Dr. Burke on speed dial, and he watches me like a hawk. You would think I was the first woman to ever give birth."

"He loves you," Jen said with a little sigh of her own. Max had been the baddest man around until the day he'd met Rachel.

Rachel sat back. "Rye loves me, too, but he doesn't feel the need to know where I am and what my blood pressure is twenty-four hours a day, seven days a week. I swear Max wouldn't let me drive until Rye had it out with him."

Callie had gone a little white in the face, and suddenly she was staring out at the street.

Rachel continued to praise her "reasonable" husband, missing the tells Callie was giving off. "Rye is the reasonable one. If I didn't have him, I don't know what I'd do."

Oh, but she remembered what Callie looked like when she was hiding something. She shook her head and pointed to Callie. "I don't think so. She knows something."

Now Callie's face flushed, and she had to stifle a laugh because her friend's glasses went the slightest bit foggy.

Rachel swung her head around like a predator sensing an easy kill. "What do you know, Callie Hollister-Wright? You tell me right

now."

Callie's fingers drummed nervously against the tabletop and she shot Jen a stare. "Thanks a lot. Now I'm going to get in trouble. Fine. Rye's not as reasonable as you think, but he is way sneakier than Max. The reason he's okay with you driving is that he had a GPS installed on your vehicle. It tracks you, and Nate and Rye both have the codes so they know where you are all the time. That's why Max backed off."

"That son of a bitch. I swear if I could get my foot more than three inches off the ground I would shove it up his ass. Reasonable? He's…" Rachel's eyes got watery. "He's so sweet." Tears began to fall. "And Max. I love them so much."

Rachel buried her head in Callie's shoulder and started to cry. Quigley got off the ground, and suddenly his head was in Rachel's lap. He whined a little as though he couldn't stand his mistress's tears.

"Hormones," Callie mouthed as she patted Rachel's hair. "She'll be fine."

"Max says I can't go anywhere without Q." Rachel's words came out in gasps between sobs. "He's trained the dog to come find him if my water breaks. I spilled a glass of water on the floor the other day, and ten minutes later Max was trying to take me to the hospital. Do you know how crazy you have to be to train your dog like that?"

"Crazy in love," Callie said soothingly.

Max was crazy in love with his wife. There was no question about that. For Max and Rye, Rachel was the sun in the sky. It didn't come as a surprise that they felt the need to watch over her every minute of the day. They wanted to know what happened to her. They wanted to be there if she came to harm, to love and protect her. If Rachel had been arrested like Jen had been, they would have been right on the case.

Like Stef.

"How did Stef know?" It suddenly struck her that Rye wasn't the only sneaky bastard. "I didn't think about it at the time. This morning was crazy but it's coming together now. Nate said something about a PI. I thought the police called because they found his number in my phone. I didn't know who to use as next of kin. I didn't put an emergency contact in my paperwork. But that's not what happened, is

it?"

Callie continued to soothe Rachel, but her eyes flared briefly before she answered. "I believe he set an army of private investigators on your ass the minute he found out you had left town. He knew you were going to Dallas before the bus stopped in Tulsa."

Damn him. He was so confusing. "Why?"

Rachel's head came off Callie's shoulder, and both of them turned to her before glancing back at each other.

"Is she really that stupid?" Rachel asked, her voice going husky. She picked up a napkin and wiped at her eyes. Q settled back down.

"Yes," Callie replied, "but I have hope for her. At least she's finally asking the question."

She shook her head because the answer they were pointing her toward didn't make a lick of sense. "He was a jerk to me. He told me flat out that he couldn't have a relationship with me."

"Yeah, and he probably chose to tell you this after he slept with you." Rachel's face was still blotchy from her crying, but a sympathetic look took over. "Men are dumb. So dumb. Not that Max and Rye were. I mean, they're dumb in other ways, but they knew their hearts. Stef is plain dumb."

Jen looked to Callie. Callie was Stef's best friend. She'd stood by him for years. She was as close to him as a sister. Surely she would defend him.

"He's also a bit of an ass at times, and Rachel's right. He's dumb as a post when it comes to this," Callie said.

"Are we talking about my boy?" Stella set down three mugs of what looked like hot chocolate. "He's always behaved like an idiot when it comes to Jennifer. He's smooth as glass around those other women he brings into town, but he practically falls all over himself over one of my waitresses. I always knew he had good taste."

"How can you say that?" She was completely at a loss. Her world was spinning on its axis and stopping in a completely foreign place. "He ignored me for eighteen months. I begged. I pleaded. And he said no every single time."

"And the minute you turned your back he stared at you like a lovesick puppy dog," Stella explained. "I know that boy. Hell, after his father left I practically raised him. Love him like he was my own.

You're the only woman he's ever really fallen for, and it scares the crap out of him."

She didn't understand anything. "Why? It wasn't like I was playing hard to get. I walked in and practically fell at his feet. I found out about all the pervy things he liked and said, hey, I can do pervy things, too. I bought BDSM books. I learned the lingo. I was the easiest lay he was ever going to get, and he turned me down. So one of you has to explain how all this rejection equals true love."

"Do you know Lana Wilson?" Callie asked.

Jen felt her heart drop. Sure she knew her. Lana Wilson was gorgeous and loaded. She was a stunning, curvy blonde bombshell. She was everything a man could want. Lana never had a hair out of place. She wouldn't be caught dead with paint under her fingernails or smelling like turpentine. She was Stef's sub. God, how could she have forgotten about Lana? Was she still around? Was she the reason he didn't want his dad in the guesthouse?

"I can see you do," Callie said with a nod. "He had a training date with her twice a month for the last three years. He hasn't seen her since the day you walked out."

She felt her mouth drop. Stef took his role as a Dominant seriously. "Why?"

Callie's shoulders came up in a shrug. "He won't talk to me about it, but if you ask me, it's because he was committed elsewhere and he finally got it through his thick skull that his feelings weren't going away."

Why was he stubborn? "Damn it, I've never told that man no. Why would he push me away? I slept with him. I gave him everything I had. I told him I loved him. Why did he dump me?"

"His mom," three voices said in perfect harmony.

"Thanks, that clears up everything." She wanted to pull her hair out. "One of you explain, now."

Stella scooted in beside Jen, her hand running soothingly across Jen's as she urged her to take a sip of the cocoa. "Stefan's momma was very young when she married Sebastian. She was twenty-four, and she wasn't ready to be a wife or a mother."

"She was older than me," she said, more to herself than anyone else.

"Yes," Callie agreed. "I never met her, but I saw a picture of her. She was stunningly beautiful, a pageant queen. She was Miss Oklahoma or something. She met Stef's dad and married him within six weeks."

"And had Stef a year later," Stella explained, her voice even, though Jen could see her eyes tightening. "I have all of this secondhand, but she didn't like living in Dallas. She wanted to go to LA and become a movie star. Sebastian wanted a wife. She wanted a sugar daddy. When Stef was five, she walked out on both of them. Sebastian was devastated. He left Dallas and ended up here for a couple of years. When he went back, Stef stayed. But I think his parents' divorce wrecked him. It's not you he's scared of. It's the fact that you're twenty-three, hon. He doesn't think you know your mind yet."

A whole bunch of things fell into place. Every fight and argument she'd ever had with Stef suddenly had a sheen of clarity. He'd always argued that she needed to work on her art rather than chasing around a man. He'd claimed he didn't have time for her. He'd pushed her away and then pulled her back when there was the slightest hint of danger.

God, he was a dumbass.

And yet she couldn't be too intelligent since her heart, her stomped-on and busted-up heart, was already softening. It had been burst and broken, and at the slightest sign of hope, it perked up and held out its stupid hands and wanted a hug from the same man who'd damaged it in the first place.

"He missed his mom?" Jen couldn't stand the thought of it. In her mind's eye she could see him as a child, alone and abandoned. She'd heard that part of the story. Sebastian had left, and Stef had been raised in Bliss. The vision of a lonely boy caused her eyes to water and her mind to race. She remembered all the times she'd told him she wanted nothing more than a fling. It had all been a manipulation. She'd thought that once she had him in bed, she could convince him that she was girlfriend material. When he'd turned her down, she'd pouted and ranted and made an ass of herself.

"He would never admit it, but yes, he missed her terribly." There was a gleam of moisture in Stella's eyes, but she sniffed it away. "His father made a mess of things because he couldn't commit after she

left. Stef had made friends here and wouldn't go back to Dallas. Sebastian let him stay. Stef built a life for himself out here. He also built up some strong and high walls that kept a lot of people out. Then one day, he fell for you. You walked out at the first sign of trouble."

She turned quickly because she wasn't at fault here. "I left after he told me it would never work. I left after he told me how much he regretted what was the best night of my life."

Stella nodded. "Yes, you left rather than fight for him or for your life here. You left because you were mad."

"I left because I was embarrassed." The truth hit her like a ton of bricks. She hadn't left to spare him. She hadn't run away because there was nothing for her in Bliss. Everything she cared about was in this tiny mountain town, and she'd left it behind to spare herself some momentary embarrassment.

"What were you embarrassed about?" Stella asked, her tone grave, as though the next answer truly meant something to her.

She felt the tears begin to roll down her cheeks. "I was embarrassed that he couldn't love me back. I was embarrassed because I knew I would never stop loving him, but I couldn't make him love me."

"Oh, baby girl, that is nothing to be embarrassed about." Stella pulled her close. "Every woman in the world has loved some man who didn't deserve her. That's no reason to give up your home and your friends."

"And it's not true," Callie insisted. "I don't care what he said. He missed you. Look, Jen, I don't know what happened that night. He won't talk about it. I do know that he bought a dozen red roses from Marie and Teeny the next day, and he tossed them in the garbage outside your place when he realized you were gone."

Rachel had tears streaming down her cheeks, too. "Max said Stef has been very enthusiastic in their fistfights since Jen left. It's a sign that he misses you." Rachel sobbed into her napkin. "Sorry. I can't help it. I don't care what the doctor says. I think I'm having a litter. There has to be more than one baby. I'm a whale."

Jen couldn't help it. She laughed through the watery mess of her tears. Something heavy had lifted from her, and it felt good to cry and laugh and just be with these women. It didn't matter that every tourist

in the place was watching them like they were crazy and all the locals were on their cell phones telling the people who weren't there about the waterworks.

"So Stef is dumb," Jen acknowledged in a rush of joy.

"Very, very dumb," Callie agreed with a smile.

Dumb she could handle. She reached out to pick up her cocoa, but she met Stella's hand, and the mug spilled off to the side, dripping to the floor.

Q was up and running for the door, his big body hitting it with a force that sent it flying open. She got a glimpse of the dog as he ran through the snow.

Rachel pointed to the street beyond the window. "We've got about five minutes before Max gets here. He's at the feed store. Ever since Dennis bought it and turned it into a church on Sundays and started only giving discounts to those who attend services, Max has been on his ass. Better order him a burger, or better yet, call Zane. He might need a beer."

"Don't worry about it, hon." Stella got up and started mopping up the mess. "Hal keeps a bottle of whiskey in the back. If that doesn't work, we can call the doc. I've heard he keeps tranquilizer darts around for Mel. I figure they'll work on Max, too. I like that doctor, I tell you."

Stella walked off, her boots clanging lightly on the floor.

Callie leaned forward, her elbows on the table. "So, you going after Stef?"

That was the question, wasn't it? How much did she want him? A whole, whole lot, her heart replied. It was pounding at the thought of going another couple of rounds with Stef.

"I can't change how old I am." It was a barrier she would have to find a way around.

Rachel put a hand on her stomach. She looked more peaceful than before. "You have to bust those walls down. He'll get it through that thick skull in the end. You're his woman. You have to prove it."

That, she decided, might be easier said than done.

* * * *

Alexei had to move quickly to get out of the way of the enormous animal that burst from the diner's doors. He thought it was a dog, but it might have been a small bear. Oddly, it wasn't the weirdest thing he'd seen this afternoon.

This was a strange place, but friendly. The people were talkative and open. He'd spent much of the hours since he'd left Ivan walking around the town. He'd browsed through the stores with their odd combination of ticky-tacky tourist merchandise and gorgeously made works of art. All around him the mountains climbed their way to a gloriously blue sky. Even in the winter, the world here seemed full of light. He almost never saw blue sky in Moscow. The sun rarely came out and even when it did, he did not join the people who lay on the grass, soaking it up. No. He stayed to the shadows always.

Was it any wonder the people here seemed so happy? They were surrounded by beauty. He'd found himself wandering. Up and down Main Street, people were out decorating and putting up small booths for the festival that was set to begin the next day. There was a happy hum of energy from the tourists who grabbed ski wear and fuzzy socks with bears on them.

This was a good place.

"Hi," a breathy voice said.

He looked down at the small woman with dark auburn hair. She was petite, with a curvy body that had his eyes roaming. His flare of attraction was shoved aside as he read the tight shirt she was wearing.

Stella's Café. Like the women in the picture he'd found at Jennifer Waters's apartment.

His stomach churned as he remembered he had a job to do.

"Would you like a booth or a table?"

His eyes briefly skimmed her nametag. Holly. Holly was a lovely woman. Luckily, she was not the woman he was looking for.

"I will sit at counter, thank you." Weariness overtook him as he slid onto a seat at the counter. He'd briefly forgotten himself. He sent Holly a tired smile and ordered a cup of coffee.

"Anything else?" Her bright green eyes were wide with expectation.

It was a polite question, but somehow it didn't have the inquiry of a server to a guest. There was something about her that made him

think she wanted to please, wanted to give. He found he couldn't disappoint her. She was sweet, and if his circumstances were different, he would try to seduce her. How long had it been since he'd taken a nice girl out? Never. Nick was right. He didn't know what normal was. His brother died when Alexei was a teenaged boy. All he'd thought about since was revenge. As he climbed up through Pushkin's organization, the women he'd had access to had mostly been prostitutes or the sort to couple with gangsters. Not a one of them saw past his wallet or his position. Not a one of them had looked at him with wide eyes and a truly soft smile.

"You pick for me?"

Her head cocked a little to the side, and she bit at her bottom lip, causing Alexei to shift uncomfortably in his seat. She was so beautiful.

"Savory or sweet?" Holly asked.

"Sweet." Definitely sweet. She would be sweet. She would be sweet in his arms. She would make sweet sounds. And her taste, that would be sweet, too. He would bury his face between her legs and lap up all the sweet cream he would draw from her.

She clapped her hands together. "Excellent. Stella makes the best chocolate pie ever! Be right back."

He took a long, deep breath and tried to get his dick under control. He was always in control. He was on a mission, and that mission had nothing to do with a woman named Holly with soft breasts and wavy auburn hair that would look beautiful spread across a pillow.

There was movement to his left as someone sat down next to him. He turned to see a man with reddish hair settling into the last chair left at the counter.

"Cup of coffee, please?"

Alexei sized him up immediately. This man oozed authority. There was a hard line to his jaw and a stiffness to his bearing, as though he was always ready for something to go wrong, and he would be the one to fix it. He knew the instinct well because he saw it himself, felt it, every day.

"Sure thing, Caleb," Holly said, turning toward the new guy. "You need a menu or do you want your regular?"

And just like that, the man named Caleb turned into a sputtering mess. "I…yeah, great. Great. Regular sounds good. I'll take that."

Holly shook her head, but there was a teasing grin on her face. "I have no idea how you can eat the same thing every day, Doc." She placed a piece of pie in front of Alexei. "There you go, big guy. You make sure you tell me how you like that pie. There's more where that came from, you know."

He bet there was. Holly turned, and he couldn't help but admire the way her ass looked in a pair of jeans. She was luscious. Those cheeks of hers were round and curvy. Damn, but he'd like to get his hands on her.

He shifted to grab some sugar for his coffee. Cold green eyes stared right through him. The man named Caleb wore a frown that would have intimidated a lesser man. Unfortunately for Caleb, he wasn't a lesser man. He had sat with a gun aimed at his head, not knowing whether he would live or die on more than one occasion. He found the man's jealousy amusing.

"I am not trying to steal girl," he assured the man. "But I am not blind."

"You could be," Caleb shot back.

He shrugged before digging into the pie. Holly had been right. It was excellent. "I don't to be seeing ring on her finger."

Now the man was staring at his coffee. "I didn't say she was mine. She's a nice woman. She doesn't need some tourist pawing at her."

"I will attempt to keep paws to self, but if you want woman, you should take her. She is too lovely to be alone for many times."

"Thanks for the advice, but I think I can handle it." Caleb turned away, his part in the discussion obviously over.

The door to the café swung open, and Alexei turned to see two boys walk in. They were twins, with dirty blond hair, oversized coats, and hockey sticks. Neither boy looked like he could handle a hockey stick. They were slender, with not an ounce of muscle between them. They shrugged out of their coats and took a seat in one of the empty booths. Their heads sagged as though the weight was too heavy to carry. Each boy had sad brown eyes that stared at the tabletop as though it was the only thing in the world.

Holly set Caleb's mug in front of him. She noticed the boys and walked around the counter to move to their booth. She got to one knee, and if the booth hadn't been so close, he wouldn't have heard her soft words.

"They wouldn't let you play again, would they?"

Both heads shook.

"Little pricks," Caleb muttered under his breath.

He was curious enough to risk the man's wrath. The boys, though American and twins, somehow reminded Alexei of himself at that age. There was something in the way their heads hung in disappointment and the way they clutched those sad hockey sticks. "Those young boys?"

Caleb's eyes flared as though he'd forgotten he wasn't alone and was pissed to be reminded. He shook his head as though to clear it, and his voice got low. "Nah, those are the Farley brothers. They're twelve and flat-out geniuses when it comes to school, but they can't get the boys from the next town to let them into their hockey game. It must be lonely for them. They're the only kids their age here in Bliss."

He turned back, and the kids were accepting comfort from Holly. An older woman with frothy blonde hair and cowboy boots was serving them hot chocolate and ruffling their hair. They seemed like nice kids.

"They are not picked for team?" He should let it go, but somehow he couldn't. "Perhaps they were too many players?"

"Nah, they're just not very good," Caleb said with a little snarl. "Those other kids are jerks because they think Will and Bobby are nerds. They have genius-level IQs and have photographic memories. You know what a nerd is?"

He searched his brain and came up with the slang. "Yes, this is smart person. I do not understand why your country does not like the smart persons. In Russia, these boys will one day make all the money and get all the womens. Why does this mean they cannot to play hockey? How will they get better if no one will let them play?"

He would never have learned if Mikhail had not taken the time to teach him.

"They won't." Caleb's mouth became a stubborn line. "I swear,

sometimes I'd like to take those other kids by the throat and teach them what it means to be a bully. But I'm not supposed to do that anymore."

Alexei slapped him on the back as an idea occurred to him. "Then we should put your anger to the management."

One reddish-brown brow rose. "Excuse me?"

He searched for the words. Sometimes English was hard. "We should to teach the boys. If they learn, then they play. No one will call them nerd when they learn to put their asses on other boys."

"God, I hope you meant to say put the other boys on their asses," Caleb said with a shake of his head.

"If that mean to hurt them in an entirely legal fashion, then yes. This is what I mean. I am good hockey player. Do you play?"

"Yeah," Caleb said, his lips curling up. "Actually, that sounds like fun. I wouldn't mind a little practice." He turned and slipped out of his seat. "Holly, can you get us a thermos of coffee? Come on, Bobby and Will, the big Russian guy and I are going to teach you how to put the older kids on their asses—I mean butts."

Alexei paid his tab quickly and was rewarded with the twins' shining faces, and Holly, who looked at him like he was the nicest man alive.

She could never know the things he'd done.

But maybe he could help a couple of kids out.

He followed Caleb and the boys out the door in time to dodge two men in cowboy hats running for their lives. The large dog he'd seen earlier ran behind them.

"Sorry, mister," one of them said. "We gotta move. Our wife's having a baby."

His English must be really bad, Alexei decided. It almost sounded like they shared a wife. He found that idea entirely entertaining.

"You coming, mister?" one of the young twins asked.

"Sure," he replied and followed his new friends.

Chapter Eight

Stef strode through the double doors of Trio with one thought on his mind—get Jen and go home. He'd searched all over the fucking town for her. From the moment he'd realized she'd left the house, he'd been looking for her. He'd tried Stella's, where he'd found out she'd had lunch with Callie and Rachel. He'd moved on to the Trading Post, where Teeny and Marie had admitted they'd talked to her for half an hour about everything that had happened in Dallas, including her unfortunate incarceration. Marie had made it plain that she blamed him. Jen wouldn't have gotten into trouble if he'd had enough of a brain to marry her. Laura Niles at the Stop 'n' Shop had said roughly the same thing.

How had she left everyone high and dry, but he was the villain?

"This place is new, Stefan. It used to be a hardware store, I think."

And he'd done all of his roaming with his father riding his ass. He wasn't sure how much worse the day could get.

"Mr. Weldon died back in '05, and he didn't have any kids. The place was empty until Callie's husband decided we needed a bar he didn't almost get murdered in," Stef said under his breath as he looked around the little tavern.

It was filled to the brim with tourists. The damn Winter Festival. In all the drama of the day, he'd forgotten that it started tomorrow. He'd promised Callie and Rachel that he would help with several of the events. He was supposed to host the final night's dinner and call out the raffle prizes. Could he get out of that? *Shit*. Rachel would probably get upset. A stiff wind was all it took to get her crying these days. He was stuck. That was exactly what he needed, his whole damn town overrun with strangers while he was trying to keep an eye on Jennifer. Despite what Nate had said, he would feel better when that painting turned up.

"Which husband is that? Nathan, or the large, ill-tempered character?" His father glanced around the place with the same enthusiasm he'd shown all day. Everywhere they'd gone his father had tried to talk to people, to find out everything that had changed in the years since he'd left.

And ill-tempered was a good way to describe Zane Hollister. "It was the big one, Dad."

His father's brows came together in a concerned *V*. "And you say that Maxwell and Ryan are involved with a single female as well?"

"Yes," Stefan replied shortly. After the incident he'd started to mentally refer to as Anal Plug Armageddon, his father had all kinds of questions about the relationships in Bliss. He'd been shocked to discover that ménage was rapidly becoming a way of life in the little mountain town.

"But you aren't sharing Jennifer with someone, are you?"

He reminded himself that he was thirty-two years old, independently wealthy, respected in the art world, and responsible for himself. So why did talking to his father about sex make him feel like he was an eleven-year-old boy who had gotten caught with a *Playboy*? Of course, when he'd gotten caught with a *Playboy*, it had been by Stella, who'd given him a stern lecture about respecting women and taken it away. Max and Rye had been pissed off because it was the only one they had. Two days later, Mel had replaced it. He'd given Stef a lecture, too. Mel had advised him to always make sure the women in his pornography were humans.

"No, Dad. I'm not even dating Jennifer, much less passing her around to my friends."

And he wouldn't. Not ever. He loved Max and Rye like brothers. He felt the same way about Nate, and he'd gotten to where he was rather fond of that Neanderthal, Zane. But he would never understand how they could share the woman they loved.

He didn't love her. Perhaps if he told himself that a hundred times a day he could believe it.

A soft, twinkling laugh flitted through the bar. There were many people talking and laughing, but that one sound had all of Stef's attention. He could pick Jennifer's laughter out of a crowd of a hundred thousand.

His father pulled at his coat sleeve. "So you merely tie her up? You don't date her?"

Stef's back was suddenly ramrod straight as his eyes found her. She was sitting at the bar with Callie on her right, accepting a glass from Zane. That wasn't what had his back up. It was the cowboy sitting beside her, his hand possessively resting on her back, mere inches from her perfect ass.

James Glen. He was a rancher who had inherited an enormous spread from his father a few years back. He was twenty-five and a known playboy. He smiled at Jennifer, leaning in like they were having an intimate conversation. He was tall, dark, and very much the asshole since he was busy trying to horn in on another man's woman.

Damn it, he couldn't think that way. Except that technically she *was* his. He'd signed a bunch of paperwork making him responsible for her. Yeah. She was his. He just didn't love her, and she wouldn't be his forever. He would do well to remember that.

"Stefan," Sebastian said, his impatience obvious in the tone of his voice. "I asked you a question. I'm trying hard to understand this lifestyle you seem to have chosen."

"It isn't a lifestyle. It's who I am, and it's private." He tried to keep the irritation out of his tone. He was fairly sure he was failing miserably. While his father had been reacquainting himself with the town, Stef couldn't help but think about how many years had gone by. Every time his dad marveled at some new store in town, Stef would think about the fact that if he'd ever come to visit, he would have known. He would likely have been able to figure out Callie wasn't his son's girlfriend if Sebastian had given a damn.

"But I'm your father."

"No, you are the one who provided the male portion of the DNA that created me." He couldn't quite keep the cruelty out of his voice. "Mel was the one who taught me how to shoot a gun, and he was the one who told me about sex. Do you have any idea how difficult a conversation that was? He's legally insane, but he did it. Stella made sure I had lunch on the weekends when the nanny took off and didn't bother to bring in a replacement. Callie's mom took me to the doctor when I was sick. You are not my father, and you have no place in my life. So back off."

He stalked away. He didn't look back because he was sure of what he would see. His father's illness seemed to have brought on some need to bond with the child he'd left behind, but Stef didn't have the time or patience to deal with him right now. His father had been sick, and he hadn't bothered to tell him. Why should it mean anything at all to him? His father didn't need him in any way that counted. His stomach was in knots. His hands were shaking with the force of his rage.

She thought she could ignore him?

He'd been the one to get her out of jail. He'd been the one to move heaven and fucking earth to get her out of that hellhole, and she was flirting with James Glen, who couldn't tell a Klimt from a Jasper Johns because he spent all of his time knee-deep in cow crap. He had no interest in who Jennifer Waters was as a person or an artist. He liked her tits, and she was smiling at him. She was giving him her softness.

Stef pushed through the crowded bar. He plowed his way through the tourists and locals who called out his name. His vision tunneled down to Jennifer, the rest of the world falling away. Her generous lips opened, and another long, sexy laugh came out of her throat. She put a hand on James Glen's forearm as she said something low and seductive.

"Stef, are you okay?" Callie asked.

He barely heard her. He did catch Zane's smirk.

"No fighting in my bar, Talbot," Zane ordered.

He'd paid for the damn bar. He should be able to do what he wanted in it. And what he wanted to do was fuck up James Glen's

unlined, pretty-boy face.

"Hey, Glen, you want to move your hand off the girl's ass?" He felt his every muscle go hard and his heart start to pound. Why was he doing this? His rational brain knew he needed a bit of distance between himself and the way-too-young-to-ever-settle-down girl, but the caveman in him wanted that fucker's hand off his woman's ass.

James Glen turned, his Stetson moving as though it always sat on his head. "You got a problem, Talbot? I was just welcoming a friend back into town."

"You bet I have a problem," he spat.

Jen looked back at him. "What's wrong with…" She stopped, and a smile curled on her lips. She forcibly removed James Glen's hand from her waist. Her smile was wry as she looked back at him. "Better, babe?"

The endearment did weird things to his heart. It was a term for equals, for partners. He shouldn't take it seriously. "You need to come home with me. You've had a rough day."

"Yes, I have. I could probably use a little stress relief," she said as she brought the wineglass to her lips. "Can you think of anything that might help?"

His cock stuck up her ass? That might help. His cock fucking her tight little asshole would relieve an enormous amount of his stress. Just like that, he was hard and ready to fuck. Damn, he was glad he'd left his coat on. He grasped on to the only non-sexual thing he could think to say.

"You stole my snowmobile."

Callie laughed. "That's the worst diversion tactic I've heard yet. And it was me. I stole the snowmobile. I hate driving that damn SUV of Zane's. It's like he has to prove how big his penis is. It's unwieldy."

"The SUV. Not my dick, that's completely wieldy. I wield it often and totally in her direction," Zane said with a grin.

"Are you going to arrest me?" Jen asked with a laugh. "Because I think I'll appreciate Bliss County Jail way more than where I woke up this morning. Zane was telling me Nate's new admin, Hope, takes food orders for the poor people Nate tosses in there."

"Stella and I split it," Zane explained. "She takes the lunch

orders, and I get anything after 7:00 p.m. You would be surprised what some well-made fries can do to liven up a prisoner's day. I make sure they're hand cut. I figure if I feed 'em properly, maybe they won't sue Nate. So far we're good."

Jen shook her head. "See, this is why I love small towns. No one offered me fries in the Dallas lockup. Though I did get a thorough body cavity search from a woman named Mildred."

"That must have been horrible for you, darlin'," James said, his hand stroking hers.

Stef felt his blood flare, but Jen moved the cowboy's hand off her wrist.

"That's sweet, James, but seriously, I belong to him. He might be too dumb to admit it, but he'll do that thing where he starts a fight, and he'll probably get his ass kicked, and then I have to listen to him whine."

"I don't whine." What the hell was happening? He'd expected her to spit bile his way, not sweetly tell everyone she belonged to him. Because she didn't.

Jennifer shrugged. "That's not what Max says. Max says you whine every time he kicks your ass."

"Max lies," he retorted. "And he doesn't kick my ass. I hold my own. I have since we were kids. Let's go home."

She hopped off the barstool. "Okay."

Just like that? Where was the catch? She'd been the brattiest thing he'd ever met for a year and a half. Now she walked to him, placing her hand in his and turning her perfectly serene face up. He was at a loss. Did he lead her out or wait for the other shoe to drop?

"Should we get your dad?" Her hand squeezed his when she said the word "dad," as though she knew how conflicted he was and offered her support.

He found his fingers lacing through hers. "I left him in the front."

Her eyes scanned behind him. "Well, now he's sitting at a table with Hiram and Stella."

He turned and saw that his father was laughing, his head thrown back, his face more open than he could ever remember it.

"You're going to have to talk to him, you know," Jen said, her eyes narrowing in obvious concern.

"Why?" He didn't have to do anything. As far as he could see, he didn't have anything to say to his father.

"Because it's the right thing to do." She started walking, her hands still laced in his, forcing him to follow. "Leave him the keys. We can drive the snowmobile back. Somehow I think someone will take Callie home."

She took the lead, pressing through the crowd, holding on to him. She stopped in front of the table where the mayor of Bliss sat holding court with some of the town's older residents.

"Good evening, Sebastian," Jen said with a sunny expression on her face.

His father's smile was slightly tight, as though he didn't approve. "Jennifer."

If it bothered Jennifer, she didn't show it. "Please, only Stef ever calls me Jennifer. My friends call me Jen."

One eyebrow cocked up. "Stefan isn't your friend?"

Her hand squeezed his as she replied with a little laugh. "Stefan is a complete coward. Calling me Jennifer is his way of distancing himself. You'll note he doesn't run around calling Max Maxwell or Rye Ryan. It's okay. We're going to work on the problem."

"Jennifer." He bit out her name between clenched teeth. She was pushing him. *Why?*

Her hand came up and rubbed across his chest. "It's all right. No one thinks less of you. Everyone gets scared. Now, give your dad the keys, and I'll get my coat and meet you outside."

She released his hand and strode off toward the front of the tavern. *Coward?* She'd called him a coward in front of his father.

"Now, Stef, you need to take a break and think about what you're going to do next," Stella said sternly.

He didn't need to take a break. "I'm going to blister her backside. That's what I'm going to do."

Stella's relief was obvious in the relaxed line of her mouth. "Oh, good. I thought you were going to do something stupid."

"Stella, how can you say that?" Sebastian slapped a palm on the table. "I might not like the girl, but I certainly don't want my son to inflict injury on her."

Stella's eyes rolled. "You've turned into an old man. Stef, don't

listen to him. I knew your father when he was younger. He wasn't always a dried-up old prude. And listen here, Sebastian. That girl is the best thing to ever happen to your son, and one day he'll wake up and see it. Maybe, if he's smarter than his father, he'll reach out and grab her. Maybe he won't wait twenty years, because let me tell you, if he does, she won't be sitting around waiting for him."

Stella pushed out of the booth and strode away. Stef could have sworn he saw tears in her eyes. The crowd swallowed her up.

Hiram put a wrinkled hand on Sebastian's shoulder. "That was to be expected. Let's have a beer. I've missed you, old friend. Let me tell you about all the craziness around here. These young folks are very entertaining."

Stef shook his head and turned from the sight of his father and the elderly mayor of Bliss. It struck him suddenly that his father had a life here at one time. He'd lived here and built the manor house and the guesthouse. He'd been a part of Bliss. He'd seemed happy here and always spoke of it with an obvious fondness.

Why had he left?

Because people left. That was what they did. His mother had left. His father had left. Jennifer left. People picked up and left when he became difficult, and he couldn't quite figure out how to not be difficult.

He didn't like the direction of his thoughts. It made his stomach twist and turn. It was easier to focus on the fact that Jennifer had defied direct orders. He was responsible for her. He'd signed papers that made him accountable for her behavior. She'd been in jail. She'd left Bliss, and not six months later she was involved with some unsavory people. The minute she got back, she started looking for more unsavory people. He pushed through the crowd, scowling at anyone in his path. He was satisfied with the way they made room for him, shuffling out of his space as though no one wanted to get too close. He found her at the door, talking to Logan Green, Nate's deputy sheriff. She laughed at something he said and gave him a big hug that seemed like it lasted far too long. Logan was about Jennifer's age, perhaps a tiny bit younger. He was far more suitable for her than a thirty-two-year-old man.

"Beat it, Logan," Stef growled as he got close enough to be

heard. His dick didn't care who was more age appropriate. "Go find Hope and bug her."

Hope was the new receptionist at the Sheriff's Office. Logan spent an enormous amount of his time flirting with the slightly older woman.

Logan's eyes flared briefly, but he seemed to get the point. He headed straight to the bar.

"Very friendly," Jen said, shaking her head at him.

A nasty impulse clutched at his gut. He took Jennifer by the arm and led her down the narrow hallway toward the small office Zane kept.

"Hey, I thought we were heading home," she protested as she struggled to keep up with him.

"I have a few things to say to you that can't wait." He punched in the code for the door and the lock gave way. It was a good thing Zane was so predictable. Callie's birthday was something he knew by heart.

"Don't," Jennifer said softly as he closed the door behind her.

They were locked in together. He couldn't miss how intimate the tiny room was. It was the first time he'd gotten her alone since she'd been back. No, it was the first time he'd allowed himself to be alone with her. He was in control. She was an artist he liked. She was too talented to be allowed to waste it all. That was why he was here. That was why he had gone to Dallas.

Then why had he bought her flowers on that day when she'd left? A little voice was sighing in his head. Why had he been ready to apologize and ask to start over? Why had he told Lana he couldn't see her anymore? Why hadn't he been to the BDSM club in Denver in months? Why had he turned down invitations to play parties?

Stef hated that fucking voice.

"What do you think you're doing?" He turned on her, though the small room didn't allow much distance between them.

"I am begging you not to do this," she said, her fists clenched at her sides. "I am trying to get along with you. I'm trying to be understanding."

"Really? What are you trying to understand, love?"

"Why you act like such an ass," she said and then groaned. "See, I did not mean to say that. I meant to be sweet."

"Tell me something, did you mean to drape yourself all over James Glen?" Stef felt his hands twitching. She was so close. He could smell her. She'd taken a shower at some point, and her hair smelled like citrus. God, he loved that smell. She always smelled sweet, with a hint of bite underneath. She was a juicy grapefruit who needed a spoonful of sugar. His cock ached. He was so hard he could pound nails.

Her eyes became wide orbs in the low light. "What are you talking about? I never touched him. He was being friendly."

"No, he wasn't. He was being horny." There had been nothing at all friendly about the way James Glen's hand had been ready to cup her ass. It had been a prelude to an invitation to go back to his ranch where he would have done any and all manner of nasty things to her. James Glen had been looking for a lover for the night. Stef should know. He was desperate as hell, too. Why had he brought her back here? It was too quiet and intimate.

"Well, good for him. Maybe I should take him on. It's been a long time for me," Jen snarled. Her foot stomped at the floor, her face blushing in frustration. "Damn it. Stop it, Stef. Stop it now. You're making me say things I don't want to say."

"I'm not making you do anything." This was what he needed. He needed a good fight to remind him why she was a bad idea. She was a brat who always tried to push him. She'd tried anything and everything to get her way. Maybe now she was trying to make him jealous. It was working. "You were the one making a spectacle of yourself. You were the one flirting. Tell me something. Is your taste in men really that bad? James has fucked just about every girl in southern Colorado. You want to be next in that long line?"

Her face flushed, her eyes narrowing to angry slits. Her mouth opened, and he knew venom was about to spew out of that pretty mouth of hers. Then it closed. Her shoulders relaxed, and her hands went, shockingly, to the waistband of her pants. He watched in a mixture of abject horror and rampaging desire as she pushed her jeans over her hips and presented that gorgeous ass to him.

"How many, Sir?" Her voice was calm, but there was a throaty, aroused quality he couldn't mistake.

He coughed. He couldn't help it. He couldn't find air to breathe

in. Her palms were pressed against the wall, her ass thrust out and prepared for the slap of his hand. She was a bit awkward, but her presentation was close to perfect. Everything about her called to him, and he wasn't sure he could refuse the invitation.

Those twin globes were beautifully round and juicy. There were two perfect dimples above her ass, calling to him to kiss the skin there. The line dividing her cheeks was a sweet arrow leading to her pussy. Of their own volition, his hands moved out to caress her ass. Her skin was soft and hot against his fingers.

"Ten," he heard himself say. Ten smacks. Two for letting James Glen touch her. Two for smiling at Logan. Six for leaving him. Even as he thought it, he knew he wasn't being fair. Nothing about this was fair. His brain felt fried. The only thing he could see was her soft, white flesh. She was ready for him. She was submitting to him.

"Yes, Sir. I'll count." Her voice was breathy and deep.

She was manipulating him. There was zero doubt in his mind and he also knew that it was going to work. This was much more effective than yelling at him.

Her jeans were around her knees. They were skinny jeans, tight when she wore them, and they formed a near perfect binding now. She couldn't move freely. Her legs were tied together as surely as if he'd wound a rope around them. If he shoved his cock in, it would be tight, so tight. He would have to fight his way in. Thrusting would be hard. He would have to force his dick in and then grind in a slow circle until she moaned and he felt her pussy vibrate around him, sucking at him, milking his cock. Then he could let go. He would come until he had nothing left. He would grind into her until he was dry and she was full, the exchange complete between them.

Fuck, he didn't want to wear a condom with her. He hadn't the first time and didn't want to now. He wanted to fill her up with nothing in between them. His cock was obsessed with getting inside her bareback. He couldn't do this. This wasn't some sub he was training. This was Jennifer. He couldn't send her away at the end of the weekend. He had to see her every day.

Stef tried to take a step back, his thighs coming in sharp contact with Zane's desk.

"Is there something wrong, Sir?" She hadn't moved from her

position, but her head was turned as she attempted to look at him. "Did you change your mind? I did spend some time with the doctor. Maybe I tried to seduce him, too."

It was the smile on her face that did it.

He reached out and picked up the ruler on Zane's desk. It was flexible metal with a corked back. He tested it against his palm and then brought it down on her ass.

Jen gasped. Her body stiffened for a moment. He waited for her to get back up and tell him to go to hell.

"One," was all she said.

His cock felt like it was trying to claw its way out of his pants. The ruler in his hand felt good, but something was off. "This is wrong."

Now she stood, a fine sheen of moisture in her eyes. "No, Stef, don't stop. I want it. I like it. This isn't some lifestyle I want to live, but I love to play with you."

He turned quickly, looking for what he needed. Earbuds. They were connected to Zane's laptop, but he easily removed them. She wasn't where he'd left her. "Did I tell you to move? That's two more. Now, give me your hands."

She turned, hopping because her jeans were caught at her knees. "Sure, let me get out of these."

"Two more for questioning me, love," Stef said with great pleasure. Ten had been far too easy, but Jennifer seemed determined to give him more. She didn't seem to fear him at all.

Her mouth opened, then closed, and she held her wrists out to him without another protest. He wound the earbuds' plastic wire around her wrists, palms together. He worked quickly, winding it in a pattern that would restrict her movement but not damage her nerves in any way. Now that he was tying her up, a sense of calm, almost fatalistic acceptance had come over him. He should walk out the door, but he couldn't. He needed her. He'd never needed another woman the way he did her. She'd haunted his dreams since the day he met her.

She was an addiction, and he was going to fall off the wagon for the night.

"I like the way those jeans keep your legs together. They make a

good binding." He picked her up and moved her to the desk. "Lean over, put your hands out, chest against the desk, ass in the air. I owe you some discipline, love."

Discipline. Even saying the word made his cock jump. Saying the word while he contemplated Jennifer's gorgeous ass had his breath ragged. He had to remember to stay in control.

She did as he asked, sliding seductively against the desk. Her eyes were hot as she craned her neck to look up at him. "Is that all you owe me, Sir?"

He brought the ruler down on her perfect ass. A pretty line of pink formed, and her flesh quivered. He owed her so much more than a spanking. "What else do you want, Jennifer? What else should I give a bratty submissive who doesn't know her place?"

A couple of hours at his feet might start to satisfy the Dom in him. She could kneel at his feet in the studio while he painted. When he needed to relax, he'd open his pants, and she would suck his cock. Otherwise, she would sit there, and he could stroke her while he worked.

A slow smile crossed her face, like a cat who had found the most perfect cream. "Where's my place, Stef?"

Beside him, underneath him, with him always. But he would never let her know that. He wanted something she couldn't give him. He wanted something that wasn't fair for him to ask of her. He was a selfish bastard. If he had his way, she wouldn't have a career at all, and she was far too talented for that. Tonight was all he could allow himself. "This is your place. Right here. Right now. Bound and waiting for me."

He brought the ruler down in short arcs, spreading the spanking all across her gorgeous ass. He counted in his head because he didn't want to hear the sound of his voice. He preferred the breathy, desperate gasps and moans that escaped her lips. She was trying so hard to hold still for him. Her chest hitched, and her ass swayed as though anticipating the next stroke. He slowed down after stroke number five. Anticipation was part of the game.

Her skin was pink and perfect. No welts, just a nice, hot color. By the time he reached eight, her head was pressed to the desk and not a single snappy remark had come out of her mouth. She simply

whimpered, and the sound went straight to his cock.

"I didn't like that rancher's hand on your ass, love," he explained as he put his own hand on her warm flesh.

"Yes, Stef," she said, a dreamy quality to her voice.

She was so submissive when it came to this. She would rail and rage at him outside of sex, but she was a kitten when he got her pants off. The combination was intoxicating. "No more ranchers. He wouldn't understand you anyway."

"Yes, Stef."

That's what he wanted. *Yes, Stef.*

His hand moved up and down, the ruler snapping back after each tap. He rained down on her until he was perfectly satisfied that she was on the edge. Her breathing was choppy, and she was trying to clutch the front of Zane's desk with her bound hands.

Stef stopped. What was he doing? He'd lost count. He wasn't sure how many he'd given her. Damn it. He never lost count. He was shaking as much as she was, his breath sputtering in and out of his chest. He'd come close to losing control. He could have hurt her. He hadn't even talked about her safe word. Had he hurt her?

"Are you okay?" he heard himself ask, though he was afraid of her answer.

"No, damn it. I am not okay." She pounded her bound hands on the desk.

His heart felt like it would fall out. This was one of the reasons he'd stayed away from her. He couldn't keep himself in check around her.

Jen made no attempt to get up. She wiggled her ass, pressing her legs even closer together. "Look what you did. I ache. I swear to god, if you don't fuck me, I'll hate you for life."

The way she moved had her pussy on full display. He felt his mouth fall open as he caught sight of her wet lips. She was swollen and so wet she glistened in the low light. His hands came out. He put his left hand on her hips, steadying her, while his right hand slid through her juices. He was fascinated by the way his hand looked against her soft, pink flesh. It was a gorgeous coral color, but the juice gave it a sheen he'd love to capture on a canvas. If she were his submissive, he'd order her to spread her legs so he could paint her. He

would look at her pussy until he could get its perfection just right. Georgia O'Keeffe would have nothing on him. Jennifer's pussy really was a flower opening up for him.

She sighed, her body relaxing as though she was finally getting some much-needed relief. "Yes, that's much better than what Mildred did to me."

He couldn't help his chuckle. Her humor always brought him back to earth. Sometimes he lost himself, but she knew how to bring him back. It was good to know he pleased her more than some guard from the county lockup. He let a single finger circle her clit. "I take it Mildred wasn't a skilled cavity searcher?"

Her hips swayed, inviting him in to play. "I'm sure she's really good at finding any drugs I might have shoved up my hoo ha, but all in all, I didn't care for the experience. She definitely wasn't as good at spanking me."

His hand came straight out. "She hit you?"

"I was joking," Jennifer said quickly. "No one hit me, except you, and that was very erotic. I was neither sexually nor physically assaulted while in prison, as I told the good doctor. I'm fine. I'm of sound mind, and I would really like to have an orgasm."

He slapped his hand across her ass for teasing him. He'd been horrified at the thought of her in a cage at the mercy of guards. It wasn't something to joke about. "You didn't let Caleb look you over. You simply walked out and didn't even bother to leave a note telling me where you were going."

Maybe he hadn't spanked her enough. If they were at the guesthouse, he would tie her to the St. Andrew's Cross and use a single tail on her.

"I was hungry," she said, biting her lip, a sure sign that she was nervous. She would always nibble on that plump bottom lip when she was attempting to find the right thing to say. "I'm sorry. Next time I'll let you know when I'm fleeing from the somewhat insane doctor you sic on me. Now, let's get to the good part. Come on, I can see that you want me."

He was sure she could. His cock was standing at full attention. His slacks were pressed out as far as the wool would go. Still, he had standards to uphold. "You're not supposed to be in control of this."

But she was. He could see it. She'd herded him to this place. First, she'd left and sent him running around town to find her. Then, she'd waited in a bar, where it was inevitable she'd get hit on. This was what she wanted. She'd turned sweet and submissive because she'd changed tactics on how to get him to give her what she wanted. It worked so much better than the way she'd tried to deal with him before. She was much more dangerous this time around, and he'd thought she was fatal before.

Her face turned up, and all of the sauciness was gone now. "Please, Stef. Don't think. Just for tonight. We can go right back to circling each other warily in the morning, but I need you tonight. I need you so much, babe."

Her words sliced through him. She'd been through hell, and she'd smiled all day. Stef felt his heart seize. She needed him. He needed her. Damn it.

He got to his knees and did what he'd wanted to do for six months. He shoved his face into her pussy and surrounded himself with her. He buried his tongue in her pussy and let his senses fill. His mouth was full of her tangy, sweet taste. His nose breathed in the scent of her arousal. His skin pressed to her softness. The connection he'd felt to her from the moment they met was fully open, and he gave in.

"Oh, yes, Stef, please."

His ears took in the sounds of her growing need. She pressed against him. He pulled her open gently and lapped at every inch of her pussy. He ate her, not wanting to miss an inch of her delectable flesh. He fucked her with his tongue, pressing up into her cunt over and over. He showed her exactly how he wanted to fuck her. When he got his cock in, he'd show her no mercy. He stabbed at her with his tongue and then countered with long, luscious strokes until the cream poured out of her, honey across his tongue.

He had to press in to get his tongue to her clit, but he managed it. Her clit felt like it swelled against the tip of his tongue as he lapped at it. Every breath he took was filled with the smell of her arousal. A primal need ripped at his gut. This was what he'd been missing. This hot urgency that had little to do with lust and everything with need, it was what was missing from his previous sexual encounters. Those

had been fun. Jennifer was more.

He began his journey from that pulsing little nub all the way back to her ass, where he kissed her pink cheeks as he pressed a finger deep inside her. He slid in easily. She was soaked with cream. It poured from her body, a gift to him.

"God, that feels so good," she said on a low moan. He added a second finger and twisted up. He scissored them inside her, seeking that spot that would make her groan. "So good."

It would feel even better once he got inside her.

"You haven't had anyone since me." He didn't make it a question. He knew. She hadn't made love with anyone. And neither had he. He couldn't.

"No," she replied, her hips pumping against his hand. "I don't want anyone but you. I never have since the day I laid eyes on you."

Sweet words. He felt the same, but he'd lived far more than she had. He had almost a decade on her to figure out that he wasn't cut out for one woman.

That voice was back. *If you aren't cut out for one woman, then why did you stop seeing Lana? Why haven't you taken a lover in the whole six months she's been gone? Not one single training session, not even one without sex involved. Since you started having sex you've never gone six months without it, until you met her.*

He couldn't go another single night.

He fished through his pocket and found the condom he kept in his wallet. Despite what had happened all those months ago, he needed to protect her. The pill didn't always work. They'd been lucky the first time. He wouldn't tie her down like that. The vision of his kids with Jennifer playing with Max and Rye's and Callie's assaulted him with a sweetness he couldn't have imagined.

He pushed it ruthlessly aside. A child would be a cage for her. Her future was far bigger than being a wife and a mother.

He opened the condom. He hoped it wasn't expired, because he wasn't going out to the bar to see if Logan had one on him. He pushed his slacks down, freeing his rampaging cock. He was throbbing, desperate. There was already arousal seeping from the head, and he could practically feel the blood pulsing. With shaking hands, he slid

the condom on. He managed it and then pressed his cock to her soaking flesh, making his dick wet and ready to fuck. He slid through her labia before lining himself up to her pussy.

She was so tight this way. She was tight and perfectly helpless underneath him. He wished he'd taken off her shirt. She should be naked, but there was no time. He had to get inside her. He pressed in and held her hips. This was what he'd needed for months.

Under him, Jennifer was trying to push back against him, trying to take him deeper inside.

"Calm down, love." He ran his hands along her skin, reveling in the connection between them. One hand at her waist, he let the other force its way to her breasts. Her nipples were pebbles against his fingers. "Let me take control. Don't fight me."

She stilled beneath him. Her willingness to trust him gave him the control he needed. Her pleasure was at stake, and he didn't intend to fail her. He pressed in, her pussy tight all around him. He pushed in until he was plastered against her, his legs flush against her thighs, her ass pressed against his stomach.

"You feel perfect," he said as he twisted his hips. The sensation raced from his cock up his body.

He pulled out a short distance and then pressed back in. He loved the sound of her pussy sucking at his cock. Regretfully, he slid his hand back down her body and circled her waist for better support. He reached around to find her clit with his fingers. He pressed on the little nub in time with his thrusts. He wouldn't last. She felt too good, and it had been far too long for him to last any length of time. He wanted her with him so badly. He circled his hips, seeking her G-spot while his fingers rubbed at her clitoris.

She went wild beneath him. Her whole body shook as she came. She pushed back as she screamed out her orgasm.

Her pussy spasmed around him, and he couldn't hold back. His balls drew up, and he forced his cock as deep as he could go. His own moan filled the room as he came. He ground into her again and again, until he was empty. He let himself fall forward on top of her, his chest to her back. He let himself relax, a pleasant languor infusing his blood.

"Thank you, Stef," she said, pressing her cheek up to his, seeking

connection. "I know you don't believe me, but I missed you. I missed you so much. I won't leave again."

He could feel her heart pounding against his, but now his sleepy pleasure was replaced with panic. What had he done? That hadn't been sex. He'd made love to Jennifer again, and she was promising him things. She was saying exactly what he wanted to hear.

Stef pulled himself up and quickly cleaned up, tucking the used condom into a tissue and tossing it into the trash can. He righted his clothes and turned to her.

She'd managed to stand up, and she looked so young and sweet standing there.

"Too much, too soon, huh?"

"I don't know what you're talking about," he muttered. "I need to get you home. It's getting late."

She held her hands out. "Fine. I'll play it your way."

He quickly unbound her hands, and she pulled her pants up.

Stef did not miss the final phrase she uttered.

"For now."

Chapter Nine

Alexei stopped and stared at the big screen outside his motel room. He felt a smile cross his face. The movie was something in black and white with an old American actor. He searched his memory. Cary Grant. It was a screwball comedy that he'd seen before, and it never failed to make him laugh.

There were at least twenty cars out in the parking lot of the drive-in portion of the Bliss Movie Motel. There were even a couple of people huddled in lawn chairs close to the snack bar. They held mugs of something steaming hot and passed popcorn between them. The rooms all around him had open curtains that people watched out of. He'd had to move quickly to not block the show.

Only one room was dark. His. He hoped Ivan was still sleeping.

Nick's words were playing through his head. *You don't have to give up your whole life. I gave up mine. Listen to me, cousin. I wish I could go back to her, but there's too much blood on my hands. Don't make the same mistake.*

He didn't have a woman. He wouldn't have a woman like the one Nick had given up. The most he could hope for was a night or two in a woman's bed, and that was all he would ever get.

Or an afternoon spent doing something good. Yes, he could have

that. He'd had that this day.

He paused outside the door because he knew what it meant to go in. It meant he had to go back to work. He preferred to stand in the cold and remember the afternoon he'd spent teaching two awkward preteens how to handle a hockey stick. That had felt good. It felt right to teach something that brought joy. He'd even enjoyed the time he'd spent with the crusty doctor, though the man hadn't warmed to him at all.

It had been easy to forget for a moment why he was here. After he'd spent a few hours with the boys and the doctor, he'd headed back to Stella's where he had dinner and then moved on to the tavern next door for a drink.

That was where he'd been reminded that he wasn't here to make friends.

The girl had been there in the tavern. Jennifer. That was her name, and it looked like she wasn't alone. He'd been surprised when the whole bar had stopped and a good portion of the patrons moved into a small hall where they kept whispering to each other and shushing anyone who talked too loud. When the door everyone was interested in had opened, a couple had emerged to triumphant shouts and catcalls, and one large man who claimed they'd ruined his desk forever.

He'd recognized her immediately. She was the brunette from the photo, the one they were looking for. His heart had seized as he realized that perhaps the job would not go as easily as he had hoped. The man with her had been shocked at first at the large crowd listening in on his lovemaking session, but he'd scooped the woman into his arms and scowled at everyone he passed. He was protective of the woman. He had to be the man who'd gotten her out of Texas. Stefan Talbot, the one Nick was worried about.

Alexei would have to get the woman alone. He would have to try to reason with her. Perhaps if he kept quiet about having found her, he could distract Ivan. Once he had the painting in hand, he could force them to leave quickly and with no bloodshed.

Cary Grant took a pratfall that had everyone laughing. What would it be like to live in this small town? Quiet and protected. If he was ordinary, he would march back to the diner and invite Holly to

come out with him. He would buy her popcorn and make sure she could see the movie screen. He would treat her like a lady.

That wasn't going to happen. He'd told his cousin the truth. There was no way he could back out now. He shoved the key into the lock and opened the door to his room. The best he could hope for was a good night's sleep, with no dreams of blood and screams.

He closed the door behind him quickly, not wanting to let the chill into the tiny room. It was quiet, with the single exception of the faucet in the bathroom running. He glanced around, but Ivan had woken up and was in the bathroom. The room was still neat as a pin with the singular exception of the bed Ivan had slept on. Both of their suitcases were where they'd been when he'd left, but Ivan's was open.

A low hum came from the bathroom.

A chill went through him that had nothing to do with the cold outside. Ivan only hummed after a job, one he particularly loved. He only hummed after he'd drawn blood.

With reluctant hands, he pushed open the bathroom door.

"Watch it," Ivan said. A wide grin was on his face as he washed blood off his skin. His shirt was off, showing his chest and its intricate tattoos. "Careful where you walk. I don't want to get blood everywhere."

Alexei's stomach rolled. Lying in the bathtub was a pale, slim brunette, her brown eyes open but unseeing. Her throat had been slit by a professional.

"It wasn't her," Ivan said gruffly. "I thought I had gotten lucky. I picked her up outside a gas station when I went to fill the tank. She was trying to hitchhike. I thought she was trying to get away. Apparently, she's some tourist who fought with her boyfriend. Bah, it looked like her."

Alexei swallowed, trying desperately to contain his nausea. It was one thing to kill other thugs, but this was different. In the past, he'd killed rival mob members who were out to kill him. They were bad men and it didn't bother him that he'd been their end. This…this would haunt him. This was flat-out murder, and he'd had a hand in it.

"We need to get rid of her before the cleaning crew comes in the morning," Ivan said as he reached for a cigarette. He lit it quickly and seemed completely at ease as he looked down at his handiwork.

Alexei had to give him credit. Ivan was a professional. There wasn't a drop of blood outside the tub. The woman's body was small and fit into the tiny, utilitarian tub neatly. They could wash away the blood. They couldn't wash away the body.

"Come, my friend, don't look so down." Ivan stretched his long limbs. "We'll get rid of this one and start again tomorrow. She's out there. We'll find her. Don't worry."

Ivan walked out of the bathroom, mumbling something about a tarp. Alexei was left with a girl who couldn't be more than twenty-five. She looked to be about the same age that Mikhail had been when a gangster had murdered him and left his body in the river. He didn't know her name. His heart ached because someone out there would miss her.

And he knew how that felt.

* * * *

Sunlight filtered into Jen's room. She could feel it on her face, but she wasn't ready to open her eyes yet. She wanted to stay in the amazing dream she was having, the one where Stef didn't fight her anymore, where he understood she was different from his mom and they would be okay. In her dream, Stef had kissed her and taken her to his room where he'd promised she'd never leave again.

Unfortunately, that had not been how her evening had ended. She took a deep breath and shifted, her mind playing out the fiasco that had happened after she'd gotten Stef to make love to her.

It had been utterly ridiculous for him to think for a second that she had a thing for James Glen. The cowboy was hot, but he had nothing on Stef. And Logan was even worse. Logan was still a kid. He was barely…twenty-two. *Damn it.* Logan was almost her age.

It wasn't the same. Logan still lived at home, and she'd been on her own most of her life. Her mom had loved her, but she wasn't exactly a "dinner on the table at six" mom. Jen had learned to take care of herself at a young age. She was surely more mature than Logan.

Now Zane Hollister and the rest of Bliss—she was questioning their maturity after their actions the night before. Who stood outside a

locked door and listened in on two people making passionate, beautiful love? Who cheered when the door came open?

Of course, the proper way to handle such an awkward situation was to be brazen through it. She would have taken a bow, but Stef had to play the caveman. Stef, who had public sex in BDSM clubs, if the stories were correct. Stefan Talbot, Mr. Dark and Brooding Sexuality himself, had turned a bright red. He'd hauled her up into his arms and growled at anyone who got in his way. He'd had a few choice words to say to Zane, and then they'd been off. He'd shoved her on the back of the snowmobile and told her to hold on.

Then he'd dumped her in her room.

So much for making love.

She wasn't giving up, though. Nope. She was thinking positive. She tried to pull the covers up. After talking to Callie, she was more certain than ever that all Stef needed was a little push. Of course, she'd thought that was what she'd given him when she'd leaned over Zane's desk and let him use that ruler on her ass. She could still feel it. It had hurt, but there was something erotic about the pain.

There was nothing erotic about the chill, though. She tugged, but the blanket wouldn't move. She sat up, and her heart melted, the chill of the morning gone the instant she saw the man who had fallen asleep at the foot of her bed.

"Stef?"

He came up so fast he started to roll off the bed. His body hit the hardwood floor, and he cursed. His hand came up to hold his head.

What was that silly man thinking? She held the covers back, offering him some warmth. He was wearing jeans and a sweatshirt, but it was chilly. He still had to be cold. Though she expected a fight, he immediately crawled under the covers.

"Stay on your side, but open your legs," he demanded in a husky voice.

The morning was looking up. She hauled one leg up slightly to give his hands entry. She screamed when it wasn't his hands he put there.

Stef's ice-cold feet found a place between her nice, warm thighs. "Please, Jennifer. I'm so cold."

She growled but lowered her leg, making a nest for his cold feet.

A chill went through her, but Stef sighed with pleasure. He huddled close to her, his body at a silly angle so he didn't have to move his feet.

"I hate being cold."

"Hello, maybe you shouldn't live nine thousand feet above sea level." Her teeth chattered as his ridiculously cold hands settled on her waist.

"I was born in Texas. Heat is in my blood, but I got to Bliss as fast as I could," he said.

She was still cold, but the idea that her body heat was warming his gave her such pleasure she didn't complain. This was what she wanted from him—intimacy. "Why didn't you crawl into bed with me? It's warm under the covers."

His mouth turned down. "I didn't mean to fall asleep."

"You just meant to come in and stare at me while I slept? That's very creepy of you." She softened her words with a smile. He was weird and intense. She was cool with it. It was simply who he was. He could stare at a canvas for hours before he even opened a tube of paint. She remembered one afternoon where he'd stared at that blank sheet, and she'd stared at him, the hours rolling by as they were both lost in their own worlds. It had been a good afternoon.

"I'm not usually so weird," Stef said, his voice calm, but she heard the gravity in it.

"Really?" She couldn't help the sarcasm. He was absolutely the weirdest person she knew, and that was saying something. "Let's see, one, you're an artist, and a really well-known one. That's strike one. Artists are weird. Two, you're a Dom. You like to spank girls and tie them up, and there are things in that guesthouse that I don't even know what they're used for."

His feet rubbed against her skin. "When did you go to the guesthouse?"

"Callie took me. I was curious. She even showed me where the peepholes and the hiding spots are. Per—vert. As for your third strike, you live in Bliss. You're out. Own up to it."

"I never claimed I was normal," Stef replied. "But then, anyone who claims to be normal is probably lying or miserable because they don't know their own natures. Humans are freaks. It's better we

accept it. Are you going to deny that you liked your spanking last night?"

A warm rush of arousal poured over her. "Not on your life. Don't misunderstand me, babe. I love every freaky inch of you. You might be a complete perv, but I wouldn't have you any other way. If it makes you happy to sleep at the end of my bed like some crazy stalker, then I'm fine with it, but you could have crawled in with me."

He pulled his feet away, and suddenly his hands cupped her face, and his eyes were a serious, stormy gray. "This is a bad idea, but I don't think I can stay away from you."

Finally, some progress. She snuggled close and was perfectly happy when his arms crept around her. "I don't want you to. I never wanted you to."

"You might after you figure out what I want," he murmured. His hand stroked her hair as he spoke. "I want to train you. I want a Master/sub relationship. It's all I can do, Jennifer. For the time it takes to clear up everything, I think we should play together. I'll understand if you don't want that. I think we'll end up in bed either way."

She didn't want to stay out of his bed. And he was fooling himself if he thought all he wanted was a D/s relationship. "I've read up on BDSM. I might be a novice, but I know a little something."

His hands were creeping up the tank top she was wearing. "Are you sure? I can be a bit demanding when it comes to play."

He was already demanding. He already pushed and pulled her this way and that, and she wasn't even getting regular sex for it. "I think I can handle you."

"So young. So naïve."

So full of shit. "Bring it on, Talbot."

Something hard flinted across his face. "Fine. Show me your breasts."

She threw the covers off and had that tank top over her head in a heartbeat. The room was still chilly, but the cold wasn't what had her nipples puckering. She was finally in bed with Stef, and she hadn't had to force him there.

"And your pussy."

She pushed the pajama bottoms she had on off, along with the bikini panties she was wearing.

"Spread your legs."

His voice had lowered a couple of octaves, and it poured over her skin like thick, rich honey. She complied, though it felt awkward. Stef sat up and looked down at her. He didn't say a thing, merely sat there. His stormy eyes took in every inch of her skin. She wondered briefly if she should put on a show but thought better of it. He was staring at her the way he looked at a piece of art. Just his eyes on her made her skin heat up.

Why this man? She asked herself the question as she lay still under his considering gaze. Life would be easier if she could love someone simple. Stef was beyond complex. He was outrageous, kinky, sexy as hell, and the most loyal man she'd ever met. He'd helped out almost everyone in Bliss. Everyone knew he was the world's worst sucker for a hard luck story. Don't have health insurance? See Stef. He'll pay for your medical bills. When drought had threatened the local ranchers, they didn't go to the bank, they went straight to Stef Talbot. When Zane and Callie and Nate needed a loan to start their tavern, they had applied to the bank of Stef. He really was the king of Bliss, but sometimes he held himself apart. He needed to know that the people he helped loved him, too. She was pretty sure he never thought about that.

While Stef stared at her, his eyes fastening on her pussy, she stared back at him. He was a work of art. His jaw was a strong line. She would use a single, thick brushstroke to capture its stony grace. His skin was smooth and sun-kissed, gold and tan, blended with cream. His hair was longer than usual, falling above his eyes in midnight locks. And his eyes. She'd always loved his eyes. They were ever changing with his mood. They went from flint gray when he was angry to a warm, almost misty tone when he softened. When he was aroused, there was a storm in those eyes that always pulled her in.

Her whole body flushed with desire, and he hadn't touched her yet.

A slow smile creased his perfect face. "Very good, Jennifer. Now get dressed. I want to show you something."

She sat up, more than surprised at his command. "What?"

He gracefully rose and stretched his long limbs. "I said get dressed. My father is running around the house somewhere. I don't

want him to see you naked. He already thinks you're a felon."

"I don't really care what your dad thinks," she managed to state evenly. She wanted to move on to the more immediate subject. "What game are you playing that you think you can get me all hot and bothered and then leave me this way?"

A low growl came out of his throat, and suddenly his body was pressed to hers. His weight held her down, and the menace in his face did all kinds of things to her heart rate. "I am not playing a game. I am the Master, and you are the sub. That means you do what I tell you to do when it comes to sex, love. I know I can't expect you to listen to me when it comes to anything else, but I am the Master in this room. Now, you have a choice to make. Accept my will or tell me no and this is done."

She clenched her fists. It wasn't fair, but this was the way it was with Stef. If she wanted a chance to prove they belonged together, this was what she had to do. In return, he would coddle and protect her. He would lavish her with affection. The fact that he was willing to cede that he didn't have the final say outside of sex was actually a win. She knew that wasn't the deal with his other subs. He was in control of every aspect of life during their time together. She was different. It would have to be enough for now. "I can't get dressed with you on top of me, babe."

He rolled off her, getting to his feet and holding his hand out. Jen let him help her up. She tossed on the tank and her PJ pants. He'd picked up her panties and shoved them into the pocket of his sweats.

"You don't need them," he said almost defensively. "No panties for you."

His kinks made her smile. She imagined what he'd do with her underwear. She doubted he would simply toss them in the laundry. Not her Stef. He'd carry her underwear around with him all day. He wouldn't pull them out and show them to his friends. He would keep them in his pocket. Every so often he would put his hand in his pocket and caress them and remind himself that she'd said yes. "Good because I don't need them."

He flushed as though her acceptance of him pleased him on a fundamental level. When she was properly attired, she took his hand. He led her through the gorgeous manor house his father had built. He

was silent as he moved from the west wing to the east wing. Jen had spent enough time there to know where he was going. His studio. Most of the east wing's second floor had been transformed into the most amazing studio, with big bay windows to catch the early morning light.

"You still haven't explained how you came to sleep at the end of my bed," she said as they passed the grand staircase.

"I told you, I wanted to check on you. And it's not really your bed, is it? It belongs to me."

She chuckled. In Stef's mind, everything belonged to him. He firmly believed the whole damn town was his. She wasn't an idiot. "Well, you shoved me there, so I'll call it mine. And really, where was I going to go?"

He stopped, his handsome face frowning down at her. "As you rarely stay where I put you, I will have to decline to answer that. I don't know. It could have been anywhere."

She groaned but followed as he continued walking. "Are we going to talk about last night?"

"I thought we had, and why bother? We could simply read about it in the paper this morning. I'm sure a reporter was at Trio last night, waiting for the story like everyone else."

"Is that what's bugging you? It's no big deal. Everyone would have known we had sex in Zane's office anyway. I was totally going to tell Callie, and she would tell Nate and Zane and…well, she would tell everyone. Really, it saved Callie a whole bunch of phone calls."

His brows came together in the middle of his forehead. "I didn't like the fact that they listened in. It was private. I'm thinking about sending the health inspector to Trio. I'm also thinking about buying a bunch of rats and releasing them in Trio about twenty minutes before the health inspector gets there."

"Don't, babe. Once the Hollister-Wright clan came crying to you, you would end up paying for the exterminator. Save yourself the expense."

"Maybe not," he replied, stopping in front of the door to his studio. "Maybe I'll tell the bastard to go to hell and that he's not welcome in my town anymore."

"Oh, they won't send Zane to talk to you," she said. "They are

way smarter than that. Callie will come to your door with those sad-puppy eyes, begging you to save her livelihood. She'll talk about her future children who will starve, and it will be their Uncle Stef's fault."

He moaned and then opened the door. Early morning light flooded the studio, a vibrant, clean illumination that had her gasping. Stef had redone the studio. Before it had been stark and masculine, with nothing in it but art supplies. It had been a refuge for him. He'd once said he liked it because there were no distractions. She'd complained there was no comfort, either.

Tears pricked at her eyes. There was a big, comfy couch in one corner, and a small fridge and table. Two easels sat side by side in the perfect spot to catch the light. The big bay windows, once bare, now had gorgeous, gauzy, white window treatments. The room was still stark, but femininity was encroaching, like something inevitable.

He really was dumb.

She turned and threw her arms around him. "I love it."

He stood there for a moment, but finally his arms came around her. His voice was gruff. "I'm glad, but I didn't do it for you. It was time for a change."

So dumb. He could talk about how their relationship was all about sex, but he'd never done this for a sub before. He'd practically rebuilt the room to her specifications. She decided to let it go for now. She pulled away reluctantly. "Well, it's beautiful."

He stepped back, awkward for once as he turned a hand out. "Your supplies are over there. This is the stuff I managed to get boxed up before we left. It will be a couple of weeks for the rest of it. These arrived this morning, along with your work. I had it all crated and shipped overnight. I opened it, but I haven't taken them out yet. I thought you would like to do it."

She shuffled over to the lovingly crated box that contained the three works she hadn't been able to sell at the gallery. The gallery. Her stomach churned, but she put aside the bad stuff. If she told Stef she'd had a horrible dream about that place last night, he'd have that doctor back checking her for signs of PTSD. Or he'd go out and buy a therapist for her. She concentrated on the good stuff. "I sold some paintings while I was in Dallas."

She hadn't sold anything while she'd been in Bliss. Stefan was a

world-renowned artist, but she was just starting out.

"Really? That's great, Jennifer. I told you that would happen when you concentrated," he murmured, a smile on his face. "You have a great eye and a way with colors."

She pulled out the first of the three paintings she had left in her apartment, setting it on the easel. It was the last one she'd finished, with its glorious rushes of green and that shadow of a man. It was the painting she'd redone because she wasn't happy with the colors. Funny, they seemed perfect to her now.

"I'm going to give this one to Rachel." Rachel needed a baby gift from her. Callie said Rachel had been inundated with baby clothes, and Max and Rye had purchased every safety item known to man. Maybe Rachel would enjoy something to brighten up the house. "I missed her shower. This has to be better than what Nell gave her."

Nell and Henry had given her a gift certificate to offset the baby's carbon footprint for the first year of life. Nell had purportedly explained that Rachel was on her own after that and had given her a lecture on green diapering practices.

"I think she'll love it," he said with an indulgent smile on his face.

A sense of satisfaction poured over her. Maybe if she told him more about her sales, he would see that she was concentrating on her work. "And, who knows, maybe it'll be worth a lot someday. I got five thousand for the three I sold. Let me tell you, that came in handy."

Stef's face got a bright, brilliant red. "That fucker. I swear if he wasn't already dead, I would kill him myself."

She started at his outburst. "What are you talking about? Who's dead?"

He stopped, a red flush spreading across his face. "Renard. I'm sorry I didn't tell you until now."

"Whoa." She didn't like the man, but she was surprised he was dead. He'd been a halfway decent mentor until he'd thrown her in jail. A chill went through her. "Is it over the painting?"

He nodded and put a comforting hand on her shoulder. "Probably. The police found his body yesterday. They think he was involved in a drug deal gone bad. He was apparently paying for some

cocaine with the painting. I don't want you to worry. You're safe here."

As she had no idea where the painting was, she wasn't terribly worried. But something else struck her. "Why are you upset that Renard sold my paintings?"

Stef sputtered, his normal grace deserting him as he seemed to realize he'd made a mistake. "Nothing. I was surprised. I would have thought you could get more for your work."

There was only one reason he would be upset that she'd only gotten five grand. Her smile slipped away completely. "You bought them."

It felt like a crushing defeat. She'd gone about in a haze after the sale of the first one. After the second two, a confidence had settled over her. Now that was stripped away. She hadn't truly accomplished anything. Stef had merely stepped in and played god again. Deus ex machina. That described him. He played god and then left her alone again.

She slid the painting back into the crate. "Maybe I'll get her something else."

"Jennifer." He strode across the space between them, filling her senses. "It was the only way I knew to take care of you. And I paid way more than five thousand. I gave him twenty because I wanted you to be okay. I wanted you to have the things you needed."

Those damn tears were back. She fought hard not to shed them. She crossed her hands over her chest. "I needed *you*, Stef. You weren't about to give me that. You won't give me that now, either, will you? You'll follow me across the country and pay way too much for paintings no one gives a damn about. You'll move heaven and earth to get me out of jail, and you'll toss me over a desk when you get a little horny, but you won't tell me you love me."

His jaw hardened. "Don't make more of last night than there was. And don't make more of our relationship. I'm attracted to you. You're submissive, and I'm a Dom. It's inevitable that we would be together when we're living so close together. But this is a D/s partnership, not a love affair."

A weariness stole over her. Could she really fight him? How long and hard would he fight before he got over his fear? Maybe he

wouldn't ever get over it. He loved her. She felt it, but it didn't matter if he never accepted it. It didn't matter if she wasn't good enough to risk his heart for. "Fine. It's just sex. Got it."

He sighed, the hardness flitting away. "Does it have to be like this? Can't we be friends? I like you. I think you're an amazing artist. I think you have a bright future, if you concentrate. You don't have to be stuck here. You could be in New York selling in galleries."

He was always pointing out the future he thought she should have. He didn't ask her opinion. He merely stated what he considered the best possible future for her and pushed her to take it.

"Great, I'll look forward to it," she said, stepping away from him.

He really did treat her like a child. He'd told her he wouldn't mentor her then did it at every opportunity with all the subtlety of a sledgehammer. It didn't matter that she didn't want to go to New York. It didn't matter that she could see herself being perfectly happy selling her stuff to the tourists who came through Bliss. Stef had decided what her future should be, and he wouldn't let a little thing like the fact that she loved him mess that up.

His dark hair was shaking slightly. It was the tiniest bit overgrown, curling a little around his ears. He was so masculine compared to the metro guys she'd been around in Dallas. "I wish I could help you settle in, but I have to meet Rye. I have to help him set up the pony rides for the kids. And I should probably take a shower. If you need anything, talk to Mrs. Truss. If you're hungry, there's probably a buffet set up since we have so many guests. When I get back, we'll talk, okay? Maybe later I'll take you into town. Would you like that?"

"Sure," she forced herself to say.

He ruffled her hair like he would a kid. There was an affectionate smile on his face, like he'd never tied her up and forced his dick inside her body. He turned and walked out.

Jen shivered and wished she'd put on a robe. He'd taken all the warmth with him.

She looked around the gorgeous studio and saw it for what it was—a pretty cage. He would keep her here, and then he didn't have to deal with her in any way he didn't control.

And he'd been in control the whole time. Even when she was

away from him, he'd pulled the strings. He'd watched her and bought her paintings and stepped in the minute she got in trouble. He'd hauled her home, and now he'd detailed the terms of the relationship. She was perfectly free to love him with all her heart as long as she obeyed him in the bedroom and understood he wouldn't acknowledge that he loved her back.

Screw that.

She would do the bedroom stuff, but he was already going back on his promise to not dominate her outside of sex. Her gilded cage was proof of that.

"Stefan?" a voice called.

She turned to see the door to the studio opening. Sebastian Talbot stepped in looking dapper in wool slacks and what she suspected was a cashmere sweater. The elder Talbot was a lovely man. His hair had gone to silver, but she could tell where Stef had gotten his looks. Of course, like the younger Talbot, this one had problems with her, too.

"He isn't here, Mr. Talbot. He's cleaning up, and then he's going to help out at the Winter Festival."

Sebastian's hand rubbed at the back of his neck in a sign of obvious frustration. "He told me I should stay in right after giving me a list of things to do. I don't remember him being this bossy."

Jen snorted as she picked up the canvas. She should repack it. She wasn't going to work for a while. It was time to take a break while she thought things through. "You haven't been around him much. He's the bossiest person I've ever met."

Sebastian's face fell a bit, but he took a breath and gave her a tight smile. "Yes, I suppose you could say that. He also knows how to find talent. That work is lovely. Truly beautiful. The colors are amazing. It's not Stef's work, though. He has the best luck when it comes to finding new artists. I wonder if he would let me buy that one. It would be perfect in the new offices."

She felt a smile creep over her face as she made a decision. "Sorry, this one is for a friend, and the other two are going into the auction pool for the festival. But, if you like, I do work on commission. Feel free to contact my agent, oh wait, that's me."

She hauled out the other two paintings. She would do what she'd wanted to do with them from the beginning. She would share them.

"This is your work?" Sebastian studied each as she pulled them out. He had the same serious concentration on his face that Stef got when he contemplated a new work. Sebastian Talbot was a connoisseur. "You're talented. I believe I would hire you. My company prides itself on helping talented artists."

"You can tell me all about it on our way to Bliss," she explained.

His eyes flared. "But Stefan told me to stay in."

Jen shrugged. "He told me, too. Are we going to do what he says? Here, help me with these. If we hurry, we can get out of here before he even gets out of the shower."

A smile spread across Sebastian's face as he picked up the canvases. "I believe we might get along, dear."

Jen returned his smile. She was probably going to get into serious trouble with her Dom, but she had the feeling it would be worth it.

Chapter Ten

Stef slammed out of Rye's truck. He stalked around the horse trailer and threw that door open. All around him the festival was starting up, and heads turned at the noise he was making.

Rye Harper's eyebrows rose to the brim of his hat. "You are as touchy as Max today, Stef. You want to talk about it, or should I say *her?*"

The amusement in Rye's voice irritated him. "I'm not touchy."

Rye's twin Max walked up from the small corral he'd been putting up. There was a carousel wheel on the inside of the corral he would attach the ponies to when the time came. Yes. He could see the mistake he'd made now. He should have tied Jennifer up before he turned his back on her.

"That's not what I heard. I heard there was a lot of touching going on last night at Trio," Max said, smirking.

Rye slapped at his brother's chest. "You stop that. Rachel said to go easy on him."

Max snorted as he pulled out the ramp and stomped up. "Yeah, I got the lecture last night. Stef is confused, and we need to give him space and crap."

"I am not confused."

Rye's hand came out to grasp his shoulder. "You got woman trouble, man. We're all confused about women. Even after you marry 'em and get 'em pregnant, it doesn't get easier."

Max led a pony down the ramp, one hand on the rope, the other gently patting its head. "Hell, no, it gets harder. And he doesn't even have a brother to hide behind when the going gets tough."

Rye's lips quirked up. "I have to plead his case from time to time, keep him from sleeping in the barn with Q. Sharing has its advantages."

Max hooked up the pony, giving her a pat. "Stef isn't going to share Jen."

"Why not?" Rye asked. "He's always shared before. I heard James was sizing her up last night. From what the grapevine says, James is an open-minded man. Ever since his brother left for New York City, he's been looking for someone to share with."

"His mind is going to be opened by my fist if he hits on her again," Stef said before he realized he was being baited. He'd walked right into the trap. "You two suck."

He picked up a heavy coil of rope and turned from his friends, preferring to get to work rather than standing around and listening to their juvenile teasing. In an hour or so, the tourists would be out in full force and there would be a line of kids a mile long waiting to ride.

The grounds crew had been hard at work. Main Street had been shoveled, and the park grounds were pristinely clean. Tents and stalls were going up all over the place. Generators were humming, and he could already smell popcorn and funnel cakes. This was one of his favorite times of the year, but he was in a foul mood. He knelt in the hay that Max had lined the stall with, his hand moving smoothly, working the rope.

"Shoe's on the other foot, huh, Stef?" Rye asked, standing over him.

"No idea what you're talking about." But he had a nasty suspicion.

"Rachel. Nate and Zane. Hell, you're practically the cupid of Bliss," Rye stated.

Stef snorted. "Hardly. I merely let Rachel use the guesthouse, and Bliss needed a sheriff."

"Yeah, and Rachel came up with that plan all by herself, and it never once occurred to you that Callie had been pining for those two for years. You can pretend all you like, but you have a hand in everything that goes on here. You make sure everyone in Bliss gets what they need even if you hide the fact that you're doing it," Rye said, his boot tapping with impatience. He stopped suddenly and knelt down to get to eye level. "Man, you can't expect the rest of us to butt out."

"I sure as hell can," he replied irritably.

"Ain't happening, man." Max attached the third pony to the wheel and started to walk them around, getting them warmed up. "Nobody is going to stay out of it. You and Jen are all anyone's talking about."

"Damn it." He had to tie the knot for the third time. His concentration was shot, but it had been for months. "Well, you should tell everyone that I'm not Jennifer's boyfriend."

"Really?" Rye asked, his voice rising in surprise. "After the way you carried on with her last night at Trio, I think people will be surprised."

He had the perfect answer for that. "I'm not her boyfriend. I'm her Dom."

There was a loud snort from Max. "You owe me ten, brother."

Rye cursed under his breath. He walked up to his brother and pulled out his wallet. His blue eyes were slits of irritation as he handed over the cash to his brother. "You're a dumbass, Stef."

He tightened the rope, securing the gates of the corral, and got to his feet. "Why? Why am I a dumbass? Look, I like Jennifer. I'm attracted to her, but she's only twenty-three. She's intensely talented. She won't stay in Bliss forever, and it would be wrong to tie her down."

"Yes," Rye said with a fist pump.

Max frowned and handed the ten back.

He was tired of being left out of the joke. "Explain, assholes."

Max leaned against the truck. "See, Rye and I had a couple of bets concerning the state of your love life."

"Classy," Stef shot back.

Rye ignored him. "First, I thought you would do the right thing

and cave. There's no way you dominate that girl long term. You only like it because those subs tend to overlook your perversions. Jen is a perv herself, so I thought you would get it."

"I knew you were dumb as dirt," Max supplied.

Rye shook his head. "He didn't. Rach did. She talked him into it. She thought you were a dumbass. She thinks you're going to try to hide behind all the BDSM stuff. Now, we also had a bet on why you would potentially be such an idiot."

"I said you were afraid of commitment because you get so much tail at those clubs." Max grinned as he adjusted his Stetson on his head.

"But I knew it was because your momma left you when you were a kid and then your dad went back to Dallas without you," Rye said, as though he was mentioning the weather and not psychoanalyzing his best friend.

He felt his heart clench. It wasn't true. He'd gotten over that a long time ago. He was glad she'd left. If she'd stayed and been his mom, he wouldn't have been raised in Bliss. He wouldn't have found his home if he hadn't driven her away.

Fuck. He was thirty-two. He was old enough to know that his parents' divorce had nothing to do with him. He was old enough to be over it. His treatment of Jennifer had everything to do with her age and her talent and nothing to do with his childhood.

"Is he freaking out?" Max asked, leaning into his brother.

"I am not freaking out," Stef shouted. "I'm tired of everyone being in my business."

"Deal with it," Rye said with a shrug. "Welcome to Bliss. We show you we love you by being all up in your business. Damn it, Stef, we want you to be happy. Can't you see that?"

"If you want me to be happy, quit talking about me." The words felt stubborn. When had he stopped being open with Max and Rye? He used to tell them everything. He used to share everything with them, including women. When had he started to pull away from his brothers?

"No," Max replied, his face a firm mask of mule-like confidence. "That's not going to happen."

"Stefan, are you all right?"

Stef brought his head around at the sound of his father's voice. "I'm fine. I thought you were staying at the house."

"That was your idea, not mine." His father was wearing a nice coat, and he'd found some proper boots. He stepped forward with a smile on his face. "I always loved the Winter Festival. I wanted to come out. Hello, Maxwell, Ryan."

"Mr. Talbot." Max and Rye nodded their heads in unison.

A nasty impulse took hold of Stef's gut. He had a way to make Max uncomfortable. As uncomfortable as he'd made Stef. "You know, Max, Dad found out I'm not with Callie."

Max smiled. "I'm sure Zane and Nate were quick to tell him all about it."

"He thought I'd been covering up my sexuality all these years because I was afraid to tell him about us." Let Max stew on that. Max was usually a powder keg of anger. Questioning his sexuality would surely get him furious.

Max looked from Sebastian to Stef to his brother, his face slack-jawed. Rye doubled over immediately, but Max simply stared for a moment. Then he sighed.

"Damn, I thought we could hide our love for a few more years," Max said, his face lighting up.

Stef took a step back as Max walked toward him, his arms open. A bit of mirth lit inside Stef. *Idiot.* He was such an idiot. "Max. Don't you do it."

"We don't have to hide anymore. We can let our love flow." Max batted his eyes and puckered up.

Stef couldn't help it. He laughed. It came from deep down in his soul. He loved Max. He loved Rye. They always brought him down to earth, no matter how far he got away from it. They, along with Callie, were his anchors, his true family. "I fucking hate you."

Max punched him viciously in the arm. "You can't shame me, asshole. I got a girl pregnant. I'm comfortable with my sexuality."

"Hey, you don't know that," Rye interjected. "That could be my baby."

"Prove it," Max shot back, circling Rye. "I bet the baby looks like me."

Rye pushed at him, a wide smile on his face. "I bet the baby

looks like me."

Stef couldn't help it. "I bet the baby looks like me."

Max and Rye both rounded on him. Stef had the good sense to back up. "It was a joke."

"So is this," Max said, his fist rearing back.

Stef easily avoided him. It was nothing but play. Sometimes he and Max turned into eight-year-old boys. This time Rye joined in. Rye tackled him, and Stef hit the ground. He brought his boot up and caught Rye in the gut.

Max pulled on Rye's coat, hauling him up. "He's gone. He shook his head, said something about those Harper boys being a bad influence, and walked off. We can stop."

Stef looked up at his friends. They'd done the whole fake fight thing to get him out of talking to his dad? Rye held out a hand and helped him up.

"You're going to have to deal with him, you know." Rye sounded as sure as Jennifer had when she'd said the same thing.

He brushed the snow and straw off his coat. "I know."

But first he would deal with his willful sub. He felt in his coat pocket. Her silky panties were still there, but so were a few other items. He knew exactly how he would handle her.

* * * *

"They're beautiful," Holly said, staring at the canvases Jen had brought into the town hall. "They'll go for a lot of money, sweetie. It's a great thing you're doing."

Holly pushed a piece of paper in front of her, which she quickly signed, officially donating her work to the charity auction. Stef would probably throw a fit, but it made her feel good. Her pride had been bruised when she found out the only person who had bought her work was Stef, but Holly's admiration meant something.

"And can you keep this one until I can get this out to the Harper Stables?" she asked as she turned over the painting she'd decided to give Rachel.

Holly patted the covered canvas. "Absolutely. I'll lock it up. Just let Rachel know where she can get it."

"Thanks." Jen pulled her gloves back on and walked to the front of the town hall. The whole place was decorated in a winter theme. She smiled and waved at the people signing up for volunteer work or paying their entry fees to various functions. There was a snowboarding competition this afternoon, it looked like. The first round was today, and the championship round followed tomorrow. A line of young men stood waiting to get their numbers assigned.

She pushed through the double doors and crossed the street to get to the park grounds. The heavenly scent of coffee filled her nostrils and reminded her that she'd skipped breakfast in an attempt to avoid Master Stefan. She frowned. Maybe that had been a mistake. She'd agreed to the whole Dom/sub thing and then immediately did what he'd asked her not to. She was going to get a spanking.

Yeah, she was totally looking forward to that.

"Hey!" Callie jumped up and down, waving her gloved hands. She stood in the coffee line. "You want something?"

"Yeah, a coffee would be great," Jen yelled back. She marched through the neatly plowed park grounds to where Rachel stood, Quigley sitting at her side. She was bundled from head to toe. She felt a rush of affection for the pregnant woman.

She'd missed her friend's pregnancy. How had her mother done it? How had she walked out on the people she knew? Her mother hadn't been a bad person. She'd been flaky, but sweet. When Jen thought about her, it was as a smiling, laughing presence. There wasn't a mean bone in her mother's body, yet she'd walked out on everyone who ever cared about her because it was easier than fighting.

Or, was it that her smiling mother couldn't handle the responsibility? Being a part of a community, of a town or a family or just a group of friends, meant working at it. It meant putting them before yourself at times. That was what her mother couldn't handle. Hell, if Jen didn't call her, she wouldn't ever speak to her mother. She often worried about what would happen if her mom lost the cell phone she'd given her. Her mother would just be gone.

Like she'd been gone all those months.

"Hey," Rachel said, walking over. "I'm supposed to be the hormonal one. Why are you crying, sweetie? What did Stef do?

'Cause I can sic Max on him."

She shook her head. "It wasn't Stef. It was me. I left."

Rachel reached out, putting a hand on her shoulder. "Yes, you did. The going got tough and you walked. You left your friends, and you didn't look back. You didn't write. You didn't call. You cut us off like we didn't mean a thing."

Well, that was Rachel. If she wanted constant sympathy, she should have gone to Callie. Rachel told it like it was.

"I ran once," Rachel continued. "I left everything behind, and do you know why I did it?"

"Because you had a crazy stalker guy after you," she managed to get out.

"Yes, but more importantly, I didn't have anyone to help me. My folks were gone. I didn't have a family to rely on. My friends all gave up on me. I was alone. You weren't. You are never alone when you're here." Rachel stared at her. "So my question to you is, how long before you run again?"

"Never," she stated resolutely. "I am never leaving again. This is my home. I want a life here, and if that's a life without Stef, then I'll make it work. I'm going to try this thing with him for a while because I love him, but if he can't love me back, then I'll open my own studio, and I'll make a home here."

Rachel's lips curved up slightly. "Are you making your stand then?"

"I am making my stand." She would have Stef or she wouldn't, but she wouldn't leave her home again. She wanted everything that went with this crazy place. She wanted to gossip and be gossiped about. She wanted to get pulled into Nell's volunteer work and chase aliens with Mel. She wanted to go to town hall meetings. She wanted to love her friends and neighbors so much that they could fight and still be friends. She wanted roots more than she'd ever wanted anything else.

Rachel smiled brilliantly and pulled her in for a hug. "Then I'll stand with you. But you should know I'll kick your skinny ass if you try to leave again." Rachel shook her head. "Damn, girl, eat a burger sometime. I hate you."

"No, she doesn't," Callie said, walking up with her hands full of

covered coffee cups. She shook her head at Rachel. "What is wrong with you? You've moved way past hormonal. Pregnancy is making you mean if you've got Jen crying."

Rachel snorted. "I didn't make her cry. She's all emotional about being home. I called her a skinny bitch."

Callie nodded as she passed out the cups. "Oh, that's sweet. Here's your tea."

Rachel grumbled but took the cup. "I miss coffee. And I need a damn beer. Oh, look, it's a supermodel."

Laura Niles walked up with a little wave. She looked practically perfect in her tailored coat, skinny jeans, and knee-high boots with what looked to be a five-inch heel. She strode over confidently, her blonde hair curling in waves. "Thanks, sweetie. Can I touch today, or will I get my head bitten off?"

Rachel grinned. "Sorry, I'm taking the hormone thing to its fullest horror. I've found the rounder I get, the more crap people are willing to take from me. Go ahead. Rub for luck."

A wistful look came over the beautiful blonde's face as she touched Rachel's stomach. "He kicked."

"Yeah, he does that all the time now."

Jen felt her heart clench. "It's a boy?"

"According to the doctor. I'm going to be hopelessly outnumbered," Rachel said. "He claims there's only one in there. Christopher Stefan Harper."

"Stef?" She was going to cry again.

Rachel nodded. "Yes, Stef was the one who made me realize I could handle both those men. He was the one who brought us together."

"If we have a girl, we've decided to name her Stephanie," Callie said with a hopeful smile. "Because he brought us together, too."

Laura straightened up, brushing away a tear. "Stef is good to everyone here. Thanks, Rach. You know I have to get my baby fix every so often. Now, Callie, do you know where Nate is? I need to talk to him."

"He's back at the station last I heard," Callie said.

Laura waved good-bye and started to walk toward the station house, those impressive heels somehow not sinking into the ground. If

she tried to walk in those, she would be slogging, but Laura Niles seemed to float gracefully above the surface.

"I hate her," Rachel said, shaking her head.

"No, you don't," Callie immediately replied.

"She doesn't waddle," Rachel pointed out. "I waddle. I also bet she doesn't pee forty times a day and worry whether or not she'll fit into the bathroom stalls. I worry I'm going to get stuck and Max and Rye will have to grease me down to get me free."

"Well, she doesn't have two superhot cowboys to go home to." She was starting to get back into the rhythm. She relaxed and looked forward to the day.

"She doesn't need them," Rachel replied. "She can go home and make love to her footwear. Damn, I'd like to get into that woman's closet."

"Who's that?" Callie asked, her jaw dropping just a little.

Rachel's eyes widened, too. "No idea. Wow. He's big."

"And gorgeous." Callie sighed.

Jen followed their line of sight. Two big men stood across from them at the funnel cake stand. One was huge. He had to be six foot five at the least. He was big and broad, with inky black hair peeking out from under the hat he wore. He turned to her, and his dark eyes held hers for the briefest of moments before sliding away. He leaned over to talk to his slightly smaller companion. The smaller man had nothing on his friend. She doubted anyone would look at him when they could stare at the gorgeous god of a man next to him. His eyes were too small for his face, his mouth slightly crooked.

"Aren't you two married?" Jen asked. "Seriously, you have four guys between the two of you."

"We're married, not blind," Rachel shot back.

"Jennifer!"

She started at the sound of her name booming across the grounds. Stefan stalked toward her, walking right past the big guy they were staring at. He wore jeans, boots, and a heavy sheepskin coat. His Stetson sat firmly on his head. Ah, his cowboy clothes. He wore them when he helped out at the stables. Normally he was in slacks and designer shirts, but her heart always sped up when he went country. He was tall, and his lean strength was on display even under the coat.

He was beautiful.

"You two might not be blind, but Stef seems to think I'm deaf," she said with a shake of her head. Once again he'd made her the center of attention. Everyone was looking her way.

Her friends simply sighed and watched as Stef moved toward her with predatory grace.

"You are in trouble, sub," Stef said with silky menace.

Yep, it looked like she was.

Chapter Eleven

The sick feeling in the pit of Alexei's stomach wouldn't go away. Though the day was cold, he couldn't feel it. He couldn't seem to sense anything but the hollow feeling that permeated his center.

"You want some food? You haven't had anything all day?" Ivan asked.

Because he kept seeing that girl with the unseeing eyes, her throat split like an unhappy smile. He'd gone through her wallet. Cindy Pope. Aged twenty-one. She had a student identification card as well as her driver's license and some card that gave her permission to be horny. Ivan had laughed at that, saying something about sluts needing licenses in America, but Alexei knew what it was. It was a joke some friend had given her. Cindy would probably pull it out from time to time and laugh and remember the good time she'd had.

Cindy had no more time. The last moments of her life had been filled with pain and fear, and more than likely gratitude when it was all over. Snuffed out by a monster doing his job.

This was what he'd become. This was how he was different from Nick. Nick hadn't pretended to be anything he wasn't. Nick dealt his death from the outside. Alexei had infiltrated his enemies and done their dirty work. He'd given up who he was and what he'd believed in

to get revenge for his brother's death, but it struck him as he was helping Ivan dump that young woman's body that it was he, himself, who had truly betrayed Mikhail.

"One," Ivan said, switching to English as they reached the front of the line.

"Yes, sir," a friendly-looking man said, turning to the woman operating the fryer.

"Alexei," Ivan said, slapping him on the chest. "Alexei, are you seeing what I'm seeing?"

Probably not since all he could see was cold limbs and vacant eyes. He forced himself to focus. He let his eyes wander to the place where Ivan was gesturing. There were three women standing together talking. One was painfully pregnant, a large dog at her side. The other was a cute woman with dark hair and glasses, and the third…

He was glad he hadn't forced food into his stomach because it would surely have come up as he looked at the tall brunette with the slender frame. She was hauntingly familiar. He'd stolen her picture from her home, and it was still in his pocket. She was smiling like she had the night before in the tavern.

"It's her." Satisfaction dripped from Ivan's tone. He had switched back to Russian.

"I don't know." Of course, he was sure it was her, but he had to try. He had to stall Ivan. His head was spinning. He didn't have a plan, but he knew he had to do something.

Was he really considering it? Was he truly thinking about giving up his revenge? A cold, hard knot formed in his chest. No. He couldn't. Perhaps he was a bad man for it, but he couldn't let Pushkin go. Mikhail would forgive him one day, but he was the man Pushkin had made him.

Still, he hesitated at the thought of the artist in Ivan's tender care. She could give up the painting, but Ivan wouldn't let her live. He couldn't.

"It's her."

"You can't be sure," Alexei murmured. "You were wrong last night."

Ivan's shoulders shrugged. "Bah, these American girls all look alike. Maybe we should simply start asking. These people seem dim

enough. We will say we know her but can't find her."

He knew how to counter that. Ivan had gotten into plenty of trouble for bringing attention to himself. "Better not. When the girl turns up dead, they will remember."

"And we'll be halfway to Moscow by then."

He pressed on. "And the next time Pushkin needs something done in the States, he'll look to someone else."

Ivan growled. He liked moving up in the organization. Traveling and talking to other syndicates was a sign that a man was moving up. He wouldn't jeopardize that.

"We have to be patient," Alexei advised. "It's a big festival. We just need to get close. Someone will say her name, and then we will know."

"Jennifer!"

Alexei was startled at the shout. He turned, and a tall cowboy strode past him, his every muscle giving off the signals of one angry man. The cowboy walked quickly, but Alexei was almost certain it was the same man from last night. Stefan Talbot. The one Nick had warned him about. All around him people whispered as he moved through the crowds.

"Or we could get lucky." There was a smirk on Ivan's weasel-like face. He took the fried bread the stall owner passed to him and began to eat with singular satisfaction.

The cowboy, who had inadvertently given away young Jennifer, took her by the elbow. The artist's eyes rolled, but she followed along. Her friends didn't seem alarmed by the man's actions. They simply shook their heads and went back to talking.

"Smile, Alexei. We'll be on our way home tonight. Stick with me. I'm lucky, my friend. I'm going places."

Yes, Ivan was going straight to hell, and damn if he wouldn't be there with him.

* * * *

"Is there any point in letting you know you're hurting my arm?" Jen asked the question despite the fact she knew the answer.

Stef was in full-on Dom mode. His gorgeous face was set in

stubborn lines as he led her into the warmth of the town hall. He passed the long lines of people waiting to sign up for activities and completely ignored Nell when she tried to get him to sign up for her "Vegans Do It Humanely" newsletter.

"Not really," he said shortly, though she noticed his hold loosened.

"You're mad."

"I am not mad, love."

Yep, he was mad. He'd stopped using contractions. He got clipped and formal when he was mad.

"I am merely irritated by your obvious lack of understanding," he continued as he turned down a hall that led to the city offices. It was quieter in this part of the building. "I was under the assumption that we began a relationship earlier today, one in which I called the shots."

"In the bedroom," she replied.

He stopped in the middle of the hall. "I asked you to do one thing. I asked you to wait for me. You were to wait at home while I helped Max and Rye, and then I was going to come and get you. Was that such an unreasonable request?"

"It seemed like it at the time." At the time, she'd been a bit miffed.

"You have never driven in the winter in the mountains. The whole time you lived here, you never had a car."

She growled inwardly. That request seemed more and more reasonable with every word he spoke. "Your dad drove me."

"It has been a long time since he drove himself anywhere. He has a limo. I asked him to stay at home, too."

"Yeah, he wasn't happy about that. Stef, you have to talk to him. He came all this way."

His eyes hardened. "I have been here for almost twenty-five years waiting for him. He can stand an afternoon."

"Babe, he's been sick," she pointed out.

Something dark passed over his eyes, and for a second, she wished she could take it back. His shoulders squared again, and the brief flare of pain she'd seen was covered up in bravado.

"Are you going to obey me, or do we quit here?"

It was so much easier to not fight him now that she saw his

arrogance for what it was. King Stefan tried to keep everyone at arm's length because he needed the control. He needed to be needed. He needed to have a place here, and the only way he was sure of that place was to be the generous benefactor, to be useful to everyone around him. But what did Stef himself need?

He needed *her*. She felt it deep in her bones.

"I'm not quitting, babe. I told Rachel, I'm making my stand."

His stance relaxed slightly. "Well, love, make your stand in here."

He used a key to open the door to an office in the hallway. Jen briefly saw the nameplate. *County Engineer*.

"Nice, I didn't even know we had one of those," she said as he hustled her in. He flicked the lights on, and she glanced around the room. "Oh, it's you."

It had to be. No one else would have hooks in the ceiling. Oh, sure, to the untrained eye it probably looked like he was a man who liked heavy hanging plants, but she knew the difference. Stef liked to be perverse in a lot of different places.

There was a click as he locked the door. "I like to do my part to help the community. I almost never use this office, but it's here if I need to take a meeting with someone from out of town. Most of the people in town prefer to hold meetings at Stella's. The coffee is better. I'm mostly in charge of planning and beautification. Now strip."

He stared at her, one brow arched, his back against the door.

It looked like she would make her stand without any clothes on. She shrugged out of her coat and kicked off her boots.

"Fold them, please." Stef's voice was deep and steady, but she could see that his eyes were heating up. They were a glorious slate color as he watched her.

At least he'd said please. Jen carefully folded the clothes as she took them off. She shivered despite the heat coming from the vents above. It was still chilly. Her nipples were hard nubs pointing in Stef's direction. Now that had nothing to do with the cold. They always pointed Stef's direction. A quiver started in her belly. She was alone with Stef, and all of that intensity of his was focused on her.

"I'm going to teach you some things." His sensual lips moved,

but his eyes never left her body. "Your training begins now. Do you understand why I intend to punish you?"

She swallowed. *Punishment*. He made the word sound like dirty, sick pleasure. "Because I disobeyed you."

"Yes." He slid his hands into the inside pocket of his coat and came out with a plastic bag. "You disobeyed a direct order given for your safety and my peace of mind. I didn't ask you to stay home. I told you to. I understand that might upset you, but from time to time I will have things I won't move on. This isn't a one-way street. It might seem harsh to you, but I assume there are some things you will be unmoving on."

While he spoke, he set the bag on his desk and then slid his coat off his shoulders. He hung it up, along with his hat, and went around to the front of his desk.

She stood still, waiting for his orders. It might not be the bedroom, but it certainly felt intimate. She'd agreed to play his submissive. "I didn't know I had that power over you."

He turned his face to her, a slight smile on his mouth. "Really? So I'm allowed to fuck other girls, am I?"

She felt herself flush. "I will cut your balls off."

She immediately regretted her words, but the image of him with another woman made her want to rage. She'd had to handle it when they weren't together. It might only be a D/s relationship, but she simply couldn't watch him with someone else. She waited for him to put her in her place.

He simply chuckled lightly as he pulled out office supplies. "I rather thought so. As I prefer my balls attached to my body, I think I'll forgo the other women. See, you have unmoving edicts, and so do I. One of my unmoving edicts is that you remain alive and in one piece."

"Well, if you put it that way," Jen grumbled. He was making her crazy. She was standing there naked, and he was playing with paper clips. He pulled at one and then another.

"I didn't realize I had to put it a particular way." He twisted the metal clip over his forefinger. "Perfect." He laid the first one down and went to work on the second. "As far as unmoving edicts go, let me give you a second. I realize that sharing seems to be all the rage

143

amongst the women of Bliss, but you should know that I will not be jumping on that particular bandwagon. Don't go looking for a third."

That was the furthest thing from her mind. She could barely handle Stef, much less a friend of his. "You're safe. I know Callie and Rachel go on and on about how hot the sex is, but they have to do the laundry, too. Other women see hot double penetration, and all I see is double the underwear to clean. And I bet they eat a lot, too."

Stef laughed, the first time today he'd laughed for her. "I don't think you'll have to do much laundry at the estate. However, you deeply underestimate my creativity if you think I can't find a way to fill every hot hole you have, love. On your knees, Jennifer. I'm going to teach you the slave position."

She sank to her knees, grateful he'd had a plush carpet installed instead of the stained concrete that covered the rest of town hall. She settled into a sitting position, the carpet soft under her legs. Of course, Stef would have his comforts. She threaded her fingers together behind her back, thrusting her breasts out. She breathed deeply and straightened her spine. Her knees were splayed wide so her pussy was on display for him. She lowered her head submissively. It wasn't more than a few seconds before his boots came into view.

"Very nice. Tell me, and think carefully about the answer, where did you learn this? You have perfect form."

The jealousy dripped from his every word. She was glad her head was lowered and her hair covered her face because she couldn't help but smile. He thought she'd had a previous Dom. "I learned it from books. You would be surprised what you can find these days. I love a couple of authors, but Amber Rose is the best. She describes this position as a Dom favorite. I wanted to know what you liked, Sir."

His hand lifted her chin up. "Not Sir and not Master. My name is Stefan."

"But I thought your subs called you one or the other."

"They weren't mine," Stef explained. "They were women I trained for brief periods of time."

"I thought that's what I was." She pointed out his faulty logic gently.

"I would prefer Stefan." He stepped back.

She kept her gaze on him. He might not recognize it, but he was

starting to bend.

"Stay in position. I need to decorate these lovely breasts," he said, holding the clips in his hand.

"Those are paper clips." She watched as he got on his knees in front of her. His hands came out to cup her breasts. Her skin quivered under his touch. Amber Rose hadn't covered office supplies in her books.

"Are they? I think I can make them into something much more interesting. Don't move. Stay in your position. These lovely breasts of yours are my playthings."

His fingers were callused from holding a brush for long hours. It wasn't merely from painting though. Stef worked with his hands all the time. He worked the horses at the Harper Stables. He helped build with his neighbors. He was always using those hands to create. Now his strong fingers pinched at her nipples, creating a deep ache in her pussy. He plucked at a nipple, rolling it between his thumb and forefinger. Her pussy was already wet, and she could feel her body begin to hum.

"I love the color of your nipples, perfect innocent circles of rose and brown." He leaned over, his husky words sliding over her flesh like a warm blanket. He lowered his head, and his tongue came out. The sight of his tongue curling around her nipple caused her to moan. He sucked the tip into his mouth, sending sparks shooting from her breast to her pussy.

"This isn't torture, Stef." It felt like heaven.

He came back to his knees, a slightly sinister look on his face. He winked at her and held up the paper clip. "Oh, it will definitely be torture, love."

He pinched her nipple with one hand and then slid the clip on.

She gasped as her nipple was caught in the clip. It didn't hurt exactly. He'd stretched it out so it didn't bite, but it held the flesh in a tiny vise. Already she could feel the pull of the discomfort. It reminded her that he was in control. She was a plaything, clamped and ready for his pleasure.

He quickly clamped the other breast and looked at his handiwork.

"You're so fucking gorgeous, love." His cock was straining at the fly of his jeans. His dark hair fell over his forehead. "I know those are

improvised clamps, but they still hold you well. All the blood is pooling in those pretty nipples."

He flicked one with his forefinger. She shivered at the touch. She was so sensitive. One flick of his fingers had her panting and ready to do anything he asked.

"See what I mean? You should know that I like toys. I like expensive, perverted, twisted toys, but I can torture you without them. Anywhere, anytime. I'll find the tools I need. I'll make sure to discipline you whenever it's required."

Yep, she wouldn't be able to walk through an office supply store again without wondering exactly what dirty things Stef could do to her.

His hand went between her legs. He slid his fingers over her mound and into the slick folds of her labia. It was all she could do to keep her position.

"And, love, if you ever disobey a direct order given to keep you safe and whole again, I will clamp this little gem." He rubbed the pad of his finger over her desperate clitoris. It was a fleeting touch that tantalized and tormented. "I will clamp it, and I will torture it. I'll bring you to the edge a hundred times, and a hundred times I'll step back. You'll beg, and you'll plead, and you'll think I'll give in, but I won't, because a bratty submissive will not get pleasure from me. Do you understand?"

"Yes." She would agree to anything to get him to touch her again. He was ramping her up. She'd never been so hot. Before, their encounters had been quick and furious, but this slow tease was building to something explosive.

"What did you say?" Menace glittered from his hard tone.

"Stefan." She quickly corrected herself. "Yes, I understand, Stefan."

"Excellent. Let's move on to the next phase of your punishment. Surely you didn't think a couple of clamps could make up for what you did? What does a disobedient sub deserve?"

Hopefully a mercy orgasm. "Whatever her Dom deems fit, Stefan."

"Good answer. I think a disobedient sub should learn to take a plug."

Her ass clenched at the thought. He was going to shove a plug up her ass. Her breath caught. She'd known he would want it, but she'd been worried it would turn her off. Now, the thought of presenting her ass to him had her heart speeding up. Subspace, she thought, looking for the word. Pleasing Stefan suddenly seemed like pleasure in and of itself. This was what the books had talked about.

"You said you've read up on BDSM." Stef got to his feet. "Show me. Present yourself to me." He held a hand out to help her up.

She held his hand and stood. She could feel the clamps moving as her breasts swayed. This was why he'd done it, so she would be aware of her nipples at all times. She felt wobbly, but she managed to stand and walk to the big mahogany desk that dominated the office. She placed her hands flat on the desk, kept her spine straight, and shoved her ass in the air. She looked across the desk. Now she could see what was in the bag he'd taken out of his coat. The clear plastic plug and tube of lubricant were unmistakable.

"You came prepared." At least he wasn't going to use a highlighter or a glue stick.

"Always," he said. Jen felt him reach for the bag. "Keep your eyes front."

She gritted her teeth. Not being able to see what he was doing was going to be torture in and of itself.

"Your skin is beautiful, Jennifer."

He placed his palms on her shoulder blades. She relaxed at the contact. Somehow she didn't feel as off kilter when he touched her. When he touched her with those hands of his, she felt like a work in progress, like a sculpture he was molding lovingly. She felt like she was being brought to life.

His hands caressed her as though studying and memorizing her every curve and angle. He skimmed her back and molded her hips. She felt his lips on the nape of her neck. He traced her spine with his lips, awakening every inch of her flesh. She felt his mouth on the small of her back and then his hands on her cheeks. She went onto her toes as he spread her wide.

"Look at the pretty asshole." His voice had gone deep and husky. "What a pretty little hole. It looks lonely, love. It looks like it needs to be filled."

She braced herself as she felt the cool lube hit that sensitive hole. She held on to the desk as his finger rimmed her. He massaged the lube into her ass, his finger pressing in and circling her hole. She shivered at the dark sensation of his finger working her over.

"You're incredibly tight." He placed one hand on the small of her back, holding her down as he pushed his finger deep inside her. "It's going to be hard for you to take this plug, and even harder for you to take my cock, but you'll do it. You'll take everything I give you, and you'll thank me for it."

She wasn't sure about the part where she thanked him. The sensation was strange. It didn't hurt, but she wasn't sure it was pleasure either. It was unnerving, and she felt a bit on edge as he pressed into her.

"Not sure, yet? You will be. I'll make sure you're ready for me. I can't wait to fuck this tight asshole. I'm going to ram my cock into you. You'll whimper, but by the time I'm done, you'll writhe under me. You'll cry out and beg me to fuck your ass."

His finger disappeared, and then she felt something stiff tickling at her. She couldn't help it. She clenched her muscles, instinctively trying to keep the foreign object out.

A crack whipped through the room as Stef's hand came down on her ass. Heat and a sharp pain singed her.

"Don't you try to keep me out. This belongs to me. You belong to me. Now relax and open up." He pressed the plug against her again. His voice became softer and more cajoling. "Let me in, Jennifer. I want to come in. I promise you won't regret it."

The hand on her back soothed her as he pressed the plug against her.

"Breathe out, love. Breathe out, and flatten your back."

She tried to relax. She filled her lungs and let the breath go while she pressed back against Stef's hand. She groaned as the plug breached her hole.

"Now that is a beautiful sight. You're doing so well."

She forced her ass back and felt the plug slide home. Her hands shook at the almost unbearable fullness in her ass.

He kept her cheeks open. "Do you have any idea what this does to me? I want to know you're walking around with this little piece of

plastic shoved up your rectum because you're preparing yourself for me. You're getting ready to take my cock."

Without warning, his fingers slid into her pussy.

She bit her lip to keep from crying out.

"See, the plug makes your already tight pussy even tighter. I don't have to share you with some other man to fill you up." He pressed a single finger deep inside her. "You are so wet for me, Jennifer. Someone liked having her ass plugged. Someone likes being a nasty girl."

She liked being *his* nasty girl. Somehow Stef made all the dirty stuff seem loving. His hands caressed her sweetly even as he whispered filth into her ear. He worshipped her even as he played the big, bad Dom.

"How are you going to take care of your Master, sub? You put him through hell today. He deserves some stress relief. Can you think of any way to make it up to him?"

She felt the heat of his body as he pressed against her. His fingers teased her soaking flesh as he nudged her insistently with his hard cock. Oh, she wanted him to take out that big dick and thrust it into her. Nothing else could possibly satisfy her, but more than that, she wanted to please him. This was what it meant to play with Stef, and she wanted to do her part.

"Let me please you, Stefan."

He chuckled and ran his free hand through her hair. "How are you going to do that, love?"

He liked dirty talk, so she searched her brain for the right words. "Let me suck you. Let me lick you. I want to taste you so badly."

His cock seemed to swell against her, and he pulled his hand out of her hair. Before she could move, he was hauling her up. He turned her around, and his face was ferocious with desire. His breath came out in short pants. "Yes. That will do. I'm going to teach you how to suck my cock. I'm going to teach you how to please your Master."

He pressed his lips against hers in an oddly innocent kiss. He brushed her mouth, barely a touch, but she felt it deep inside her body. He released her and sat down in his big-backed chair, slouching down slightly so his cock was up and easily accessible. "Get on your knees, but hold those cheeks together. Don't lose the plug. Hold your

knees wide, as wide as you can, and clench that rosy ass."

She did as he asked. It was hard, but she held the plug tight as she gingerly dropped to her knees in front of him.

"Open my jeans."

She put her shaky hands on the fly of his jeans. She'd dreamed about this. She'd fantasized about the moment when she would hold him in her hands and blow his mind, but it was different. Her fantasies had been about proving to him that she was his match. Now, as she slid her hands into his jeans, all she could think about was how much she wanted to taste him. She wanted to run her tongue all over him and listen to him moan, and beyond anything, she wanted that moment when they connected, when he flowed into her. Before, she'd wanted power over him. Now, she simply wanted to be with him.

"I'm crazy about you." Stef's voice was quiet in the room, but there was no way she could miss his husky declaration.

Her heart filled as he looked down at her. She was crazy about him, too. She loved him. She wouldn't ever love anyone the way she loved Stefan Talbot. Saying he was crazy about her wasn't exactly a declaration of love, but she was closer than she had been.

"Kiss my cock, love."

She leaned forward and placed a small kiss on the silky head of his dick. His cock was truly a thing of beauty. Thick and long, his cock rose from between his powerfully muscled legs. The head was a deep, rich plum. She kissed the lovely *V* on his dick, letting her tongue come out to trace the edges. A drop of pearly fluid pulsed out. She licked it up, his taste a salty intoxication.

"That's right." His hand came out to cup her head. "That feels perfect. Suck me in, just a little at a time."

She would have to take him slowly. He was large, and he would fill her mouth quickly. She gently sucked the head, her tongue swirling around, gathering his cream. She groaned as she took him in, inch by inch by inch. All the while, as she sucked and loved him with a worshipping tongue, she imagined the big cock in her mouth plundering her pussy. She never felt closer to another human being than she did when Stef slid in and out of her body.

"I don't have to tell you anything, do I, love? You know what I need. Make me come."

He threaded his hands in her hair and thrust his cock up. She opened her jaw wide, taking in more and more of him. She was patient, licking gently on the way down and sucking with strength as she made her way back up. She let her hand run down to cup his heavy balls.

Stef groaned, his breath ragged and rattling out of his chest. "Yes, love. Harder. Suck me hard."

She gave up on subtleties. She sucked, drawing the cock into her mouth all the way to the back of her throat. She drew on him over and over, all the while aware of how he surrounded her. She could taste the masculine salt of his arousal, smell his clean, musky scent. Though he was only touching her hair, she felt him everywhere. She felt the clamps on her breasts, and the plug in her ass, all signs of his possession. Her body felt hot, as though she was the one about to come. His cock swelled in her mouth. He whispered her name over and over, like a mantra. She took him as far as she could and swallowed around him as he came.

Hot, salty spurts coated her tongue. Jen groaned as she licked it all up.

When she looked at him, Stef's head was thrown back. His hands stroked her hair, but his eyes were closed as he caught his breath. His cock was still big even after he'd given her everything he'd had. Relaxed, he was still an impressive specimen. She couldn't help but kiss him again, her mouth playing over the head. His cock twitched and seemed to come back to life.

It was perfect, because she needed to play. The ache in her body was becoming unbearable. She needed him so badly. A deliciously wicked feeling came over her. She would suck him back to life, and then he would fuck her hard until she screamed out his name.

Being Stef's sub was going to be heaven.

"Very good, love," he said, pushing the chair back. "You may stand."

All of the warmth had left his voice. She looked up, and there was a hardness to his eyes that had been absent even when he'd placed the clips on her breasts.

She struggled to her feet, the plug in her butt an annoyance now. She clenched her cheeks to keep it in. For the first time since they'd

begun to play, she felt the chill in the air.

He quickly tucked his stiffening cock into his jeans and buttoned his fly. He took a deep breath and stood. He towered over her, his jaw set like granite as he stared down at her.

"You did well for a novice. No swats today, though if you disobey again you'll spend some time on my whipping bench. You'll wear the plug for the rest of the afternoon. I'll take it out when we get home. If I find out you've removed it yourself, it's twenty swats and I won't take you with me tomorrow. Is that understood?"

A sick feeling began in the pit of her stomach. She'd thought they were playing, but this felt like something else. She'd read about BDSM and the importance of punishment and reward, but she'd never realized how it would feel. As connected as she'd felt to him before, she felt alone now. Alone and naked and wanting.

A smirk played at his mouth. "Oh, love, did you think I would take care of you? You disobeyed. Disobedient subs don't deserve their Master's cock. This is what it means to be my submissive. This is what it means to be with me. Changing your mind?"

She said nothing, aware that the Jen of months ago would have immediately told him to go to hell and walked out. Anger would have been her default position. Now, all she felt was an aching sadness. They could be more than this, but he either didn't see it or didn't want it. Was she willing to give up? She stood there naked with signs of his possession biting into her and thought about what she'd said to Rachel. Whatever she decided, she couldn't do it now. Her pain was fresh. To walk out spewing expletives would simply start their cycle again. For the first time, she truly understood that this was their last shot. She would be with him or give him up.

Tears pooled in her eyes. She needed to be alone for a while, to calm down, to think.

"Can I tell you later?" Her voice was soft in the quiet of the room.

His mouth opened and then closed. He seemed briefly out of sorts before he found that Dom stance of his again. "Of course. Take the time you need. I would prefer you keep the plug in, in case you decide to stay. It would be rough on you to have to start over again."

The damn plug was the least rough thing about this. Her anus

might be stretched, but her heart was getting battered. She might have to accept that her love was no match for Stef's childhood. She nodded. If she spoke she would cry, and that wasn't what either of them wanted.

His hands moved to her breasts. She took a step back.

"Don't," he growled at her. "I'm trying to unclamp you. It's going to hurt."

He slid the first clip off her nipple. The blood rushed back in, stinging and burning. She gasped as he quickly slid the other off.

"It'll only hurt for a minute," he muttered, stepping back. "You should get dressed."

Jen covered her breasts with her hands and nodded. "I will. Could I have a minute to myself?"

"Why?"

Trust and honesty. That was what a Dom required. Well, she'd given him everything else. He'd stripped her bare and left her wanting. Maybe he should have this, too. The truth was she was far too tired and aching to prevaricate. "So I can cry for a while."

His eyes flared. "Because I didn't fuck you?"

If he didn't leave soon, she was going to lose it. "Because it was less than I thought it would be."

He laughed, but there was bitterness in the sound. "You thought I would fall at your feet. You thought you could give me a blow job and I would just fall all over myself. It doesn't work that way, Jennifer."

"I didn't think you would fall at my feet," she said wearily. He would perpetually think of her as a selfish child. "I thought we would be together. I felt so connected to you. It was like I was a part of something special—something meant only for us—but you can't have felt that. You wouldn't be able to walk away if you felt the way I did. It hurts to be alone when I thought, just for a minute, that I wasn't anymore."

He didn't seem to have a Dom homily to give her for that. He stared for a moment and then turned to go. Seeing his back to her made her heart clench. She had to turn away. He was forever walking away from her. Why couldn't she do the same? Even when she'd run from him, she'd seen him in her dreams every night. He'd come

between her and the men she'd thought about dating. She'd lived like a nun because he was always in her mind, in her work, in her heart.

She heard the door close behind him and couldn't help the sob that came out of her throat. It was time to get dressed. She needed to compose herself. She couldn't walk around the festival like this. Maybe she could find a ride home. She wanted to sink to the floor and sob, but then she might lose that goddamn plug. Her breath hitched. She felt so stupid.

"Don't."

She turned suddenly, crossing her arms over her breasts. Stef stood there, his face as open as she'd ever seen it. There was no Dom to him, simply a man who looked like he was on the verge of heartbreak.

"Stef?"

He shook his head. "I can't."

It sounded like an apology to her, something final. She didn't try to stop the tears that flowed. She felt them fall down her cheeks, hitting her naked chest. She wished she'd gotten dressed. Hearing him say he couldn't even try to love her would have been a slight bit easier if she weren't so naked.

"It's okay, Stef." He looked utterly miserable, his composure gone. She hadn't meant to bring him to that. He needed his control. She wouldn't take it from him. She should have stayed in Dallas. She would never have come back if she'd known it could hurt him this way.

"It's not. It's never going to be okay." His hands clenched at his side.

It would be once she stopped pushing him. He'd been all right before she came around. He'd been all right before she forced her way in. She wouldn't leave Bliss, but she would respect his needs from here on out. "It will be okay. You'll see. Give it time."

"I'll never be okay when you cry, love." He moved forward, but it was jerky, as though he'd lost all grace. His hands came out and hauled her into his arms. "I can't leave you like this. I don't even want to. Forgive me."

He pulled her close, pressing her against his chest so she was surrounded with him again. This time, though, she could hear his

heartbeat, feel the uncertainty in his breath. This time he was here with her in spirit as well as body, utterly and completely.

She turned her face up, a deep relief in her soul. "I love you."

His eyes closed for a brief moment, as though the words had a physical impact on him. "That means the world to me, love. I want so much more for you, though. You deserve to have more."

"But I only want you." It wasn't true. She wanted more. She wanted a life here with him, and she wanted kids someday in the not-too-distant future. She wanted what she'd never had—roots. It all started with him. He was her foundation. His strong, giving heart was everything she'd ever wanted in a man.

"I know you think you do." He brushed his lips against hers. "Can we not fight about this now? I want to erase the last couple of minutes. I want to take care of you." His hands trailed down to the globes of her ass, cupping her, pressing her against his core where his cock was stiff and full again. "Let me take care of you."

"Yes." She wanted him so badly. The weary sadness that had taken her over was shoved aside by rampaging desire. She needed him.

He took her mouth, plunging his tongue in and dominating her with a singular purpose. His tongue glided against hers in a silky imitation of what she wanted his cock to do. He rubbed his body against hers as though he could imprint himself on her.

"This is so wrong," he said.

"It's not," she tried to plead.

"Not the sex, love." He chuckled, an open grin on his face as he pulled at the buttons of his shirt, revealing his rock-hard chest. "I'm talking about the fact that my club is going to request that I turn in my leathers. I'm being a terrible Dom."

He kicked off his boots hastily and shoved his jeans off. He dropped them and left them on the floor in his hurry to get back against her. His cock stood straight out, and then it was pressed between them as he hugged her to him.

"I won't tell." She let her hands roam for the first time. His skin was soft over the hard pack of his muscled frame. Only his hands were rough and callused from work. Those hands thrilled her as he explored her body.

"Yes, you will," he commanded, and he kissed her neck. "You'll tell everyone what a big, nasty Dom you have."

She hissed as he bent his head and kissed her nipples. He was painstakingly gentle with them. "I will. I'll tell them how you torment me."

He licked at her nipples, sucking on them softly, lighting a fire in her pussy. "I'm wicked with you. I don't let you get out of line. When you get out of line, I torture you."

He was doing exactly that. His fingers split her labia, sinking in and drawing out her juices. He bent over, and his tongue found her clit.

"Oh, god, yes, you do. You're cruel. You bring me to the edge again and again. You fill my ass and clamp my breasts and make me pleasure you."

He sucked her clit into his mouth as he pressed two fingers high into her pussy. "I make you see to my needs and fill none of yours when you're a bad sub. I fuck your mouth and spank that ass of yours until it's a hot pink and you can feel the imprint of my hand on your skin. I tie you up, shove a vibrator up your pussy, and alternate between teasing your G-spot and using a flogger on your pretty backside. You never disobey me again."

"Never again."

He got up and moved to the chair. He sat down and held out his hand. "Come on, love. Come ride me."

Jen caught her breath at the sight of him. He was decadence personified. She took his hand and straddled him, her knees sinking into the plush leather of the big chair. He reached between their bodies, lining his cock up to her pussy.

"I want to watch." His head was down. His eyes were fully focused on the place where their bodies met.

There was her pervy boy. She leaned back slightly so he couldn't miss the sight of his huge dick invading her pussy. He gripped her cheeks, pulling her down inch by inch. Every centimeter was pure pleasure. He stretched her, filling her with his hard flesh, making himself a part of her.

"You're so fucking tight like this." He ground the words out as she felt his hands split her ass cheeks. His fingers touched the plug,

making her shiver. She sank her fingers into his shoulders as he gently eased the plug a little ways out. Nerves she'd never felt before sprang to vivid life.

"Oh, Stef, that's amazing." She breathed out as he fucked the plug back in.

His voice was low, guttural. "I can handle you, love. We don't need a third. I can fuck you the way you need it."

He pulled on the plug as he thrust his dick up, proving his point. Jen was filled with him. She'd never been so full. She sank onto his cock and forced herself back up, riding him like the stud he was. She found a perfect rhythm that had the plug and his cock in exquisite parallel. When she lowered herself on his cock, he pulled the plug out to almost her rim, firing off every nerve in her ass. He pushed it back in when she rose, the feeling of fullness unrelenting.

Every movement brought her closer to that magic place only Stef had ever taken her to. She fucked him with abandon, seeking her pleasure with every bit as much passion as she'd given him his.

"That's right," Stef said, his motions becoming wickedly wild. "Come for me. Come all over my cock. Make me feel it."

She felt the command in her clit. He pushed up with his pelvis, grinding against her, and she went flying. The orgasm rushed over her like a wildfire sweeping through her veins. She cried out as she fought for every second of pleasure she could get.

His body stiffened under her hands. He shook as he came, his gorgeous face contorting with pleasure.

She fell forward into the circle of his arms. Without hesitation, he held her close, their breaths, bodies, and heartbeats one.

Chapter Twelve

Stef had to breathe deeply to get his heart rate down. His blood pounded languorously through his body, satisfaction invading his veins. Jen was wrapped around him, and the world, briefly, seemed utterly perfect to him. She'd submitted in the sweetest way possible. She'd accepted everything he'd given her with grace and a gorgeous sexuality that floored him. He was the one who screwed it up.

Why had he thought he could walk away from her? He'd never been able to do it. Even when he got the slightest bit of distance, he'd come running back every time. The minute he'd seen her face fall, his heart had clenched. He'd made it to the door, but he'd shut it again, knowing he'd never be able to leave her alone and miserable.

God, he loved her.

His hands tightened. He let the truth wash over him. He loved Jennifer Waters with his whole heart, but he'd never be able to keep her. She was too talented, too young to commit herself for her whole life. She needed to see the world and everything it had to offer. Maybe in ten years or so she could make a decision, but until then he had to be unselfish.

"Stop." Her head had come up, and she stared down into his eyes. There was a plea there. "Can't we have a few days? Just a couple of

days where we don't fight or think about the future?"

She could read his fucking mind. This time around was different. Since she'd come back to Bliss, she'd been focused on him, his moods, his thoughts. It made him feel like the center of the universe. God, he couldn't deny her. Not when it was everything he wanted. He would have to let her go soon enough. He could allow himself a few days of paradise.

He smoothed back her hair and pulled her close, loving the way their bodies were stuck together, their juices mingling. She would walk around the rest of the day with a piece of him inside her. He pulled her head down. "Of course, love. I want that, too."

He let his lips play against hers. He loved how soft she was. Her lips were pliant beneath his. He could play with her all day. A week, that was all he could give himself. Otherwise, he would take her. Already the impulse was there to brand her as his. He had a sudden vision of working with her curled at his feet. Her skin was so porcelain, so perfect, that she could be his palette. He could have her stretch out when he was ready and use her torso to mix his paints. He would bend down when he needed to dip his brush in, and as for inspiration—all he would need to do is look down.

He shook his head. He was already going to that innately selfish place where all that mattered were his own needs. He would put it out of his mind for now. He had plans for Jennifer. When those came to fruition, he would have long years without her. He should enjoy himself while he could. He took a long, last drag from her lips. "What do you want to do today? Do you want to watch the snowboarding? Or we could join in the snowman competition."

A smile of pure pleasure crossed her lips. It did odd things to his heart. "We could kick everyone's ass."

He laughed a bit. "I don't know. Henry and Nell have been practicing."

Her pretty mouth went down in a frowning pout. "Well, of course they've been practicing. What else do they have to do? How do they live? I mean it, Stef. They don't have jobs. I seriously doubt that protesting pays. So how do they maintain that cabin of theirs?"

He grinned. He couldn't help it. He knew something no one else knew, and he wasn't going to tell. If Nell wanted to write crazy erotic

romance that mirrored some of the things that happened in town, and Henry wanted to help her with the business end, more power to them. The only reason he knew was he'd been the one to find them a lawyer to set up their LLC. Bliss was lawyer free. It was written into the town's charter. He'd quietly helped the pair out, and now he would be silent as the grave. "I guess they're just lucky. Maybe Henry had some family money."

What they had was a pseudonym and an e-publisher. They had made more money off Nell's crazy polyamorous romances than Stef would have believed possible. He knew that because he'd also let them use his accountant. Henry and Nell had asked him to show some discretion, and after reading their latest, he'd decided it was best for the peace of the town if he honored their request. It would make Max and Rye crazy that their adventures had been fictionalized. But it was hard, because he so wanted everyone to know just how filthy Nell's mind was. Nate had once described her as a Disney princess and Henry as an asexual college professor. Henry and Nell got nasty. Like seriously nasty if that fiction was any indicator of their real life.

Jen shook her head. She settled against him again. "Maybe."

He let his hands wander over her deliciously curved backside, and his brain moved on to more amorous thoughts than the snowman-building contest. He squeezed her ass. God, he couldn't wait to fuck her there.

There was a loud knock on the door. Stef spun his head around. Couldn't he get a fucking moment's privacy in this town?

"Stef? Seriously, take a goddamn break! We gotta move," Max yelled from the other side of the door. He knew it was Max. Only Max could make him want to punch something with the sheer sound of his voice.

"Go away!" he yelled back.

"Can't, Stef." Now Callie's voice split through his skull.

"We should start charging," Jen said.

"I might start killing." His cobbled together family was making him crazy. He squeezed her ass one last time and kissed her lips sweetly before she slid off him. He was reaching for his jeans as he looked at the door. "This better be good."

"It's bad," Callie said.

"We're supposed to take you to the clinic," Max chimed in.

He did up the fly of his jeans and felt his curiosity rise. "Why?"

"Because the doc is doing an autopsy, and Nate thought you should see it," Max shouted through the door.

"Get dressed," Stef barked at Jen. His every nerve was awake, alive, and afraid.

* * * *

Twenty minutes later, Stef stared down at the body of one Cindy Pope, aged twenty-one. There was no way he could mistake the resemblance between the dead girl and his Jennifer. They were both brunettes, roughly the same age and build. If a person just glanced at the two, they might think they were the same woman.

"I wondered why there was a backpack in our trash bin." Marie shook her very sensible head. "Teeny had gone to take the paid bags out, and she found a nice pack. And still full of her things. Such a shame."

"Well, it wasn't aliens." A no-nonsense voice spoke up. Stef turned to see a slender, petite female of maybe sixty years pursing her lips. She wore comfortable working clothes, and her long, steel-colored hair was in a braid that went halfway down her back. She stood beside Mel, her arms crossed over her chest. "They use lasers."

"Yep." Mel simply nodded his agreement and stared down at the woman like she was a font of knowledge.

Dear god, Mel was in love. Heaven help everyone.

"So, no laser, Doc?" He would leave the actual professional opinion to the man in the green scrubs. As far as he could tell, Caleb Burke might be just as certifiable as Mel, but at least he'd gone to medical school.

"Nah," Caleb replied. "It was a knife."

No shit. He felt his stomach turn. The girl was just a kid. She was lying on a slab in a clinic in a town she hadn't been born in. A sick feeling came over him, panic threatening. He'd known this wasn't over. How the hell had they caught up with her? "Same as Renard?"

Caleb's face was a grim mask as he looked back at Stef. "I

believe so, though I didn't see that body personally. The DPD sent me the autopsy report and the crime photos. I sent mine to Detective Brighton. We've agreed it's a possibility. There's no hesitation here. It's clean. Mel and his friend, Cassidy Meyer, found her in the river out by 285."

Mel let his hand drift to the small woman's shoulder. "We were out on the alien highway. Our group was securing the recon platform. Cassidy here was making sure the telescope was working. That's when she saw the poor girl. We knew it wasn't an alien thing right away. They would never kill a fertile, young female. They would probe her."

The woman named Cassidy, who Stef deeply feared Mel had probably met on the Internet, nodded her agreement. "She's a prime specimen for their fertility experimentations."

Nice. He'd found someone as crazy as he was.

Dr. Burke turned on the couple, his hand out as though seeking to ward off further paranoia. "Rachel is fine. I promise."

Cassidy waved her hand. "I know that, Doc. I don't worry about it. I gave birth to two alien babies, and they're just fine. Sweetest boys you ever saw. They both went into the Navy. Did their country and their mama proud. One of them has some weird ideas, but he's a good man. They like beets, though. Couldn't get enough of them when they were boys. We should tell Rachel to stock up."

"Cassidy raised some fine kids. You wouldn't ever know they're half alien," Mel said with a proud smile.

"I think that's all we need, Mel," Nate said, walking into the small room that currently served as the Bliss County Morgue. He was a familiar, welcome figure of authority. "And you, too, Marie. I appreciate everything. Logan can take the rest of your statements. Y'all go on. Enjoy the festival."

In a few seconds the room cleared, and Stef was left with Caleb and Nate.

"Is this what I think it is?" He couldn't help the tight, almost violent way the question came out of his mouth.

Nate sighed. "I don't know. I have to think we should consider the fact that what happened to Jen in Dallas is connected to this. We haven't had a murder in Bliss County since...well, we've had several,

but they were mostly self-defense. This is different."

Caleb pointed to the body, his finger gesturing to the line of her throat. It was split neatly, the skin blue from the cold of the river and the fact that she'd left life behind hours before. "It's a professional job. Neat, surgical. He didn't do more than he had to do here, but look at her stomach."

Burke pulled back the drab blue sheet that covered the girl. Her body was a map of blue and purple bruises.

"He beat her." He couldn't imagine what she'd been through.

"He tortured her," Caleb corrected. "There's a systematic pattern to the bruising that tells me he was controlled when he did this. There's nothing that hints at someone who was out of control. He didn't touch her face. He went for soft parts of the body. He knew what he was doing."

Nate was staring down at her wrists. "She was tied up."

Stef flinched at the chaffing on her wrists. She'd been tied too tightly. Caleb turned the wrist over. The underside was perfectly smooth.

"I would assume she was tied to a chair," Caleb said clinically. "Look, I've never worked forensics. I was a surgeon, but I know the human body, and I know about interrogation techniques. If you asked me, right now, I would tell you that this young woman was tortured. Given the relative restraint of the violence, I would suspect that the man torturing her was a professional in search of something, information most likely. When he couldn't get it out of her, he sliced her throat in a manner that would result in a quick death. Exactly what was done to Renard. He then tossed her body in the river, which is sitting at roughly fifty degrees. That kind of cold masks time of death, and due to the depth and speed of the water flow, we can't know where the crime took place. If Teeny hadn't found the pack, we wouldn't know if she'd been here or somewhere upriver."

"Logan and I have a grid to search all along the valley. Zane's down there now with Rye Harper. If we find anything that could tell us where the dump took place, it could help." Nate's eyes had taken on that steely look he got when he was doing serious police work. It wasn't hard to remember Nate Wright had once been a top DEA agent. Zane had been the same. Bliss might be a small town, but it had

its share of veteran law enforcement.

The door to the clinic's waiting room opened, and one of those former law enforcement employees walked in. Laura Niles looked slightly flustered, an adjective Stef almost never used for the cool blonde. Her cheeks were flushed, and her eyes narrowed as they homed in on Nate.

"I have been looking all over the town for you, Sheriff."

Nate's eyebrows climbed his forehead under the brim of his Stetson. "Sorry about that. It's been a long morning. Actually, I'm glad you're here. I wanted to ask you a couple of questions. You used to profile for the FBI, right?"

Laura had been one of their top profilers until an incident that caused her to walk out on a high-paying job. She'd found her way to Bliss, and now the Harvard-educated psychologist rang up tourists buying gas at the Stop 'n' Shop. She ran her perfectly manicured hands through her blonde hair, and if she had any problem standing in a room with a corpse, she didn't show it. She'd barely looked down at the body, but now she let her eyes roam over it, a cool professionalism falling over her like a cloak.

"You want my opinion about this?" She stared at the body as though it was a thing rather than former housing for a soul.

He couldn't quite wrap his brain around it, but then he hadn't worked for years in a job where death was all around him. Laura, he'd discovered, had made a name for herself by hunting serial killers. It wasn't surprising that she'd learned to distance herself.

Nate nodded, and the doctor stepped aside, allowing Laura access to the corpse.

She was quiet for a moment, and when she spoke, her tone was academic, far from the bright, friendly voice he associated with her. Even her husky Southern accent seemed to fade in favor of a flat, professional cadence. "Any signs of sexual trauma?"

Caleb shook his head. "None, but I ran a rape kit anyway. She was in the water for a while."

"We won't know how long until we can estimate a time of death." Nate was cradling his cell in his hand. His face was haggard, and the morning seemed to have worn him down. "I haven't even figured out when she went missing. Her mother talked to her last

week. She was out with her boyfriend."

"I doubt this was done by anyone who knew her, much less a boyfriend," Laura murmured.

"It's too clean," Caleb pointed out.

Laura's lips pursed in agreement. "Far too clean. This is an incised wound. It's going to be hard to determine the exact weapon beyond the fact that it was a knife. The killer stood behind the victim."

"I thought so, too." Caleb's gloved finger traced the line of the fatal wound. "It starts high and ends lower on the neck. It's also deep."

"Yes, if he had been in front of her the wound would be more shallow. This is professional. There's no passion in this kill. It was business, pure and simple, and this man takes pride in his work. There's a neat efficiency about the kill. You're looking for a hired killer." She turned on her heels and frowned at Nate. "Which brings me to why I was looking for you."

"Laura, it's going to have to wait." Nate crossed his arms over his chest. "Right now I need to call some of my old contacts at the DEA. If this is a Colombian cartel, we need to know."

Laura shook her head. "I doubt we're dealing with Colombians, Sheriff, unless Bliss has become the battleground for a nasty bit of mob warfare."

Nate turned to Laura. "What is that supposed to mean?"

She faced the sheriff, looking more serious than he'd ever seen her. "It means I don't think we're a hot spot for criminal activity. You aren't dealing with Colombians, but I would like to know why the hell the Russian mob is in town."

* * * *

The room was becoming slightly oppressive. Jen stared at the door to the clinic, wondering why it seemed like everyone in Bliss needed to parade in and out of what had recently been designated the county morgue.

"Bad business," Teeny said, shaking her head. Her little beak of a nose was turned down in what looked like sadness. "I can't believe it.

Would you like some fudge?"

She held out a tray of perfectly cut fudge. She was wearing slacks, a pink sweater, and a lovingly detailed apron.

This was an autopsy in Bliss.

"No, thanks." She couldn't think about eating now.

"I'll take some, Momma." Logan reached over and grabbed two squares, giving his mother a thumbs-up. "I'm going to take some back for Hope. Nate left her answering the phones for the day."

"Me, too," Rachel said, taking three. The dog at her feet whined. She frowned at Jen. "Don't look at me like that. Baby needs fudge."

"And cookies." Callie smiled at them, a huge tray of cookies in her arms. "Stella sent them. Apparently tragedy requires carbs. She's on a tear. She's been working nonstop. She made like a hundred sandwiches when she found out the Sheriff's Department was working on a homicide. I had to tell her that there were really only like five people working the case, but then Zane inhaled four sandwiches, and I just let her work."

"And you didn't mention this to us, why?" Rachel asked, frowning at Callie.

Callie set the tray on the small reception desk. "First, Nate asked me to keep my mouth shut."

"Since when has that stopped you?" Jen asked. It was no secret that Callie Hollister-Wright was the hub for information in Bliss.

"This is serious." Callie pushed her glasses up her nose. "I knew it would upset Rachel, and after what you went through, it should upset you as well. Besides, I only knew they had found a body early this morning. It could have been an accident. We have a town full of tourists. The last thing we need is some sort of panic."

"That is very mature of you." Rachel frowned Callie's way.

Callie nodded. "Thanks."

But Jen knew what that frown on Rachel's face meant, and she agreed with it wholeheartedly. "It wasn't a compliment. We're your best friends. You aren't supposed to hold out on us."

"But—"

"No buts." Rachel pointed a finger in Callie's direction. "Don't start talking about your husbands. Who did you call when you put that dent in Nate's new truck? Should I remind you that it wasn't Nate?

Was it Zane?"

"It was you, and you know it." Callie crossed her arms over her chest. "Of course I called you. You have a really devious mind. I would never have thought about saying I was installing a satellite radio for his birthday and getting the damage fixed so he never knew about it."

Jen grinned and gave Rachel a high-five. "I would have gone with tinting his windows. See, Callie, you can love your husbands, but your girlfriends are the ones who get you out of trouble. I should know. If you two had been with me, I'm sure one of you would have pointed out what a damn weasel my boss was. Such a jerk. I was supposed to be the artist-in-residence, but he had me doing the stupidest crap."

"Some men." Rachel shook her head. "I remember my boss at my last job before coming to Bliss. He treated me like his barista."

"Yeah, well, Jean Claude seemed to think I was a handy man. One of the last things the bastard had me do was—oh, yeah." Just like that it fell in place, and she wanted to smack herself for not seeing it sooner. The day before she'd been arrested, he'd had her mess around with the security cameras. He'd complained that the security company would take too long. *Bullshit. Bastard. Son of a bitch.* He'd set her up, and she'd been too stupid to see it.

"What?" Callie asked, her eyes round under the glasses she wore.

"I know where that painting is." Jen started for the door. "I was about to give the damn thing to Rachel as a baby gift."

"Whoa! You were about to give me a half-a-million-dollar, black-market Picasso? I thought it was just one of yours. Though they are beautiful." Rachel's mouth hung open. "That's the awesomest present ever. Way better than the baby monitor that also acts as a SETI receiver. Baby boy's going to college."

She reached for her coat. "You don't get to keep it, Rach. It has to go back, but at least I know where it is. The nasty jerk hid it under the painting I was going to give to Rachel. He pulled the canvas off and hid the Picasso under mine. I wouldn't be able to tell because he was a dipshit when it came to his personal life, but brilliant at what he did. Of course he didn't count on me being a crazy perfectionist. I decided I could do better. I painted the whole damn thing again in one

night and changed some of the colors. Renard must have called the police the minute he realized he no longer had the painting. Asshole."

Rachel flushed slightly. "Uhm, I kind of talked to Holly. The one you put back for me really didn't go with the room. I might have talked Holly into switching it with the blue one. Don't look at me like that. It's a boy. Blue is for boys."

There was no pleasing a client. Every artist knew it. "It's fine. But that means the others are potentially up for sale. I need to get my hands on that painting. Tell Stef I've gone back to town hall, and he should meet me there when he can."

Callie was right behind her. "I'm going with you."

Jen brushed past Logan and Marie and out of the door of the clinic. The glare of the sun off the snow made everything seem vital and alive. She loved winter in Colorado, but her mind was on getting to the town hall. Her heart wasn't going to slow down until she pulled the canvas off that painting and made certain that the Picasso was underneath. It was her sure ticket to getting that potential felony off her record. Once that oppressive weight was off her, perhaps Stef could see her as something other than a girl constantly in trouble.

The clinic was on the end of Main Street. It was quieter here. Up ahead, she could see that the festival was in full whirl, but here, there was an almost eerie quiet. She turned to tell Callie to follow her when she noted the two men standing with her friend.

"Callie?" Jen immediately recognized them as the two men they had seen earlier in the day.

The smaller one with the dangerous eyes was standing far too close to Callie. The big, gorgeous one was walking her way.

"Miss Waters?" His deep voice rumbled out.

"Yes." She had a terrible feeling that the smaller man wasn't helping Callie balance on the snow. She caught the glint of metal at Callie's waist and the way her face tightened. "Let my friend go."

"I can't to be doing that." There was an almost sympathetic look in his eyes, but it didn't move Jen because the bastard still had a gun in his hand. "You have something that belong to my employer."

Jen took a deep breath. Trouble, it seemed, just kept finding her.

Chapter Thirteen

Alexei stepped close to the brunette, who now resembled a frightened deer in the presence of a tiger. The fact that he was the predator was not lost on him. The gun in his hand felt pounds heavier than he knew it to be.

"Don't scream." Ivan's voice was low, but there was no way anyone could mistake the steely threat in it.

Alexei wound his hand around the artist's elbow and looked back at what was happening behind him. Ivan had the woman with glasses in a dangerous hold. His arm was securely wrapped around her waist, their bulky coats hiding the gun Ivan had shoved into the woman's side.

"You scream and I have no reason not to shoot you. Understand?" Ivan looked down at his victim.

The woman bit her lip as though forcing herself to comply when all she wanted to do was yell. Slowly, she nodded her head. She took a deep breath, and though Alexei could still see the fear in her eyes, a stubborn will took over. She would fight. That small woman, with her sweet face and round glasses, would not go down easily.

"It's going to be all right, Callie." Jennifer Waters kept her voice steady. Her jaw firmed as she stared at her friend. "I'll get us out of

this."

He hated the way his stomach churned, acid rising to his throat. He'd been worried about tears and pleading, but this suddenly seemed worse. These women were calm though afraid, their solidarity obvious in the way they encouraged each other. It was completely different from the others he'd dealt with. He and Ivan had specialized in dealing with other criminals. They had often worked over "partners" in an attempt to get information or simply to send a message. The people he'd interrogated always gave up their "friends." They begged and pleaded and lied about their partners in an attempt to throw the violence on someone else.

These women loved each other. These women, he had no doubt, would sacrifice for each other.

There were tears in the artist's eyes as she looked up at him. "I know what you want."

He had to force the words to come out harshly. "The painting. My employer pay for painting. He is not a man to cheat."

Her jaw firmed with pure stubborn will. "Well, he didn't pay me. Did he pay you, Callie?"

The woman named Callie shook her head. "Nope. I haven't had a single check come in for a stolen painting."

Jennifer nodded his way. "See, big guy, there's no reason to go all *Godfather* on us—or whatever the Russian equivalent is. I can get you your painting, and you can go on your happy way."

But it wouldn't be like that, and he knew it. They couldn't afford to leave these women alive. They would need to kill them, stash the bodies, and get out. There was far too much at stake, and this wasn't some piss-poor, mob-run rural town in Russia where they could bribe their way out of anything. Pushkin's name didn't mean anything here.

An image of his brother flashed across his brain. Mikhail had been a handsome, smiling young man who had never been impatient with his brother. He'd taught Alexei with a gentle smile. What would his brother think about him killing this woman? One day, he would have to stand in front of his brother and account for the things he'd done in Mikhail's name.

"Move." Ivan walked behind them, his gruffness letting Alexei know he was growing tired of waiting. "If either one of you makes a

wrong move, we will kill you both and then start on the crowd. If you care at all about the people around you, you will behave."

Jennifer slid her arm around his waist. She smiled, though it didn't reach her eyes. "Pretend you're crazy about me. Otherwise, people might wonder why we're walking so close. We have to get to town hall, you see. We can go in from behind, but there's a good hundred yards before we can move to the alley."

He saw what she meant. There were people milling around all over the place up ahead of them. He saw the place where she pointed, a small road that led to the back of the buildings on their left. "All right. We're just two couples enjoying day together. You can handle that, can't you, Ivan?"

"I think so." Ivan switched to Russian. "Perhaps we can enjoy much of the day. I like this one. I think she's got nice breasts under all the clothes she's wearing. Let's get the painting and then go back to the motel. We can enjoy their bodies before we kill them, my friend."

He could taste the bile in his throat but forced himself to laugh and agree with the man he hated. How much? How much of his own soul was he willing to give up? Panic threatened as he started to walk Jennifer toward the opposite side of the road. It was all happening so fast. His life seemed to be coming to a point. His revenge seemed further away than ever before, and yet so tantalizingly close. All he had to do was get the painting and take it to Pushkin.

Nick's words kept coming back to haunt him. He was giving up the rest of his life, the rest of his soul. If he walked further down this path, there would be no going back.

His feet moved along the ground, the thud in time to his beating heart. All he had to do to avenge his gentle brother's life was kill two women after watching Ivan brutally rape them. All he had to do was go against everything his brother ever taught him. All he had to do was give up his soul.

A man in a cowboy hat strode confidently down the sidewalk. "Hey, Jen! I've been looking for you. Did you hear what's going on around here?"

"Be very careful," Alexei whispered. "He will kill your friend."

"And you won't?" Her words were returned quietly.

That was the question that ran through his head. Could he pull the

171

trigger and end an innocent life?

Jennifer turned on a bright, charming smile. "Hey, James! How are you doing today?" She winked at the cowboy who stopped and stared at the four of them. "Callie and I are having fun, if you know what I mean."

The cowboy's mouth came open and then closed. Alexei felt a thrill of terror that the man would call them out.

"I thought you were with Stef." The cowboy's eyes narrowed in obvious anger.

Jennifer shrugged. "I'm with a lot of guys, James. You know that."

He shook his head. "Yeah, I heard that, too. And Callie. Biggest slut in the county. I thought I was different. I thought I meant something to you. I was willing to wait for you to wake up to what a creep Stef is, but I won't watch you go through tourists, too."

"You're an asshole, James," Callie spat out. "And Jen was right not to sleep with you. I was bored when I slept with you."

"Bitch." The cowboy named James stalked off without a backward glance.

Ivan laughed. "Dumb bitches," he said in Russian. "American women are all sluts. Perhaps they will like what we do to them, eh?"

But Alexei didn't think so. He got the distinct feeling that something was wrong. He moved along anyway, his mind whirling, seeking a way out until he knew there wasn't one.

You're the best thing I ever did, Alexei. That was what his brother had said when Alexei had asked if he minded giving up his chance to go to university. Mikhail had a promising future in the sciences before their parents had died.

He moved like an automaton toward the building Jennifer had told them would get them safely to the town hall.

A picture of his parents was in his wallet. It was hard to remember them sometimes, but they were smiling in the only picture that was left of the man and woman who had given him life. It wasn't the only thing. He was left. He was still here, still could have a life.

His parents had been gentle people.

His brother had been the finest man he had ever known.

Who the hell was he?

"You're crying." Jennifer spoke softly as they walked.

He felt the tears slide down his cheeks. Fuck. How was he going to explain that to Ivan?

"Please." The word was a puff out of her mouth, meant for his ears, his soul.

Please. Had Mikhail pleaded? Perhaps. He had a brother to raise. Mikhail would not have allowed pride to stop him. If he'd thought begging might help, he would have begged. The man who killed his brother had not listened.

Alexei turned the corner.

Who was he? A man like the one who took his brother's life? For fifteen years, all he had thought about was revenge. For fifteen years, he'd told himself that he owed his brother this violence. What a fool he'd been. He owed his brother, his precious brother, a good, well-lived life. He owed his brother his honor. Unfortunately, he also owed the woman in his arms something.

One last act of violence.

Alexei turned, quick as a cat. The gun was up, and before Ivan could wipe the lecherous grin off his face, there was a loud report and a neat hole appeared in his head. The man he'd worked with for years fell backward and hit the ground, his blood blooming across the stark white of the snow beneath their feet.

Callie shot toward Jennifer. The women huddled together, each seeming to protect the other.

"He would have killed you." Alexei lowered the gun. He could feel his face flushing.

"Thank you." Jennifer's arms were tight around her friend. "You should run. Our men will be here soon."

He was done with that.

Three men burst into the alley, two with guns drawn at the ready. He recognized one of the men as Jamie, the cowboy the women had reviled. He felt himself smile a bit. Clever girls.

"You drop that gun or I'll take your head off. Please give me a reason to take your head off." The man in the lead seemed perfectly ready to do that.

"I got them here as fast as I could," James said, looking at the women. His face was stark, and he was out of breath. Alexei

wondered if the man had started running the minute he was out of sight. "I'm sorry I wasn't carrying at the time. Walking away was one of the hardest things I ever did."

"You did the right thing, James." The head law official frowned at Alexei. "I'm serious. I want to shoot you. One of those women you were about to kill is my wife. Only the fact she's watching me right now keeps me from blowing your ass away."

"Please to not blows on my ass." Alexei dropped his gun and held up his hands. "I wish to become defective."

He could not go back to Russia. It suddenly struck him that he had something to bargain with. He had detailed workings of the Russian mob. He could tie Pushkin to American mobsters, even a few politicians.

He sank to his knees in the snow as the men walked toward him. Two in uniforms, shiny gold stars hanging on their shirts, were in front. They hadn't bothered with coats.

"Nathan, that was rude," Callie said, indignation dripping.

Alexei waited patiently as the married couple worked out their obvious disagreements concerning the treatment of prisoners. The husband frowned at the wife.

"Logan, pick up that gun," the tall man with cold eyes said in a quiet, professional voice. His revolver was leveled straight at Alexei's head.

"Yes, Sheriff." The gangly, younger man first kicked the gun away, and when it was safe to do so, he reached down and picked it up, securing it.

"This one's dead, Nate." The one the women had called Jamie, or James, stared down at Ivan's body.

"You all right, baby?"

It was the first emotion Alexei had heard in the sheriff's voice. His eyes didn't leave his prey, but there was the slightest softening of that hard-as-nails tone.

"I'm okay," Callie replied. "Jen's okay, too, thanks to him."

The sheriff's lips turned down. "I'll wait to thank him. Logan, cuff him. We'll get him back to the station and figure out just what the hell is going on around here."

Jennifer stepped forward. "You can't arrest him, Nate. He saved

us."

"It's fine," Alexei said quickly. "I will go with them. I will answer all questions. I would like to become a defective person. I have much helpful information."

"What the fuck is going on?"

A man with dark hair stepped into the alley. It only took a moment for Alexei to realize this was Jennifer's man. He could be in more trouble.

"Stef, everything is fine." Jennifer tried to step forward.

"You stay right there, Jennifer." The sheriff shouted the order.

Jennifer and Callie stepped back at his tone.

Alexei allowed Logan to pull his hands down, and he felt the cold metal snap around his wrists. He was in custody, his plans blown, his future in severe peril, but he hadn't felt so light in years.

He turned to the two women he'd blown his revenge to save. He shook his head at the thought. In saving them, he'd finally saved himself.

"Thank you," he said as the sheriff took his arm and began to lead him away.

* * * *

"I could make him defective really fucking fast," Stef said, looking at the Russian through the bars of his cell. The urge to make the asshole sorry he'd ever walked into Bliss was riding him hard. His heart had been racing from the moment he'd realized Nate had left the building. Rachel had been the one to tell him what was going on. He'd been caught up in his discussion with the doctor when he'd heard the sound of a gun going off. He'd never been as afraid as he'd been when he heard that shot. He was going to start carrying a rifle with him wherever he went so he would always be prepared.

Hope, a sweet-looking, dark-haired woman, looked at Stef, her eyes going wide.

"Sorry," Stef said. Hope had come into town a few months before and seemed shy and retiring. Though she was only twenty-five, she somehow seemed younger than her years.

She smiled shyly. "It's okay. I'm getting used to it. The sheriff

175

curses all the time."

Nate looked up from his paperwork. "I certainly do not curse all the time. And I don't think that's what he meant, Stef. I think he's under the false impression that the US is still on the lookout for defectors. Laura was right. Smart woman. She caught the other guy's tattoos when he came into the Stop 'n' Shop. It's apparently code for these guys or something. I don't know. I dealt with South Americans and homegrown assholes. The European mobster might be too much for my poor, backwoods sheriff brain." Nate was far too calm. It was making him crazy.

Of course, Jennifer standing there and talking to the same man who had kidnapped her and worked for the man who planned to kill anyone in his way made him even crazier.

Stef had to turn away. He stared out the window where the snow was falling in thick waves, blanketing everything in a fine powder.

At least it was over. He forced himself to sit down.

"Look, I've already put in a call to the feds. They can't get here until tomorrow night because of the snowstorm headed our way. If he is who he says he is, he could be important," Nate said all too sensibly.

Stef couldn't believe what he was hearing. "He's a man who almost got your wife killed."

After giving her brief statement, Zane had collected Callie and insisted she go home to rest. Nate had held her for a long time before allowing Zane to scoop her up and take her home. Stef hadn't even had a chance to hug Jennifer. She'd been a bee, buzzing around everywhere. She'd sat with Logan while he took her statement. She'd held Callie's hand while she'd given hers. Now, she sat talking to the same fucking mobster who had gotten her into the situation in the first place. She'd briefly smiled at Stef and told him she was okay before rushing off to find someone else to comfort or thank.

"Callie's going to be fine," Nate continues. "She's strong. So is Jen. You're the one I'm worried about. I thought you would be relieved this was over."

He wasn't sure it was. "Is it? We don't have the painting in hand, yet."

Nate's eyes rolled. "Well, it couldn't possibly be as easy as

walking in and getting it. I blame Rachel. Apparently she preferred the blue painting. Nell said Holly sold the green painting, but she wasn't sure who had bought it. Holly told her she was thrilled because it brought in enough money that it didn't make sense to put it in the auction. Someone paid five hundred for the damn thing."

Stef winced. He didn't agree with Jennifer's insistence on giving away her work. It was worth far more than five hundred. "And Holly doesn't remember who gave her five hundred dollars?"

"Holly left to pick up her kid. He's coming into town. She wanted to get him before his dad changed his mind. You know how she is about that kid."

Holly would drop everything for her teenage son. From what Stef understood, her ex-husband kept them apart as much as he could. "Did someone check the receipts?"

Nate stared at him as though he'd grown a second head.

"Right." Like anyone in Bliss was terribly concerned about receipts.

"Nell gave me the book. Whoever bought it paid cash and can't write to save his or her life. I tried to make out the signature, but I apparently don't read that language. Don't worry about it. I'll put out the word. We'll find it."

Nate sounded certain, but Stef wouldn't be satisfied until that painting was out of their hair.

And then it would be over, and he would have to deal with the fact that he was going to lose her. He nodded to Nate and forced himself to sit down in one of the chairs in the waiting area.

Though he'd been the one to set in motion the plan that would separate them, Stef didn't like to think about how fast it was all happening. He'd thought he had a bit of time with her. The wheels of the court system tended to grind slowly. He was certain he could get the charges against her dropped, but it would take time.

If what the Russian said was true, Finn Taylor could get the charges against her dropped by tomorrow morning.

"I did what you asked of me, Stefan. Are you sure about this?" His father sank down into the chair beside his. He watched as Jennifer laughed at something the criminal who had nearly killed her said. "You seem very taken with her. I might not understand your

177

relationship with the young lady, but I can see plainly you care for her."

He felt like he always felt around his father, slightly restless. It was as though the minute he occupied the same space as the man, Stef's skin became too tight. He shifted in his chair, wishing he could avoid all of this, but he needed his father's help on several fronts. They had talked about his plans early this morning before Stef had left. His father, apparently, worked fast. "I love her, Dad. I want what's best for her."

Just saying the words made him wish he could take them back, but he'd been compelled to spit them out. No one understood. Everyone thought he was being an ass when all he wanted was to do right by her. It was all he ever wanted.

"If you love her, why are you trying to send her away? I made the calls you asked me to. They'll take her mid-semester. They're counting her work with Renard as life experience. But, I don't think she wants to go to Paris."

Stef turned, and Jennifer was passing the man named Alexei Markov a glass of water. Every artist wanted to study at the Sorbonne. Jennifer couldn't be any different. She would be surrounded by art and culture, and he would see that she lived in style. She could study and live a bit, and then if she decided to come back to him, he could believe her.

Why couldn't anyone see that he was sacrificing his happiness for her?

"She'll love it once she gets there," Stef insisted.

His father's eyes tightened in suspicion. "Are you planning on drugging her, son? Because I think that's what it's going to take to get her on a plane to Europe."

She would go. He would see to it. She would certainly see reason. She couldn't grow as an artist here. She couldn't see the world.

His father leaned forward. The lines on his familiar face creased further as he frowned seriously. "Stefan, this is one of the reasons I came back. I want to talk to you about so many things, but this one in particular. You can't keep blaming yourself for what happened between me and your mother."

He shook his head. "What are you talking about? I don't blame myself."

Sebastian snorted lightly. "Fine, then I would like for you to stop blaming me."

"This is not the place to have this conversation." He kept his voice low. The last thing he needed was more gossip.

His father didn't seem to have a problem with it. "Well, you don't seem to think there is a place for this conversation, so I've decided to have it out here."

Like he needed this right now. "Fine. I don't blame myself, and I don't blame you. I lay the blame squarely on the shoulders of my mother. She's the one who decided to leave us in order to pursue a career in acting. She's the one who walked out."

His father leaned in. "She was very young. I knew that when I married her."

"Then why did you?"

His father seemed to think for a moment. "I was in love with her. I married your mother when she was twenty-four years old. Back then, that wasn't really so young. I was older, of course, but I knew I wanted her the minute I saw her."

Stef felt his whole soul drag. He knew that story. He'd wanted Jennifer. He'd known that first morning she'd walked into Stella's looking for him that she was special. He'd been fighting the feeling ever since.

His father had a wistful smile on his face. "I judged a beauty pageant. She won."

It should have been a clue. Sebastian Talbot had made a mistake that Stef didn't intend to make. He'd seen trouble coming and walked headlong into it. "Did she talk about her dreams for the future then?"

"Oh, no," Sebastian replied with a shake of his head. "She was set on getting married and having a family. Your mother was a lovely, funny, bright woman, but she was always mercurial. She changed her mind all the time. She was like a butterfly flitting around. I should have known, but I was young, too. I thought I could make her happy, and then you came along. I was sure she would settle in."

It was hard to remember his mother. When he saw her in his head, it was always in still form, as though he was looking at a

photograph. She was beautiful and distant, always distant. She'd been that way even with his father. "She needed more than marriage and a family could give her. I think it's like that for talented women. They need room to grow. Tell me something, Dad, do you think it would have been different if you had met her at a different time? Say, when she was older?"

His father laughed, the sound amusing but with a sharp edge. "As your mother has gone through three husbands since me, I doubt it, son."

He turned to his father, utterly startled at the announcement. He'd known that she hadn't had the career she'd planned. He'd googled her in the past, but he'd imagined her as happy and working. "Three husbands?"

His father held his hand up, indicating the number four. "Don't forget me. I was the first. Her current victim is a nice retired lawyer."

Stef felt the foundation of his world shift a bit. "How would you know? Are you telling me you kept tabs on her?"

"Not exactly. She contacted me a while back. I think it was right after she tried to get in touch with you and you rebuffed her."

He felt his face harden. He hadn't rebuffed the woman. He hadn't done anything at all. He'd simply not responded. He'd thought she'd taken the hint.

His father's hand came out to pat his shoulder like he had when Stef had been a child. "You're her only child. She realized she wasn't maternal, so she was careful. But as you get older, you feel the need to reach out, to make things right. She backed off because she didn't want to hurt you more than she had. She called me to ask about you. She came into town a few weeks later and we met for lunch. We've become quite good friends. I wish you would talk to her, but I understand it's hard for you."

A nasty suspicion seized Stef's gut. "Did she know you were sick?"

His father's face flushed. "Yes."

"But you didn't think to tell me?"

"I didn't want to worry you." He took a long breath, seeming to come to some kind of decision. "That's not true. I didn't tell you because I was afraid. I was afraid it wouldn't worry you at all. I was

afraid it wouldn't mean anything to you. It's recently come to my attention that I've been a coward most of my life. I should have called you, but I didn't. Getting on that plane was one of the hardest things I've ever done, son."

He didn't understand his father at all. "Why?"

"Because I had to face the worst mistake I ever made."

Now Stef was the one flushing. Well, he'd always known that was true.

His father reached for him. "You're not understanding me. It wasn't a mistake to marry your mother or to have you. My mistake was in leaving you behind. Stefan, I should never have allowed us to be separated."

"I didn't want to leave. I needed this place. I was happy here, so you don't have to feel guilty." He couldn't imagine what his life would have been like if he'd been forced to move to Dallas. He glanced at Nate, who was talking to his deputy, his eyes never straying far from the man in the cell. Nate had grown up in that world. Nate had taken years to accept who he was. He'd tried to fit into society's version of normal. He'd almost lost Callie in the process. No, he wasn't angry with his father for letting him stay in Bliss.

He was angry with his father because he hadn't stayed with him.

The revelation hit him straight in the gut.

He was angry, brutally angry, with his father. All the years of telling himself that he'd built his own family and didn't need anything from the man had been lies. It wasn't that he didn't love his pieced-together family. He did. But he'd needed his dad. He'd needed to know that someone with his blood wanted him for something besides convenient proof that he could procreate.

He looked down, and his hands were shaking.

"Son, I deserve everything you're thinking right now, but I'm asking you to hear me out."

Stef stood abruptly. The room seemed to be closing in on him. His father scrambled to get up as well, but Stef moved across the room from him. He couldn't do this right now. He had too much going through his brain. Everything his father had said reinforced his belief that he was doing the right thing for Jennifer, but the fact that she would soon be gone made him sick. He hadn't had enough time

with her, and he couldn't allow himself any more. If he did, he'd take over her life. He'd mold her into something she wasn't.

"Stef?"

A hand on his arm brought him back to the real world. Jennifer looked up at him, her eyes soft and filled with concern. When he focused on her, she stepped forward and wrapped her arms around him as though she could read his need to be close to her. Without hesitation, he took the comfort she offered, reveling in the way she felt in his arms.

"I'd like to go home, love."

He felt her head nod as she squeezed him close.

"You keep an eye on her," Nate said, standing up and walking across the room. His hand came out.

Stef adjusted Jennifer so she was firmly at his side as he shook Nate's hand. "I will."

He slid his hand into hers and led her out.

If he was going to lose her soon, he didn't want to waste a moment on anything as insignificant as the man who had left him behind.

"Stefan." His father's voice called out.

He didn't look back as he walked out the door.

Chapter Fourteen

Jen wasn't sure what had happened with Stef and his dad, but she knew beyond a shadow of a doubt that it was her job to calm him down. If she allowed him to, he would withdraw, pretending that there was absolutely nothing wrong. He would more than likely tell her that he wanted to work or some such nonsense and leave her alone for the rest of the evening.

That was not going to happen.

Stef pulled his Land Rover into the long drive that led to his house just as the sun was going down. He'd said little since he'd asked Max to give his father a ride back when Sebastian was ready. The whole way home, he'd concentrated on the road. His hands had been perfectly steady on the wheel, but she couldn't forget the moment when she'd seen them shake. Stef out of control made her heart hurt. It was the one thing he couldn't handle.

She knew exactly how to give control back to him.

He put the SUV in park and shut off the engine. Jen got out before he could say a word. Though she was right in front of the door that led into the house, she walked around the vehicle. She wasn't going into the house.

"Jennifer?"

She turned slightly and stared at the deliciously masculine sight he made. He was lit from behind by the setting sun. He looked every inch the rough-and-tumble cowboy in Levi's, boots, and a somewhat-battered Stetson. He looked far from the immaculate man he often presented himself as. She realized looking at him, heart racing at how beautiful he was, that she loved all of Stef. She loved the wickedly decadent artist and the doggedly loyal small-town boy. She adored the perverted Dom. He was all of those things, and she wouldn't have him any other way.

"I love you, Stef."

His boots suddenly became very intriguing, it seemed. He stared down at them for a moment.

Though her heart clenched at his silence, she realized something else. In the end, she couldn't control whether or not he loved her. She couldn't force him to see how good they could be together if he didn't want to. She could bluster and batter him with attention-seeking behavior, but in the end, he would decide whether or not he was brave enough to take the chance. All she had control over was how much she loved him. It wasn't such a selfish thing. Her love suddenly seemed vast and warm and giving.

"Don't cry."

She hadn't been aware she was, but she felt it now. It wasn't sad. It was simply the acknowledgement of overwhelming emotion. She loved, and suddenly she was a better person for it. She was larger than she'd been mere moments before.

"I love you." There was no hesitation in the words. They were strong and proud. Her love was worth something. He might deny it, but she wouldn't.

"I…that means a lot to me." His words were oddly faltering, as though foreign to his tongue.

She wouldn't push him, but she could help him. "Then come to the guesthouse with me. I want to play."

His eyes flared. "You want to play? I don't know if that's a good idea. I'm not exactly calm and in control."

"But you will be." She turned and started to walk toward the guesthouse. This was how he could get his control back. This was the gift she could give him.

He caught up to her in an instant. "You're topping from the bottom."

The outrage in the accusation made her smile. "Isn't that what every smart sub does?"

He frowned before a laugh huffed from his chest. "You're going to kill me, Jennifer."

He leaned over and gently pushed his shoulder into her midsection, picking her up in a fireman's hold.

"Hey!" The world went topsy-turvy, and then she felt a sharp slap to her ass.

"Hush, sub. You want to play? I want to play, too. But we're at least going to pretend I have some control. When we go into that guesthouse, you treat it like a dungeon. I'm the Master. You're the pretty submissive who'll do anything to please me."

And that was different how? She didn't argue with him, though. She was already getting hot at the thought of playing with Master Stefan. "Yes, Stef."

"What will please me?"

She loved the way his voice went deep and rich, like dark chocolate. "My submission."

"No clothes are allowed in my dungeon."

He set her on her feet and pulled out the key. He quickly opened the door and allowed her to enter. Jen felt her shoes sink into the thick carpet. The door closed behind her, and when she turned, Stef was staring at her, his face as hard as granite.

"I'm waiting."

She certainly didn't feel the cold now. She shrugged out of her coat and handed it to him to hang. With deliberate movements, she took off her clothes. Where the afternoon had been a flurry of passion, this was measured, and a level of anticipation permeated the room. She felt almost drugged by it. She slid her hands under the waistband of her jeans and pushed them down her legs.

"Poor darling," he said with silky sympathy. "You had to wear your plug all day. Is my slave's ass sore?"

"I can handle it, Stefan." She smiled at him in genuine pleasure.

There wasn't a hint of his earlier worry and panic. He was utterly and completely focused on her now. He was in control. "Turn around

and lean over the couch. It's time to take it out. I have more interesting things to shove up your ass than a piece of plastic."

His cock made his jeans bulge. While she'd been undressing, he'd done the same. He was down to his jeans, his perfectly cut chest making her mouth water. She wondered what he looked like in his leathers. More than likely, a lot like he did now. He was an intimidating, lean presence. Jen took a deep breath to calm her racing heart and walked to the couch with what she hoped passed for grace. She placed her hands on the arm and leaned over, presenting her ass to her Master.

"Nicely done, love," Stef purred. She shivered just a bit as his hands traced her back. "You've studied up. I can see that. I wonder how much you're prepared for. I wonder how much you can take."

"I can take almost anything except the part where you get me riled up and walk away."

He chuckled. "Yes, I can see where that would be difficult for you. How about I promise you that I won't ever leave you unsatisfied? But your satisfaction, when we're playing, comes at my discretion. If I choose to torture my slave for hours on end, that is my decision."

"I don't know how much I like the sound of that."

He smacked her ass, causing every nerve in her backside to come alive with a jittery pleasure. "Yes or no? We can go back to the house and have nice, vanilla sex. I'm all right with that, love. I really am. We can have vanilla sex and go to sleep wrapped in each other's arms. Or I can tie you up, spank your sweet ass, and torture you with vibrators and other nasty toys. I can lick every inch of your body. I can devour your pussy while I shove my finger up your ass. And I can fuck that ass, love. I'm going to ream it until you don't remember a time I wasn't balls-deep inside you. Really, it's your choice."

He punctuated his speech by running his tongue down her spine almost to the place he'd promised to fuck. It was delicious and dark and dirty, and she felt her pussy clench in response.

"Oh, Stef, I want to play." Her hands tightened on the couch because if she didn't hold on, she would fall. He was turning her into a quivering mass of desire. "Please play with me."

She felt him get to his knees behind her. He nipped at her butt

cheeks. "I'll play, love. Have I mentioned how pretty your asshole is?"

She laughed. It wasn't a compliment she heard often, but Stef said it like he was talking about her hair or telling her how nice she looked in a new blouse. He left absolutely no room for shame. "Thank you."

"I like to look at it." He pulled her cheeks apart.

"You're not painting my asshole, Stef." She had her limits.

"I don't see why not. I wouldn't sell it, of course. But it is a work of art. I could do a whole series of paintings featuring your pink parts. I love your ass and your pussy." His hand slid up to where she was already wet and wanting. "I definitely love your clit. I like to rub it and suck on it until it pokes out of its hood and begs for my attention."

Jen gasped. Her clit was probably doing that right this second because he was rubbing her in the sweetest way. He pressed on her clit and lessened the pressure, running a circle around the nub before pressing again. It lit a fire that spread from the apex of her thighs, crawling along her skin.

He pulled his hand away.

"Hey, I was enjoying that."

"And I'll enjoy this, brat." He pressed her down, forcing her midsection over the arm of the sofa. His hand slapped at her ass in ten quick, harsh licks, each one a shocking heat on her flesh. "Don't talk to me that way when we're playing."

"Yes, Stefan." She bit her bottom lip to keep from crying out, but even as she did he was smoothing his hand across her skin, the pain morphing into pleasure.

He slid his hand between her cheeks and pulled on the plug. It slid from her, leaving her strangely empty. He almost immediately pressed a finger in.

"Tight. You're still going to be tight, love, but you can take me." He groaned as he pressed deep, rotating his finger. He moved in between her legs, taking up all the space. "No one's had your ass, have they?"

"No, Stefan." She never even dreamed she'd want anyone to take her there, but she couldn't imagine not sharing the intimacy with Stef.

He'd invaded every inch of her soul. She wanted him to have all of her body, too.

"Excellent." He pulled his finger out and backed away. "Go into the bedroom, love. I'll be along in a moment. There are some toys I need."

He steadied her when she got back on her feet. Every nerve and pore in her body seemed open and aware of his presence. His lips curled in a decadent grin as he looked down at her.

"Toys? Dare I ask?" She probably didn't want to know. He was a veritable pervertopedia when it came to toys. He knew how to use them all to great advantage.

"No office supplies this time, love. We're in my dungeon. I have every luxury imaginable." He suddenly frowned. "Unless my father threw it out."

She stifled a laugh. "I doubt it." She went on her toes and pressed a kiss to his lips. "I'll be waiting."

On wobbly feet, she made her way to the bedroom. Callie had pointed it out when she'd given her a secret tour of the guesthouse. She'd gone into salacious detail of what went on, though at the time she hadn't played here herself. She had the feeling Nate and Zane had probably fixed that situation. She knew that Max and Rye had an open invitation. She entered the bedroom and wondered if there was a sign-up sheet. It might be awkward if the room was already occupied.

Then she wasn't thinking about awkwardness. Her heart raced as she looked at the newest addition to the dungeon. Stef had installed a floor-to-ceiling mirror. She stared for a moment at the reflection of herself. She was naked, but she almost didn't recognize the woman there. She looked tousled and soft. She'd always thought of herself as gangly and too thin. She didn't have Callie's curves or Rachel's petite grace, but there was an innate sexiness to the woman in the mirror that couldn't be denied.

"Yes, love, you're beautiful."

Stef stood in the doorway behind her, his dark hair ruffled. He leaned on the frame and caught her gaze in the mirror.

"I never thought of myself as beautiful. I certainly never thought of myself as sexy." She doubted she would without him. Stef brought out a version of herself she really liked. When he looked at her like he

was looking now, she felt powerful and sexy even as she submitted to him.

"I can't think of you as anything less." He tossed several items onto the bed and took a place behind her, cupping her shoulders. "You have no idea how many times I've thought about painting you, your graceful arms and long limbs." He let his hands move lower to cup the breasts that had always seemed too small to her, but felt like the perfect size when his hands were on them. "Your sweet breasts. You're my ideal model. I couldn't find a woman I want more than you."

She let her head lean back against his chest, enjoying the picture they made. When she looked into that mirror at the couple cuddling together, it was hard to believe they ever fought at all. They looked right together, as though two pieces that had been separated had finally found their way back together.

"Kiss me, love."

She tilted her head up and reveled in his kiss.

* * * *

Stef pressed his lips to Jennifer's mouth and felt himself sigh. All of the previous tension of the day melted away as he let his body mold to hers. This was what he'd needed since that moment when he realized how close he'd come to losing her.

He'd walked into the room to find her staring at herself in the mirror as though seeing herself for the very first time. He wanted her to see herself as he did—a true, amazing work of art. She was gorgeous from the top of her silky, sable hair to her dainty toes. She would probably be shocked to discover he was fascinated with her toes. She painted them pinks and purples, and one day last summer, a bright, shocking orange. He loved summer because she would glide around town in sandals, her toenails a patch of art in his day.

He ran his tongue along the seam of her lips. She always tasted sweet to him. He sometimes thought he could run his tongue over her skin a thousand times a day and never get sick of the taste.

How was he going to let her go?

A breathy cry slipped from her mouth as he moved from her lips

to her neck. He let his eyes drift up so he could watch them in the mirror. She was femininity and grace to his masculine aggression. That mewling cry went straight to his cock. Every muscle in his body seemed hard and ready to pounce, but his cock was past rigid. His cock was a throbbing, insistent rock.

He nuzzled her neck. His fingers found her rigid nipples. He pinched at them, remembering how well she'd taken his spontaneously made clamps. He had better ones now. Unwilling to wait any longer, he moved back. "Get on your knees on the bed, love. Face the mirror. I want you to watch everything I do to you."

She shivered a bit, but he didn't think it was from the cold. He could see her pussy, and it was getting creamy and soft. She was so responsive, like an instrument only he was meant to play. She climbed on the bed and turned so she could see herself in the mirror. He reached out to the nightstand table and grabbed the first of the toys he'd brought for her, a set of lovely clover clamps. Silver and ornate, they were held together by a chain that would dangle between her breasts.

"No more paper clips?" She anticipated his next command. She pushed her shoulders back, thrusting her breasts out. The pink and brown nipple pointed directly at him.

He quickly clamped the precious nubs, adjusting the tension to ensure maximum stimulation without cutting off her circulation. He would really prefer piercings. If she belonged to him, he would try to convince her to pierce her nipples. He'd play with the rings constantly, twisting them and sucking on them. He would attach pretty chains between the two and tug on them to stimulate her.

"It's pretty." She smiled at him like he'd given her a diamond necklace rather than clamping her breasts for his pleasure.

"You're prettier, love." She was gorgeous, and it went past her lovely face and sexy body. She was beautiful down to her soul. She was kind and loving. She put others first. It was up to him to make sure she got her dreams. Even if it meant letting her go.

But not yet. He could keep her for a while. He felt a stubborn resolve rise. What if he taught her? He'd never taken on an art student before, but he'd never met one with as much potential as his Jennifer. Surely he had something to teach her. His work went for hundreds of

thousands of dollars. He'd been reviewed as an artist to collect and was doggedly pursued by gallery owners. He could teach her. For as long as he taught her, he could enjoy her. He could hold her close and pretend she really belonged to him.

He traced the line of her torso down to her wet and ready pussy. He found the jewel of her clit and rubbed gently.

Her eyes closed, and her body bowed back slightly, opening her to his touch.

"Come for me. I want to watch your face as you come."

She murmured her assent as her breath caught.

Without letting up on the pressure he was exerting on her clit, he grabbed the vibrator he'd bought for her. He replaced his finger with the rabbit, pressing the outside to her clitoris.

Her eyes flew open as he flicked the vibe on.

"Oh." A delicious moan came out of her mouth.

"Keep those eyes open."

She opened her eyes. They were large and verdant green. She could never lie to him because everything about her was right there in her eyes. Now he could see her desire in those eyes. Her bow of a mouth came open as he rubbed the vibrator over and over her clit. Her hips pumped forward, pressing against the sensation.

He looked down at her pussy. It was swollen and pink, like a flower just on the edge of bloom. He hadn't needed to use the lubricant he'd brought. By the time he'd clamped her nipples, she was soaked with her own sweet cream. He notched up the vibrator, the sound buzzing against her skin.

Her eyes flared. Her skin flushed a gorgeous pink. Her breath was ragged as she moved toward orgasm.

"Stefan. Oh, Stef."

His name sounded like a breathy prayer. Her hands came up. She held on to his shoulders to balance herself as she cried out. She was so beautiful in that instant that he knew it would never be the same again. He would never want another woman. He might be able to view them as lovely on an aesthetic level, but Jennifer was everything to him.

Her body shook in quivering waves. It made the chain between her clamps shiver. He tossed the vibe away and pulled her close. His

hands tightened on the soft flesh of her ass. She didn't hesitate, merely wrapped her arms around his neck and gave herself to him. Her mouth opened on his, and he took advantage. He plunged his tongue into her silky heat. He kissed her over and over, as though he could memorize her taste. He loved the feel of her clamps teasing his chest.

He could have kissed her forever, but his cock was insistently pulsing, demanding attention. He forced himself away from her and climbed off the bed. He ripped at the fly of his jeans and had the offending garment off his body in a heartbeat. His cock bounced free.

"Hands and knees, love," he commanded as he grabbed the tube of lubricant. She hadn't needed it to take the vibrator, but her lovely asshole didn't have her pussy's cream. His whole body tingled at the thought of finally shoving his dick up her ass, forcing her to take him in a place she'd never had a man before.

He was shocked to find his hands were shaking slightly as he got onto the bed behind her. She was beautiful, the perfect picture of submission. Her golden-brown hair hanging down, she stared forward, looking at the mirror. He wondered if she saw what he saw. He saw his perfect mate, waiting for him.

Heart pounding, he couldn't wait a moment longer. He slicked up his dick, fisting himself in quick passes before moving on to the more interesting part of the preparation. He parted her cheeks and dripped the lube in between them.

"It's cold."

"Sorry, love." He'd warmed it, but then he'd spent a good deal of time getting her off. She was a dangerous distraction. "I'll warm you up in a minute."

He pressed a well-lubed finger into her. The rosette of her asshole clenched around his finger.

"Relax. Don't try to keep me out. I won't let that happen." He pushed a second finger in. She groaned as he stretched her. The deep sound made him groan a little, too. "This is mine. Say it."

"It's yours, Stef."

"Your body is mine." The possessive words rolled off his tongue. They felt right, just like she felt right. She was his, every inch of her. "Your mouth, your breasts, your pussy, they're all mine. What else is

mine?"

"Everything, Stef." She didn't hesitate. Her green eyes were clear as she looked at him in the mirror. The chain dangled under her breasts. "I am yours."

He lined his cock up to her asshole. "You're mine."

He pressed in, every inch an outrageous pleasure. She was tight around his cock, fighting to keep him out, but he gently pushed forward. He would win this little war. He would have her because she belonged to him. She would surrender everything to him. He gripped her hips and drove in with ruthless precision.

"Oh, Stef, oh. It burns. You're bigger than the plug."

In the mirror, her face was tight with obvious discomfort. He smoothed his hands over her back. "Poor baby. Is my nasty cock splitting your little asshole?"

"Yes." Her eyes flashed fire, and she hissed through clenched teeth.

She didn't look so submissive now. The thought made him chuckle. This was how it should be. He should earn her submission. He should bind her to him by taking care of her needs and wrapping her in love and pleasure. "Give it a minute. Let your body adjust, love. You were made for me. You can take me."

She lowered her head and leaned forward, flattening her back to push against him. It was just the traction he needed. With a low groan, he pushed his way in past her resistant muscles into the hot, tight clasp of her ass.

He held himself there, reveling in the feel of being balls-deep inside her.

"Are you going to get this over with?"

His hands tightened in warning on her hips. "Don't push me, love. I'm enjoying this, and in a moment, you will, too."

"I doubt that."

He pulled back a bit, with exquisite care. He watched as her muscles relaxed. He knew from having it described to him that this was the good part.

"Oh." Jen's breath came out in short, sharp pants.

"Tell me how it feels." He wanted to hear it from her lips. He inched out again.

"It's so…I don't know, but it's amazing. Do it again." Her hands clenched, clutching the comforter in her fingers. She pushed her ass toward him as though trying to tempt him to stay inside.

"Your wish, love." He thrust into her, a savage need taking over.

Her head fell forward, and she began to rock back against him as he thrust in and out. Stef alternated between watching the mirror and staring at the gorgeous sight of her ass taking his cock over and over again.

He drove forward, pulling her back so she took his full length. He watched her in the mirror. Their eyes connected as their bodies pounded together.

"I love you." She mouthed the words to him.

He loved her, too. So much. She was the other half of his soul, certainly the better part of him. She might never know how much he loved her, how much he was willing to sacrifice for her. She deserved more than he could give her. Even as he made love to her, he saw himself completely dominating her. He wanted to be the center of her universe. He wanted her main goal in life to be pleasing him. If she stayed, he would get her pregnant as soon as possible. He wouldn't be able to help himself. She wouldn't leave Bliss, wouldn't see the world, wouldn't become the woman she could be. She would be his wife, his submissive, his precious possession. How could he do that to her?

He slid his hand down to her clit. At least he could give her this. He slipped a finger onto her clit and started rubbing in perfect circles, the movement timed to his fucking. His finger and his dick worked in perfect precision. He couldn't keep her, but he could have a few weeks of joy. He could hold her and love her while she was here. He could please her and care for her so much that one day she might come back to him.

Tears pricked at the corners of his eyes. Jen's mouth opened, and she came on a low wail. He met her stare in the mirror, trying to memorize the experience. His balls squeezed up, lighting a fire in his body as he fucked her. It would be so lonely without her, but he wouldn't cheat on her. That's what it would be. She was his soul's mate, and the least he could give her was his fidelity.

The orgasm flashed through his body, flaring every nerve in his

system. He grasped her hips, pulling her onto his cock one last time, as though trying to fuse them together in a way that could never be broken.

He came, semen leaving his body in smooth jets of silky pleasure. He pushed again and again, giving her everything he had.

Finally empty, he fell forward, his cock slipping from the sweet comfort of her ass. He pulled her close, turning her so her chest met his, the clamps a reminder that, for a while, she was truly his. Her hands came up, smoothing back his hair.

"God, I love you so much, Stef."

"I love you, too." The words dropped from his lips before he could think to not say them. They fell between them like a loaded gun in his mind.

Jen merely smiled and brushed his lips lightly with hers. "I know, babe. I know."

He wrapped his arms around her and tossed a leg over hers so that he surrounded her body with his. He knew he probably seemed like a spoiled child attempting to utterly brand a toy as his, but he couldn't help it. He wanted to sleep like this, jealously guarding her against everything that might come their way.

"You'll have to forgive him, you know." She nestled her head into the crook of his shoulder.

He didn't pretend to misunderstand. She was talking about his father. "I don't see why."

She was quiet for a moment, and he couldn't help but think she was disappointed in him. It made him restless even as his blood pounded in languid afterglow.

"Why do you think he deserves forgiveness?" He wanted her opinion. He rarely asked for help in making a decision. He was very decisive, but she seemed so certain that he was wrong in this case.

Her face turned up, and the sleepy satisfaction in her eyes hit him straight in the gut. "Silly, I don't think he deserves it. You do, babe. Forgive him, because you might not have the chance to later. Forgive him. Forgive your mother. Let it go so we can move on. I promise I'll help you."

She settled her head against his again. Stef held her and thought about whether or not she would ever forgive him.

Chapter Fifteen

Alexei sat up from the strangely comfortable cot as the door to the station house came open and a large man with black hair and scars on his face walked in, followed by the woman named Callie. The big man had been the one who'd swept her out of the station earlier. Alexei was confused. He'd thought the sheriff was her husband, but the other man had kissed her passionately and spoken to her, been concerned with her every comfort.

"Damn it, Zane." The sheriff looked up from his mountain of paperwork and scowled as the couple entered. "I thought you were going to take care of her."

"Yeah, well, Callie wanted to make sure the Russian prick got fed." Zane was holding a bag in his hand.

His stomach growled as the heavenly scent hit him.

Callie slapped the big guy lightly on his chest. "Be nice."

The man named Zane shook his head. "I'm with Nate. He pulled a gun on you."

"He pulled a gun on Jen," Callie corrected. "The dead guy pulled a gun on me, and then Alexei here saved us both."

She smiled and winked at him. Alexei felt a deep gratitude toward her. It had been so long since he'd had a moment's softness.

This Callie woman had a kind heart. She practically glowed with forgiveness.

"I am filled with the apologies." Alexei couldn't say it enough.

"Yeah, well, be glad you're not filled with lead, buddy." Zane strode across the room and held the bag out. "If I'd been there, you would be as dead as your friend."

"Zane Hollister!" Callie's admonition rang through the quiet station house.

The sheriff was leaning back in his chair, obviously enjoying the show. "I told you he would have reacted exactly the way I did."

Zane rounded on the pair. "No, I would have shot his ass."

The sheriff's eyes hooded, and he sat up, straightening his spine. "I'm actually glad I didn't. He's...different than I would have expected."

Alexei listened in as the sheriff began to detail a bit of his own past to the other man. He'd spent several hours talking to the sheriff, a tape recorder between them. The sheriff had taken copious notes, and Alexei had been surprised to find that the man's attitude shifted as he spoke.

He pulled the burger out of the bag. It was juicy and perfectly American. He bit into it and thought it might be the best bit of food he'd ever tasted. When had he stopped enjoying the simple pleasures of life?

"See," Callie was saying, "he's not unlike the two of you. If your brother had been horribly murdered, you would have sought revenge."

"I don't have a brother," Zane shot back with a stubborn edge to his voice.

There was a moment of silence. It was filled with meaning as the two men stared at each other as though speaking silently. Alexei watched, fascinated, as Zane shook his head.

"Fine. But I don't have to like him." Zane turned on his boots and strode back to the cell, coming within feet of Alexei. "Thank you for saving our wife."

Yes, his confusion was back. Maybe his English was worse than he thought. "It was all I could to do. I could not to harm the women. They were innocent. Their lives are not worth revenge."

"Well, I thank you for shooting your friend, anyway."

He searched his brain for the proper American words. Americans always knew how to describe an asshole. "He was not good friend. He was, how you say, a bag of douches."

The sheriff laughed outright, and Zane's mouth tugged up. "At least he has the lingo down."

The sheriff looked genuinely amused. "He's hell to understand, man. You should have been here."

"Don't make fun of him," Callie chided. She took her place next to Zane, her arm hooking around his waist. "Your English is very good, Alexei. It's way better than Nate's Russian. And you barely have an accent."

Zane snorted, but he didn't take it as an insult. He swallowed another heavenly bite of perfectly cooked burger. "I am thanking you for the hospitality. This is good booger. Best booger I ever to eat."

Zane glanced down at Callie. "Yeah, no accent at all, babe. It's like he came straight out of Iowa."

The door to the station opened again, and a big, broad man with reddish-brown hair pounded in, brushing the snow off his coat and brandishing a file folder like a weapon. He walked straight to the sheriff's desk and slapped it down. Caleb. Alexei wanted to shrink back. He'd spent an afternoon on the ice with this man. He was a bit gruff, but Alexei had admired how patient he'd been with the boys they had taught. He'd admired much about the man. He rather wished Caleb didn't have to know what he'd done. Meeting Caleb had been the first time in years and years that he'd come close to making a friend.

The doctor didn't look back at him. His eyes were firmly trained on the sheriff. "Here you go. Do you know what that is?"

The sheriff didn't appear to take exception to the other man's outraged tone. "I could give it a good guess, Doc, but I think you're going to tell me."

"That's my autopsy report," the doctor said, slapping his hand down on the file folder. "My second autopsy of the day. Second."

The sheriff stifled a laugh. "And I appreciate your promptness. Want to fill me in on this one?"

"You want a cause of death? Single GSW to the brainpan," Caleb began. "Although this guy seriously should have died from Hep C

long ago. He's covered in tats. Laura was right. Those Russian guys love their tattoos."

"He get most in prison," Alexei said, getting up and moving to the bars.

The doctor turned and stared at him. "Are they meaningful?"

He didn't like to think about what they meant. "Yes, they detail his crimes and how many he murders. It is how you know what man is willing to do. He would have added to them for killings he do here. He talks about it on way to Colorado."

"This is a nice town, you know." The doctor's face was turning a bit red, and he reminded Alexei of an angry bull waiting for his chance to charge. "You assholes walk in here looking to do god knows what, and you wreck everything. This is a nice place where people give a shit about each other. I should not have to do autopsies. I should not have to write out the way people died of unnatural causes here."

"I am sorry. I could not save other girl. She was dead because I was…" Alexei let his eyes drift down.

Caleb stopped in front of the cell. "She died while you were out with me and the Farley twins?" When Alexei didn't answer he put a hand on the bars. "What would you have done if you had been there? Would she still be dead? Would you have helped kill her?"

His stomach churned at the thought. He'd been through the scenario in his head a million times. It had kept him up all night. He'd played it through, and he still wasn't sure what he would have done.

"Caleb, stop." Callie crossed her arms and faced the doctor.

Caleb didn't look at her, obviously preferring to expend his intimidation on Alexei. Alexei forced himself to face the man he'd briefly thought of as a friend. The doctor wasn't close to being done with him. "Why? Why should I stop? Why should I think he would have saved that girl? He almost certainly helped get rid of her body. Am I wrong?"

The burger he'd wolfed down now threatened to come back up. He could still feel the slight weight of her body in his arms. They had wrapped her in a tarp and taken her to an isolated part of the river. "I help him."

"Yeah, I thought so. I had to perform an autopsy on a twenty-

one-year-old girl today. The sheriff and I had to talk to her mother. We had to inform a mother that the child she carried in her womb is gone. The child she loved and nurtured, the child who should have buried her is gone from this earth." The doctor's voice shook. His eyes had welled up in righteous anger, and Alexei's teared up in shame.

"I am sorry." It was all he could think to say.

"Yeah, I can see that. It won't bring her back." The doctor turned. He pointed at the sheriff. "You get that asshole out of my town, Nate."

The sheriff spoke quietly, as though trying to placate the other man. "The feds are coming for him. The roads are keeping them out of here tonight, but they should make it by tomorrow night. Until then, he's going to stay right there in his cozy cell."

The doctor huffed and stormed out as quickly as he'd rushed in.

Callie's big brown eyes stared at him sympathetically. "Please forgive Caleb. He lost his wife a few years ago, and his family no longer speaks to him. Once he was a highly paid surgeon. Well, I won't tell you that story, but he's got a lot of anger. Don't take it personally."

"He is right." Self-recrimination tasted bitter on his tongue. He deserved whatever these feds gave him. He deserved whatever hell waited on him.

A soft hand covered his own. He heard Zane curse, but Callie simply tightened her fingers over his hand. "Tell me something, do you honestly believe that you would have stood there and allowed this Ivan person to kill that girl?"

He didn't recognize himself anymore. And he had no idea what the word honest meant in reference to his own life. He'd lived a lie for so long. "I don't know."

Her breath came out in a tiny sigh. "I do. I know you've been through some bad things, but deep in your heart, you're good and worthy, and you can fix the things you've done wrong. You would have stopped him. You would have saved her."

Tears fell from his eyes. The room seemed oddly still. Only Callie's voice meant anything in that moment. "You do not know me. How can you possibly know what I do?"

"Because you saved me." She leaned down and placed a single chaste kiss on the back of his hand. "Because you saved Jen. And because you saved my baby."

The men in the room gasped. Their deep, shocked voices were one. "Callie?"

She smiled at Alexei before turning, opening her arms wide. She nodded, her voice choked with emotion. "I took a test this morning. Three, actually. I was going to tell you this evening. We're finally pregnant."

The men crowded her, their arms forming walls around her. They squeezed her tight, kissing and nuzzling her.

Alexei watched the scene. He no longer cared that theirs was obviously an odd relationship. They loved, and it filled the room. They loved, and it filled him with longing. He had absolutely no one who would put their arms around him and shut the world out. He'd given up even the chance of love for the pursuit of revenge, and suddenly it seemed like a terrible thing to have missed out on.

He let his head rest against the cold metal bars. He would probably see a lot of metal bars in his future. An image of that pretty waitress slid across his mind. Holly. He would never have a chance to date a nice woman like Holly. He would be lucky if he survived at all.

"Hey." A gruff voice pulled him from his misery.

He looked up, and Zane's hand was out. It took him a moment to realize what the other man was asking for.

"You are sure?" Alexei had to ask. It felt wrong to simply accept that hand. The man should be sure.

"Yeah."

Tentatively, he put his hand in Zane's. He wouldn't have been surprised if it had been a trick. He wouldn't have been shocked if Zane had used his hold to pull him through the bars and bash his skull against them. A part of him kind of wished he would do it, but that large hand strongly pumped his own.

"Thank you. I don't know why you did it, and I don't care. You saved our wife and our baby. I don't think I can ever repay you for that."

Emotion choked him. One good thing. He'd managed one good thing. He would have to settle for that. He wasn't sure if it would save

201

his soul, but it began to make it feel lighter. "I am glad I do this."

"I'm calling Logan." The sheriff hadn't taken his hands off his wife. "I want to go home, Zane. I want to show our wife how well we're going to take care of her." He kissed the top of her head and walked to his desk.

Fifteen minutes later, they left, their arms around one another. The lanky deputy took over.

"You okay in there?" Logan's face was open and slightly curious. He was young, so young, to have a badge on his chest.

Was he okay? Perhaps not, but he was more okay than he'd been in years. His future looked bleak, but he had a chance to be something more than he'd become. He could not erase past mistakes, but maybe, just maybe, he could find a way to earn forgiveness.

"Yes. I am good."

The young man smiled. "All right, then. I'm the night shift. I'll probably fall asleep at some point in time. Just bang on the bars if you need something."

"Yes, I will bang bars." He wouldn't need anything. He settled himself on the cot, feeling lighter than he had in years. The oppressive sadness he'd felt was gone, only remnants clinging to remind him of his past mistakes.

"Oh, and your cell phone's been ringing. I know I'm not supposed to, but did you need to talk to someone?"

It must be a mistake. Everyone he knew was either dead or half a world away. It didn't matter. He lay down on the cot and pulled the covers up around his chest. It could be his cousin, but he wouldn't worry Nick with his troubles. "No. There is no one to call me. Ignore this."

Logan tipped his hat, a grin curling his lips up. "Can do. I'm really good at ignoring stuff. Only thing I'm better at is avoiding work."

The deputy sat down in his chair. He propped his feet on his desk and leaned back. He tipped his hat over his face and was asleep in no more than five minutes.

Alexei stared at the ceiling, the events of the day playing through his mind, and a deep sense of relief spread through his body. Deep in the night he heard the cell phone buzzing from its place in the small

locker where the sheriff had placed all his personal items at the time
of his booking. He ignored the sound. After a long while, he fell
asleep and dreamed about what it would be like to have a best friend
and a wife. He dreamed about how it would feel to share a life.

* * * *

Jen woke and stretched, her limbs deliciously sore from repeated
and vigorous sexual encounters with the man she could only think of
after last night as her boyfriend. A smile stretched across her face.
He'd said it. He'd said *I love you.*

Oh, he'd looked terrified at the prospect, but he'd said it, and he
hadn't taken it back or tried to pretend like it was a friendly thing. No,
he'd said it and held her and let her fall asleep in his arms and then
promptly woke her up twice more in the night for some rough sex.

She might need to take up yoga. Nell taught a class at the rec
center. Maybe limbering up would help her keep up with her old man.
She winced inwardly. *Never call him that.* She couldn't tease him
about their age difference.

A heavenly scent wafted into the room, and Jen opened her eyes
to discover she wasn't alone.

"Whoa!" She pulled the covers up because she was looking at
someone she hadn't expected.

"Good morning, Miss Jennifer."

Mrs. Truss was a solidly built woman of roughly sixty-five years
with a perfectly upper-crust British accent. The older woman smiled
down at her and placed a mug of what smelled like coffee on the
nightstand.

"Good morning." Jen glanced around the room. It looked like
Stef had put up all the toys they had played with last night, but they
were still in a dungeon. The woman's grandmotherly smile and crisp
white apron was incongruous in a room that had a whipping chair, a
doctor's table with a TENS unit, and a St. Andrew's Cross.

"Don't you feel self-conscious, Miss Jennifer. I've been cleaning
up after Master Stefan's parties for years. I received thorough training
on how to take care of all the toys and sterilize them."

Dear god, Stef had hired Mary Poppins to watch after his

collection of vibrators. "I am so sorry."

Her laughter trilled through the air. "Not at all, dear. The master is a bit odd when it comes to his sexual proclivities, but he's a dear boy. I've been with him since he turned sixteen. Miss Stella hired me to take care of the house."

Her curiosity was on full alert. Carefully keeping the covers around her, she sat up and grabbed the coffee. "Stella hired you?"

"Yes. Stella practically raised the master, you know. After his father left, Stella took over. His father hired a few nannies, but Stella watched them like a hawk after one left Stef alone for a weekend. She was only in her twenties herself back then, and she'd never had children, but she loved Master Stefan like he was her own."

Stef had been lucky. Stella was a natural mother. It had always been confusing to her why someone with as much love to give as Stella had never gotten married. As far as she could tell, Stella never even dated. She'd thrown herself into her business and caring for the people around her.

"Why did Stella take over? Max and Rye's mom was alive then. So was Callie's mom. That would have made more sense."

She shrugged. "I have my theories, but nothing concrete. Stella felt a deep connection to the young boy. He felt it, too. I came in to let you know that Master Stefan is having breakfast. I don't believe he wanted to wake you, but I thought it might be a good idea if you joined him. He's dining with his father, you see."

That could go poorly, and the last thing she needed was for Stef to screw things up with his dad. It had become apparent that part of Stef's problem was his unresolved conflict with his father. She wanted to be there to referee.

"Thanks, Mrs. Truss. I would very much like to join the Talbot men."

The older woman nodded her head as though satisfied. She started out the door but turned. "Oh, and you have a call. It's on hold. I had it transferred out here. When you're ready, pick up the phone on the nightstand, and it should come on. I'll let the cook know to set up another place. I'm happy you're here, Miss Jennifer. I think you'll be perfect for the master."

The door closed behind her, and Jen picked up the phone,

wondering who would call her here. Everyone she knew would call her cell phone.

"Hello?" Jen asked, holding the phone to her ear.

Ten minutes later, soul utterly deflated, she got dressed and placed another call, this one to Callie Hollister-Wright. After arranging her transportation, she walked out of the guesthouse. She made her way to the main house and the breakfast room, her heart sick. She had to face Stef.

For the last time.

Chapter Sixteen

"Have you thought at all about what I said to you yesterday, Stefan?"

Stef looked up from his coffee as his father took the seat across the table from him. Had he thought about what his father had told him? He'd been awake all night thinking about his relationship with Jennifer, and his father's words had played in his head over and over again.

His mother had been certain she wanted a family. His father had said it himself. She'd been sure she wanted children, had pushed him for marriage and kids. Would it be the same with his Jennifer? Would he marry her and then be left behind when she realized how big the world was?

"Of course," he said smoothly to his father. He found he'd softened toward him sometime in the night. He'd finally felt a true kinship with the man. They both loved women who could break them in two. "I want you to know that I don't blame you. You wouldn't have been happy here in Bliss. I understand and I appreciate that you were willing to let me stay. It would have been easy for you to force me to go back to Dallas. I'm truly glad I stayed here."

His father's face flushed. "Yes, you made a family for yourself

here. I can see that. But you're wrong. I would have been very happy in Bliss. I was simply too afraid to stay."

"Afraid?"

His father's hands slipped around the mug of coffee in front of him. He took a drink before sighing and sitting back. His eyes were heavy as he spoke. "Yes, I was afraid. I told you yesterday that I made a mistake in not staying here with you. I deeply regret it, and I hope you won't make the same mistake I did."

The food in front of Stef suddenly didn't seem as appetizing as it had before. He'd meant to come to the main house, grab some food, and rejoin Jennifer in the bed they had shared the night before. He'd meant to feed her from his hands and more than likely make love again. He'd realized the minute he walked into the house that he needed a bit of space. The night before he'd thought about keeping her in Bliss. He was making decisions based on his own needs rather than hers. He was heading down the same path that had ruined his father's life.

"I don't intend to make the same mistake." He forced himself to pick up his fork. "Why do you think I've made the arrangements I've made?"

Studying in France would give her the time she needed to make an informed decision. Of course she thought she wanted to get married and start a family. He knew Jennifer's history. Her mother had been a bit of a drifter. Jennifer had gone to ten different public schools. It made sense that she would want roots, but she had no idea how successful she could be, how important her work could be. She should know all the facts before she decided how her life would go. It was the greatest gift he could give her.

Sebastian's hands came down on the table, causing it to shake. "You do not understand me. You are making the same mistake. You're walking out on a woman you love."

Stef sat back, his father's outburst shaking him a bit. The man had never raised his voice before. "Mom left you, Dad."

"I'm not talking about your mother. I'm talking about Stella."

The fork dropped from his hand. "What the hell does that mean?"

"This is what I've been trying to discuss with you. You think the biggest mistake I made was marrying your mother, but it's not true. I

was impetuous when I married your mother. She was lovely, and I thought it was time to get married. Your grandfather had turned over the reins of the company to me, and then he died. Mother had died the year before him. I missed my parents terribly. I threw myself into the relationship with Jackie. I wanted so badly to rebuild the family I had lost that I convinced myself I could love her. It wasn't until I met Stella Benoit that I realized I had no idea what it truly meant to love a woman."

Stef sat back, shocked at the way his father's entire being softened at the mention of Stella's name. Had his father really had this whole life he'd never known about? Somehow, he'd thought his father simply worked. He'd always believed his father's deepest relationship was with the company he ran. He'd never thought about his father's heartaches past the wife who had left him.

"I met Stella the day we came to Bliss. You won't remember, but I didn't mean to stay here. We were going to visit my sister in Las Vegas. It was only chance that the car broke down here. It was only luck that a large section of land had just gone up for sale."

Stef searched his memory. He had a sudden image of himself as a child, a bit lost and tired from the long car trip. He'd been relieved when the car had died. His father had taken him to a diner. His feet couldn't touch the ground from the booth. He'd sat there swinging his feet back and forth, back and forth. "It was supposed to be a hotel. A ski resort."

"Yes. And we were only supposed to stay for the three days it would take to fix the car." His father relaxed into his story. "I actually thought about calling to have another car delivered. I was going to make the call while we sat and had lunch, but those boys walked in. They walked up and asked if you wanted to play. It was the first time I'd seen you smile in a month."

Max and Rye. Oh, he remembered that. They'd been grubby and disheveled from sleeping in the woods for days. They had explained that they were mountain men. Their momma let them sleep in a tent on the mountain they lived on. It had sounded like a magnificent thing to do.

"While you played with the Harper boys, I talked to the owner of the diner," his father continued. "A few days turned into a week, a

week into a month, and I bought the land from the hotel developers at twice the price."

And Stef had rarely left since. He'd gone on trips. He went to Paris and London. He'd traveled across Europe and Asia. He'd studied in New York, but Bliss was his home, his heart and soul.

Not really his heart anymore. Jennifer was his heart.

"Why did you leave? If you loved her, why did you leave?"

A look of infinite sadness spread across his father's face. "I was afraid. When your mother left, I was devastated. I felt like the world was ripped out from under me. I put everything on hold. Stella was beautiful, but in every other way she was different from your mother. In every way but one."

"She was young."

"She was twenty-two years old when I met her. She was working the diner with her mother. She was even younger than Jackie. And I loved her more than I had imagined possible. I was in so deep with her. I told myself that it was a rebound fling. I fooled myself into thinking it was casual, but one night about a year in, I almost asked her to marry me." He put a fist to his mouth as if to stop some great emotion that might come out. "I couldn't. I couldn't do it again. She said all the right things. She said she wanted to be your mother and wanted to have more kids. And I broke it off with her that night. I believed she was too young to make that decision. I left soon after."

A well of emotion caught him squarely in the chest because he knew the truth about Stella Benoit. "She wasn't too young. She stayed. She didn't lie to you or falter. She was my mother in every way that counted."

God, she had been. She'd been the one to make sure he had the things he needed. A thousand memories flashed through his mind.

Stella baking him birthday cakes.

Thanksgivings at the diner.

Shopping trips to buy him jeans, and later, she'd learned how to shop for art supplies.

Every year he'd watched as she'd matured into a woman the town depended on. A woman he depended on. He still did.

"She wasn't," his father repeated Stef's words. Tears lit his eyes. "She wasn't Jackie, and she wasn't too young. She knew her heart.

She was the other half of my soul, and I threw her away. Even though I walked away from her and broke her heart, she stayed and watched after my son."

"Jennifer isn't Stella." The words were stupid and stubborn. He knew it, but they came anyway. Jennifer was an artist. Artists were different. Artists had needs. She was gifted.

"No, I'm not."

He turned, and Jennifer stood in the doorway, eyes red rimmed and glazed with pain.

"Jennifer." How much had she heard? It was obvious she'd heard something. Her spine was straight, and there was a bag at her feet. What was going on?

She held a hand out. "Don't. I have one question and one question only for you. How were you going to make me go?"

His stomach sank, but he attempted to keep a placid demeanor. This might be a horrible scene, but if he could remain calm, they had a better chance at getting out of it without saying something neither could take back. "I take it the Sorbonne called?"

Her green eyes had lost their sparkle. "Yes. They needed some information. Apparently no one told them it was a secret."

His heart fluttered as he realized how hard she was taking this. The timing was perfectly awful on all counts. He'd certainly not meant for her to find out about it after the way she'd given herself to him the night before. He'd meant to ease her into it. And now, after making love with her and talking to his father, he wasn't even sure if he was making the right decision. For the first time in a long time, he was utterly uncertain which path to take.

"I made the arrangements yesterday," he explained in an even tone that belied the way his heart clawed at his chest. "I would think you would be thrilled, love. Learning at the Sorbonne is every artist's dream."

She shook her head. "Thanks, then, Stef. It's a nice gesture. I have to turn you down." She reached down and picked up the suitcase at her feet. "I'll come back for the rest of my stuff once I find a place to stay. If you need me, I'll be at Callie's for a couple of weeks."

He was on his feet in a second. "What is that supposed to mean?"

He'd expected fire and fury from her. The deep, abiding sadness

was unexpected. "It means I finally get it. You don't want me. You don't have to spend a ton of money to send me halfway across the world. I understand. I won't be some puppy nipping at your heels anymore. But this is my home, and I expect you to be civil when you see me. I'll be nice, too. In a while, it'll all be a distant thing. We'll be neighbors who once had a fling."

His fists clenched, and he felt his face go red. "Neighbors? I'm not your fucking neighbor, Jennifer. I'm your lover, and I'm doing what's best for you. I'm trying to make your dreams come true."

"Your dreams," she said wearily, his anger not moving her a bit. "I know you think I'm some amazing artist, but I want to paint because I love it, not because some critic says I'm the next Van Gogh. Van Gogh's life sucked. If I get to choose a happy, mundane life or artistic immortality, then bring on the babies and the laundry and the date nights. I know you think this is about me, but it's not."

He stalked toward her. His hands itched to hold her and haul her back to the guesthouse. She wasn't going anywhere. Not about her? What the fuck was she thinking? His whole life had been about her since the day she walked into Bliss. "I beg to differ, love. I called in favors, and had my father call in favors, to get you into the program."

"Stefan." His father's tone held a distinct note of warning. "Be careful what you say."

Stef ignored him. He didn't matter at that moment. Only the fact that she was defying him mattered. He might have been able to handle it if she'd fought, but the guilt she was pushing at him was a bit much. He'd been the one to get her out of jail. Now he was moving heaven and earth to make sure she could see the world. He'd called yesterday about an apartment for her in Paris with a view of the Seine and every luxury available. And she called him selfish? "Me? I'm thinking of me? Was I thinking of myself when I got you out of jail?"

"I appreciate that, Stefan."

He hated the way she'd said his name. She never used Stefan, always Stef in that casual, affectionate manner of hers. "I'm sure you do, love."

"But sending me to Paris is entirely about you."

"You're going to have to give me a bit of explanation. I think your logic is faulty." He wanted her to shout. If she would just shout,

he could let out his pent-up emotion. She just stood there looking at him with what he was beginning to believe might be pity.

"I can't quite figure it out, to tell you the truth. I only know it isn't your great and deep love for me that has you shipping me halfway around the world. It's about fear, or perhaps it's a test. Maybe both. You think that if I go off on some grand adventure I'll come back and I'll suddenly be mature enough for you to consider settling down with. But you're wrong. I think you'll just come up with something else. Maybe you'll think I need more time to be successful without you. Maybe you'll decide I'm not ready for kids. All I know is if I do this, you'll be the one making the decisions. You'll be the one deciding what my dreams are and how I'll achieve them."

"Ah, we're back to the King Stefan argument again. Yes, I'm horrible. I pull everyone's strings. Poor Jennifer. I've been terrible to you."

She sighed, her body sagging. "Not at all. You just don't love me."

"I told you I loved you. I said it last night."

"Fine. I'll rephrase. You don't love me enough."

How could he make her understand? "I love you enough to let you go."

"But not enough to keep me. Not enough to let me make up my own mind. I would have been like Stella, you know. I would have been here. I wouldn't have walked out. I can't promise that I won't want more of a career someday. I can't promise that I'll never want to spend time outside of Bliss. But there's a difference between your mother and me. I would ask you to build that career with me. I would ask you to see the world with me because none of it would matter if you weren't there by my side. She didn't leave because she needed more than you could give her. She left because there was something missing inside her, something she never had. She didn't love you. She didn't love your father. The fault lay in her, not either one of you. But I would have loved you. So much. I know I'm probably proving your point by walking out now, but I can't spend the rest of my life proving myself to you. I can't wait around for you to decide I won't ever leave, because I don't think you're ever going to believe it. I'll always

be younger than you, Stefan. I'll always be an artist. And you'll always be waiting for me to leave."

Silence hung in the air, a palpable weight keeping them apart. He stared at her across the space between them and couldn't seem to move.

"Jen?" Callie's voice echoed as she walked through the door. There was a solemn quality to Callie's tone that let him know she'd been informed why Jennifer was leaving.

"I'm coming." She turned and began walking. "Good-bye, Stefan."

She didn't look back.

"Go after her." His father was standing, staring at the door before shifting his focus to Stef.

Stef took a step back, and then another, until he found his seat. He had to force the air into his lungs as the truth crept over him. She was right and had been all along. He'd been testing her and calling it a selfless act. He'd said he wanted to wait until she was ready, but he'd been doing the opposite. He'd been watching and waiting and cocooning her in protection until *he* was ready.

She wasn't the one who wasn't mature enough for commitment.

He turned to his father. "Why did you come back?"

His father pointed to the door. "Damn it, Stefan. This is serious. That girl is leaving you."

"Why did you come back?" He shouted the question, all pretense at civility gone.

Sebastian stepped back, startled. "I came back because I couldn't waste another moment. I came back because I love you, son."

"Is that the only reason?"

His face a chalky white, Sebastian took his seat again. "No. I came back for her. She doesn't seem interested anymore. I can't blame her, but I'm going to try. I came back because I can't live another moment knowing I haven't done everything to make it up to her."

And there it was. The truth. Fear had cost his father decades. It had been fear, not abandonment that had ruined his father's life. Stef sat back as regret swirled through him.

"It doesn't have to be that way for you," his father urged.

Maybe. But maybe he'd ruined any chance he had. Would she believe him if he ran after her? The question no longer occurred to him whether or not he wanted her. He wanted her with all his soul. A new question had arisen.

Did he even deserve her?

* * * *

Alexei yawned and managed to sit up, his muscles pulling and aching slightly from the too-cramped cot. It had not been made to accommodate a man of his size. The station house was dim, the blinds still closed. He stretched and wondered what time it was. He'd managed to get to sleep. He'd been in worse places than the Bliss County Jail. He'd even found the deputy's light snoring somewhat comforting. It was a reminder that he wasn't alone. For the first time in a long time, his dreams hadn't been about blood and loss.

"Don't worry about it, Sheriff. You do what you need to do. I knew I'd be working a lot during the festival." Logan spoke quietly into the phone as though trying not to disturb his prisoner. "I'm fine. Naw, I might have snuck a nap in. I can handle things this morning. Give me the weekend off next week and we'll call it even. Thanks."

Logan put the phone down and glanced his way. "Oh, hey. Sorry if I woke you."

"Not at all. I sleep very good." He wasn't about to return the deputy's kindness with complaints. Alexei felt his stomach rumble.

Logan walked to the front window and twisted the cord that opened the blinds. Sunlight streamed into the room. The street outside was covered in a blanket of snow. A few people walked past the window, long, colorful boards in their hands. "Stella should be here any minute with your breakfast."

If breakfast was as good as his dinner had been, he wasn't sure why there weren't more people in jail. He felt unaccountably cheerful. It made no sense. He was sitting in a small jail, waiting to be taken to a larger jail where he would most likely be interrogated and potentially deported to a place where everyone would want him dead. Yet, he felt a sense of peace he'd not felt in forever. He was going to do the right thing. He was going to bring down Pushkin, but in the

proper way, in the way that would have made his family proud.

"Is the FBI still coming?" He suddenly wanted to get started. He was eager to begin this new life he'd found.

"Yes. They're driving in, though. The airports in Colorado Springs and Denver closed. There's an ice storm. We're good here, but they're going to have to fly into Albuquerque and drive up from there. I hope they know how to drive in the mountains. I doubt they're going to get here until tonight."

Patience. He would have to be patient. "It is good. Is sheriff indisposable?"

Logan's face went slack, his jaw open. "Huh?"

He would really have to work on his English. He searched for the words. "He is working on other things?"

"Oh, yes. He's helping out with the setup for the festival this morning. The finals of the snowboarding competition take place on the mountain today. We're a real small town. Everyone has to help. This festival is our biggest event of the year."

The door flew open, and a small, well-wrapped person stumbled inside. At first, all Alexei could see was a bright blue coat and a plastic bag. Logan rushed to the door and managed to catch the visitor before she went tumbling.

"Hey!" a soft voice fluttered as the woman in the coat was helped to balance by the deputy. "Sorry, Logan. I slipped on the ice. It's getting bad out there. I hope it doesn't hurt attendance. Stella sent me with your order."

"Holly Lang! Everyone's been looking for you. Damn girl, where have you been?" Logan took the bag from her hands, frowning at her.

Holly. He wished the floor would open up underneath him and swallow him whole. Sweet, sexy Holly was here, and he was behind bars. It wasn't the way he'd wanted her to see him. Oh, he knew there was no way he could have any sort of a relationship with her, but she'd flirted with him and shown him her kind nature.

She shrugged out of her coat and stomped her boots on the mat in front of the door to get the snow off them. Her pretty green eyes were on Logan as she replied. "My evil ex managed to forget to tell me our son was going on a retreat with his high school band. Jerk. I only get to see him every other week. He knows how far I have to drive, but

does he call?" Her face was tight for a moment, but she smiled, obviously throwing off her anger. "But I got to talk to him on the phone. He's doing so well. He made the honor roll."

"That's great. While you were gone, two people died and there was a shooting and a stolen painting, and guess who has the key to the mystery?"

Holly had gone still. "Died?"

Logan nodded. "Yep, murders. It's been a regular *CSI* episode around here, except without the bad jokes. Every time I tried to make one or dramatically take off my sunglasses, Sheriff slapped me upside the head."

"I'm about to do the same thing, Logan. Who got killed? Dear god, why didn't someone tell me? Stella was crying when I got in today." Holly looked like she was about to cry, too. It ate at him that he'd had a hand in that.

Logan placed his hands on her shoulders. "It was a tourist. Everyone in town is fine. And Stella's been crying a lot lately. My moms think she's going through the change. I don't know what that means. I try to avoid all talk about feminine parts with my moms."

"So two tourists died?"

"One tourist, and some Russian dude who was trying to kill Jen and Callie."

Her eyes widened. "Oh, my god! I leave for twenty-four hours and this is what happens? I think I met the Russian guy. He seemed so nice."

"It was not me," Alexei said. "It was partner, Ivan. He was not so nice."

Holly turned, noticing him for the first time.

"Hello." Her voice sounded awfully small now that she realized she wasn't alone with Logan.

"Hello."

"I remember you from the diner the other day. You took the Farley twins out. They couldn't stop talking about how nice you were." She smiled at him, her face lighting up. "What did you do? Jaywalking? Nate can come up with a lot of reasons to toss a tourist in the clink, but usually it's because he's in a foul mood. I'm afraid our sheriff is a bit of a character. He only narrowly avoided losing to a

rubber duck in the last election. What was your name again?"

Logan gestured to the cell Alexei stood in. "That's Alex Something Russian. He's a member of the Russian mob, and he's looking for a painting his boss had Jen's old boss steal for him."

"Really? So he's an actual criminal?" Holly looked between the deputy and Alexei as though trying to discern if someone was joking.

"Yeah, but it seems he's reformed. He took out the other fellow and saved Callie and Jen and Callie's baby."

Holly's startled shout echoed though the small building. "Callie's pregnant? Did I miss a newsletter? Damn it. I hate not having a phone. I had to use the Evil Ex's to talk to my boy. The minute I can afford it, I'm getting a cell phone."

Alexei's attention shifted. There was a small group of men walking across the street. He couldn't see them clearly yet, but they stood out. While everyone else was casual, there was a certain formality about these men that had him staring. They wore black coats in a sea of colorful, fun parkas.

Logan continued to talk to Holly, poking at her like an annoying younger brother. "Yes, that would have been helpful since you're the one who knows who has the painting everyone is looking for."

A cold chill went through Alexei's body. Was that? Dear god, that looked like Luka. Luka was one of Pushkin's top men.

"I do?" Holly asked.

Luka turned and pointed at the same building that housed Alexei. Bile bit at the back of his throat. The phone. His phone had gone off all night. It hadn't bothered Logan, but the trill had awoken Alexei several times. He'd thought it might be his cousin. Now he knew who had been so determined.

Logan gestured toward the cell. "This guy came to town looking for a stolen painting. Apparently Jen's boss in Dallas hid it. It's behind one of the paintings Jen gave you to sell. The one for Rachel. You sold it to someone, but we can't read the receipt."

Now Alexei could see that Luka had two other men with him, Oleg, Luka's brother, and Pushkin himself. His hands tightened around the bars. Pushkin had come after the painting. Alexei knew Ivan had called in and informed Luka where they were going, but he'd never imagined that Dimitri Pushkin would come himself.

217

"Oh, well, that was—"

"Is that my food?" Alexei interrupted them with a short bark. He had seconds to decide what to do. A plan flashed through his brain. It was probably a terrible plan, but it was all he could come up with. The three men were moving with purpose toward the office. There was no time. If they walked in, they would simply kill anyone in their way. At least this way they had a chance.

Logan picked up the Styrofoam container and walked toward the bars. "I think it's pancakes and sausage."

The minute the deputy was in reach, Alexei reached out and grabbed him by the neck. He heard Holly gasp. The tall deputy didn't weigh much. It was easy to haul him close and grab the gun out of his holster. Alexei turned him quickly, pulling his back against the bars. He wrapped an arm around the deputy's neck. He could break it if he wasn't careful.

"I need you to be listening. There are very bad men be coming into station house. They will kill you both unless you do this right."

"Yeah, well, I'm getting the feeling you're the one who is going to kill me." Though Logan's voice was steady, it was soft. A fine tremble went through the younger man. "You get out of here, Holly."

"Don't. If you run, they will stop you. They will be here in seconds." He softened his hold but didn't let Logan go. There wasn't time to run. Pushkin and his men crossed the street, moving ever forward, snaking through the crowd toward their destination. "You cannot to tell where painting is. If you tell, you die."

"Fine. If I don't tell?" Logan asked.

"You be beaten badly." The deputy would be tortured, and Alexei would have to wait and watch until he could gain the advantage.

"Why should I trust you?" The question came from between gritted teeth.

He put his heart and soul into his reply. He had to make Logan believe him. "Please to trust. Please, I can't…I can't take more killings. I will help as soon as I can, but there are three of them and one of me. I will have to go with them for while. But help will come. It will."

There was no time to get Holly out. She stood staring at them, terror in her eyes. He had to deal with her, too. Pushkin was at the

door. The outer doors opened with a swooshing sound. In a moment, they would be inside, and he wouldn't be able to explain.

"I need you to listen, Holly. I want to see you safe. You must to take the gun. Hold it on the deputy like you are trying to get me out. You are my ho."

Her spine snapped to attention, and her green eyes flashed. She took the gun from him anyway. When their fingers touched, Alexei felt a jolt of connection. "I am so not your ho."

Panic threatened to overtake him. "You must pretend. If you are mine then they will not rape your body and slit your throat."

Logan nodded, his head tapping against the bars. "I think you should be his ho, Holly."

"Fine, but I'm not happy about it." She held the gun out, her hands trembling.

The door opened, and Luka walked in first, with Pushkin behind him.

"It took you long enough." Alexei switched to Russian. "I was beginning to believe you would leave me to rot in this hellhole."

Pushkin surveyed the room while Oleg bolted the door. "I suspected something had gone wrong when neither you nor Ivan would answer the phone. Ivan told me you were having difficulties. I do not like difficulties, so I come myself. I'm not happy, Alexei. The trip was horribly long, and we had to drive through a storm. Where is Ivan? And who is the girl?"

"Mine. The girl is mine." He brought his arm back through the bars, freeing Logan, who slumped to the floor as though overwhelmed. "Holly, dearest, you can put the gun down now. These are my friends. I told you about them."

He sent a silent prayer that she would be able to play along. They were locked in with men who wouldn't think twice about raping and killing her. Oleg prowled around the room, looking for anyone else they might have missed. He was too close to Holly for his comfort.

The gun came down at her side. "Does this mean we can get out of here, baby?"

Luka reached down and hauled Logan to his feet. "You open the door and let my friend out."

Logan stumbled a bit as he dug into his pocket for the keys. His

eyes came up and met Alexei's. There was a wary plea in his gaze, but there was strength there, too. The deputy was young, but a stubborn will lit him now.

The cell swung open, and he grabbed Logan by his shirt, pulling him forward savagely. He brought him close and whispered. "Survive. Tell them you know nothing. I won't leave you, but you must survive."

"Just get Holly out," the deputy whispered.

Alexei let his voice rise as he shoved Logan back. "I promised you payback, you swine."

The other Russians laughed.

"Did this skinny thing give you trouble, Alexei?" Luka asked, his Russian dark and thick with menace.

"He's like all pigs. Police are the same everywhere." He stalked out of the cage and slid an arm around Holly, pulling her close. He slid the gun from her hand to his, the weight a welcome burden. He was armed. He would find a way. *Patience*. But first, he had to get to the bad part. "Ivan is dead."

A loud curse filled the room.

"How?" Pushkin grunted the question.

"I can guess." Oleg brought his booted foot out and kicked the deputy squarely in the gut.

Alexei's arm tightened around Holly as she stiffened. He saw how she bit back a cry. This would be hard on her. He pressed her face into his chest. "It wasn't this cop. It was the sheriff. Ivan was foolish. He killed a girl and didn't do a good job hiding the body. The police came after us, and Ivan pulled his gun. I knew I could escape with Holly's help. I thought it was better to stay alive."

Pushkin circled Logan like a shark playing with its food. "Where is this sheriff?"

Logan's throat worked up and down. "At the festival. He won't be in today. I was only in because we have a prisoner."

A predatory smile crept across Pushkin's face. "I noticed you have *Closed* sign on your door. That is quaint...and helpful to us. Tell me something, Alexei. Do you know where the painting is?"

This was the bad part. His gut felt tight as he did what he had to do. "I don't, but he knows. He talked to the sheriff about it. They have

stashed it. They don't mean to turn it in. They mean to sell it. Like I said, police are the same everywhere."

Oleg reached down and brought Logan's head up by his brown hair. He spoke in thickly accented English. "This is true?"

"I don't know. I don't speak Russian, asshole. I have no idea what any of you has said for the past couple of minutes." Logan's whole body was tense, but the words spat from his mouth.

Pushkin slapped him, the sound reverberating through the room. He switched to heavily accented English. "Then let me speak your language. You will tell me where my painting is."

"Can't help you, buddy. I don't know nothing about art. I'm just a country boy." Logan's face was bright red, the imprint of Pushkin's hand plain on the skin.

Pushkin snapped, and Oleg began to drag Logan toward a desk in an office at the back of the room. It was far from the front door. That desk would serve as Logan's torture chamber. All the while Luka watched Alexei, his gun close at hand. His eyes were on the woman in Alexei's arms. He got the feeling Luka wasn't convinced that all was as it seemed.

He would have to wait.

He prayed Logan would survive the experience.

Chapter Seventeen

Stef's first instinct was to find her. His second instinct was to tie her up, throw her over his shoulder, haul her ass back home, and never allow her to leave again.

That was why he was attempting to ignore his first instinct.

"You want to hand me that rope, or are you going to hang yourself with it?" Rye stared at him, his hand out.

Stef passed him the rope but thought seriously about hanging *him* with it. *Asshole.* Rye had it all. Rye had a wife and a brother and a baby on the way. Rye never fucked things up the way he did. If Rye had been Jennifer's lover, he wouldn't have hesitated. Rye rarely questioned himself, and his easy confidence pricked at Stef's finely held temper. Still, he'd come here to look specifically for Rye. He was restless, utterly uneasy, a need rolling in him that was going to find its way out. He'd realized he could pick a fight with Max or Zane or he could try…talking about his feelings. He just wasn't sure where to start. "Here you go."

Rye took the rope and started to put together the corral. He and Max were expanding their pony rides. It had been a big hit yesterday, with long lines of kids waiting to ride the gentle horses. He couldn't help but think about the fact that it wouldn't be too long before Rye's

son would be learning to ride. Rye's son would grow up in Bliss. He would run wild in the wilderness with his brothers and sisters like he and Max and Rye had.

A sudden image of his own kids running around Bliss and sleeping on the mountain made his heart feel too big for his chest. He would have told anyone who asked that he didn't want kids, but he'd lain awake last night thinking about the fact that Max and Rye's and Callie's kids would be here soon. Everyone was talking about the fact that Callie was pregnant. He wanted kids. He wanted his and Jennifer's babies to grow up with their cousins.

"Are you going to talk about it or did you come here for a nice long brood?" Rye asked as he pulled on the knot he'd tied.

Brooding hadn't gotten him anywhere. "I'm afraid."

Rye tipped back his hat and placed one hand on his hip. "I know you are. You've always been afraid of this."

He was startled by the statement. "What does that mean? I've never had a real relationship until I met Jen."

Rye nodded. "That would be my point. Hell, even Max had a girlfriend or two. I've known you most of my life. The truth is I don't remember much of a time before I knew you. I watched you push away most people."

"I didn't push away you and Max or Callie."

"We're safe. You needed us, and we needed you. And you made damn sure we needed you."

This was a dangerous conversation. Without meaning to, he even took a step back. "I don't know what you mean."

"Stef, it's nothing to be ashamed of, but it's become a habit with you, and it needs to stop. You buy people's affections, at least that's what you think you're doing. We met during the summer. I remember it like it was yesterday. When Max, Callie, and I were going to have to go back to school, what did you do?"

God, he felt like he was fucking eight years old again. Vulnerable. Needy. Desperate to keep his newfound friends. "I asked my dad to bring in a tutor because the bus trip was so long into Del Norte."

"Is that really why you did it?"

He shook his head. He remembered, too. He remembered

pleading with his father. He hadn't needed to. His dad had been more than happy to do it. His father had paid for tutors for the Bliss kids from that point on. They'd converted part of the mansion into a schoolroom that had housed them through high school. "No. I was afraid the three of you would get to school and find other friends, and I would be out."

"I know, brother." Rye walked over and put a hand on his shoulder. "I know that's why you did it. I know that's why you built the town hall, and that's why you give loans to anyone in Bliss who needs one and never charge interest or even ask them to repay you."

The money didn't bother Stef. His father had set up a trust fund he would never be able to get through in one lifetime. "If they can, they will. If they can't, then I won't miss the money."

"Stef, you throw money around this town."

King Stefan. He could hear Jennifer say the words in his head. *Pathetic.* He was still a boy trying to tie people to his side.

Another voice spoke up as Max walked around the side of the trailer. "Man, you have to know that we don't love you because you paid for our school."

Max's face was bunched up, his brows forming a *V* over concerned eyes.

"He knows," Rye said with more confidence than Stef felt. "He just lets a lot of the past get in the way. He's real damn good about figuring out everyone else's motivations. He's not so smart when it comes to his own."

"Is that why Rach keeps calling him a dumbass?"

He felt himself stiffen. "Your wife has very little respect for me."

Rye shook his head, a laugh escaping his lips. "Our wife loves you. But she thinks you're wrong about Jen. I remember the day Jen walked into town looking for you. She wanted art lessons or something."

"She'd made a study of my work. She wanted me to mentor her." When he thought about it, he'd taught her a few things, just nothing of value. He hadn't taught her how much he loved her.

"She tracked you down to the diner," Rye continued.

Max smiled at the memory, obviously caught in it. "Stella thought she'd have to toss you out. You two sat there for eight hours

talking and arguing."

He'd been in love with her about twenty minutes after meeting her. She'd been so vibrant. She'd argued with him about the importance of the Impressionists and held several wrong views of the eminent Jackson Pollock, but he'd been utterly fascinated with her, hanging on to her every word.

"And the next day, you told her politely that you didn't teach art and holed up in your studio for three weeks," Max said.

He'd brooded. He'd worked. He'd done just about anything to avoid that girl with the killer smile and a saucy comeback to everything he said. He'd been afraid of her then. He was terrified now. Only now, he was starting to be more afraid of being without her.

"You think you're sending her away because you want her to have the things she needs, but, damn, you're trying to make her grateful to you," Rye pointed out. "Can't you see this is the same thing as what you did back when you were a kid? You think you can buy her a career and she'll be happy and grateful, and she won't leave you because you made it possible."

Max nodded sharply. "Rach is right. He's a dumbass. Jen already loves him. No woman puts up with the shit he's shoveled out if she isn't in love."

"He thinks she's too young, but she's not. He thinks she wants some megapowerful career, but she doesn't," Rye said. "She wants to live here in Bliss and paint and have a happy life with the man she loves. You took me aside the day I finally got together with Rachel, and do you remember what you said to me?"

"I said she's ready." Stef felt his heart seize. What if she really was ready? What if he was just a dumbass who let his past hold him back? What if he chucked that past aside and went after what he wanted?

Rye and Max looked at each other, doing that weird twin thing they'd always done, as though, at times, they spoke to each other without saying a word.

"She's ready, Stef. Go get your girl," they said in perfect harmony.

A blanket dropped over his soul, a warm, perfect feeling of

complete certainty. She was his. He was hers. They didn't have to follow anyone's path but the one they set themselves. She wouldn't leave. If she wanted to see the world, she would turn to him and tell him to show it to her. And he would. If she wanted to show in galleries, she would turn to him and ask him to help her. And he would.

He was her slave, and she would never leave him behind.

"I've got to find her." Now that he'd made the decision, he couldn't stand the thought of a moment going by without telling her. Telling her? Hell, he'd probably have to beg her. Maybe if he offered to turn the trip to Paris into a honeymoon, just maybe, she wouldn't attempt to cut off his balls with a rusty knife.

"She was with Rachel and Callie. They were heading to the diner," Rye said.

Nope. If she was with Rachel, she would definitely try to cut his balls off. He smiled at the thought. Jennifer was a lot like Rachel, brave and unwilling to take a bunch of crap from anyone. Except him. She'd taken his crap for a while now, and he swore he'd never give it to her again. He had other things he wanted to give.

The phone in his pocket rang. He reached in and pulled it out, hoping it was Jennifer. It wasn't. He slid the bar to answer the phone anyway, stepping away from Max and Rye. He couldn't ignore this call.

"Finn, what's up? Have you managed to get the charges dropped?" He prayed the answer was yes. Before this moment, he'd been willing to allow justice to move slowly. Jennifer couldn't start her new life until the charges against her were cleared. Now that her new life would be with him, he wanted that cloud out of the way immediately. He was doing it again. He was trying to give her what she wanted, what she needed, so she would be grateful. He wasn't going to change. He would always move heaven and earth to get her what she wanted. But from now on, he would make damn sure it was really what she wanted. "Give me some good news, man."

"The charges have been dropped." Finn's voice came over the phone loud and clear. "The DA filed the papers this morning. As of 8:00 a.m., your girl is free and clear."

He clenched his fist in victory. Now nothing loomed over them.

They were both free and clear. "Finn, you've done an excellent job. Please let your Master know how much I appreciate everything you've done for me. I'll talk to my father about transferring some of Talbot Industries' legal work your way. We're always getting sued for something."

Finn laughed over the phone. "Don't get me wrong, Mr. Talbot, I would love the work, but I didn't really have much of a hand in this. The police found the painting."

"What do you mean they found the painting?" He stopped, his feet halting as though a wall had been thrown up in front of him. The painting was supposed to be here. Why had those Russians come to Bliss and taken Jen if they weren't looking for the painting? "The police found the Picasso?"

"Yes, it was hidden in a vault at the gallery. I have no idea what kind of games Renard was playing, but they go deep. The guys at McKay-Taggart connected him to the mob, believe it or not. Taggart is still worried about a couple of things, but I personally think everything is fine. He's a little on the paranoid side."

A cold feeling stole over him that had nothing to do with the temperature. "The Russian mob? What is Taggart worried about?"

"Yes, that's what he found out. Big Tag didn't like how things went down so he pushed the investigation a bit. But I don't think it has anything to do with Jennifer. Renard did odd jobs for the mob, but he was specifically involved with something called the Pushkin Syndicate. The Russians have started to make a fortune selling masterpieces lost during World War II. They turn up now, and the mob is selling them on the black market for extravagant sums. Apparently Renard served as a go-between. Guess he screwed up somewhere. I'll send you a copy of the report. Taggart is an expert on the Russian mafia, it turns out." Finn sounded confident, even as Stef felt his stomach doing a triple loop dive straight to his feet. "And tell Jennifer that while going through Renard's records, we found an order for one of her paintings. Renard was holding it for a buyer. It looks like she's doing well. Twenty-five-thousand dollars is a lot for a new artist. Maybe she can still talk to the buyer, now that she's out of this mess."

But she wasn't. Oh, she wasn't even close to being out of it.

Taggart had been right to not stop. This had never been about the damn Picasso. It was about the very paintings he himself had brought with them, the ones Jennifer had put in the auction. She was right in the middle, and she didn't even know why or what they were really coming after her for, though Stef had a horrible idea. "What else was Taggart worried about? She's never gotten that much for a painting, Finn. I bought the others."

Finn paused as though realizing something was wrong. "Shit. Uhm, Big Tag said he didn't like the fact that apparently Dimitri Pushkin left Moscow yesterday morning. He took a private plane, but Big Tag has some sources who can check passport records. He landed in Denver late last night. Do you think…"

He shoved the phone into his jeans. Without pausing to say good-bye to Max and Rye, he took off running for the diner. He had to find her and find that painting.

* * * *

Jen sniffled and dragged great breaths of air into her lungs as she sat in a booth at the diner.

"Asshole." Rachel slapped at the table in a much-appreciated show of female solidarity. Rachel had shown up at Callie's cabin just as Jen and Callie had gotten back from Stef's. The women had commiserated with her before Rachel announced she needed breakfast.

"He's my best friend, but I'm with you on this one, Rach. Asshole." Callie's sweet voice always sounded odd when she cursed.

"Fucking asshole." Zane's did not. Zane sounded perfectly comfortable calling Stef all sorts of vulgar names. His huge frame dominated the booth at Stella's.

She felt stupid. Here she was crying in the middle of a diner. She'd managed to hold on to her self-esteem for a little while. She'd gotten to Callie's. She'd moved her pitiful belongings into the loft, climbing up the ladder into Callie's childhood room. There was a mattress on the floor and a small dresser. She'd sat on the cot and stared out at the mountain knowing Stef was sitting in his place. She'd sat there for an hour wondering if he even noticed she was gone.

Why did she have to love an idiot?

"It's not working," Zane whispered to his wife. "You said it would work. I think she's still broken."

"I am not broken." She frowned at Zane. He sat looking so manly and hunky hot. Now he was madly in love with his wife, but he and Nate had put Callie through the ringer once, too. It was just what men did. "And you're an asshole, too."

Zane's handsome face lit with surprise. He stared at Jen openmouthed before turning back to his wife, obviously seeking wisdom. "Why am I an asshole? I drove you to pick her up. I cleaned out the loft so she would have a place to not be homeless in."

Jen sniffed, a nasty feeling in her gut. She didn't particularly want to have anything to do with men right now. It didn't matter how nice he'd been to her. "Do you have a penis?"

Zane stared at her like he suspected the question was a trap. "Last time I checked."

"Then you're an asshole." She couldn't help it. She picked up her napkin as a sob escaped. God, she ached. It was a real, physical pain.

Rachel's hand came out, patting Jen's back. "Let it out, sweetie. Don't hold back just because one of them is around."

"One of them?" Zane asked, clearly confused at his persona-non-grata status.

Callie sighed. "Yes, baby. You have a penis. That makes you the enemy right now. Jen just broke up with the love of her life. Do you really think she wants to be comforted by you?"

"Max heard Jen broke up with Stef. Did you see how he treated her? He tipped his hat and ran the other way," Rachel explained as she wolfed down her pancakes. "Rye wouldn't even get out of the truck until she'd walked on by."

"I couldn't leave Callie," Zane explained. "I haven't trained an overgrown dog to follow her around."

Q's head came up over the table. His tongue came out as he looked at Rachel's plate. She patted his head to settle him back down.

"Don't you dare," Callie said.

Jen listened to her friends. They were trying to be helpful. They were trying to be supportive, but they had families and futures. Rachel was just about to give birth, and Callie had announced she was

pregnant like five minutes ago. Jen wasn't anywhere close to being ready for a baby, but she knew damn well she wouldn't want any baby but Stef's.

She wasn't going to have a family. She looked at big, gorgeous Zane, who worshipped the ground his wife walked on to such an extent that he was willing to share her with his best friend. Rachel had two husbands. Jen couldn't even keep one man interested in her. Nate and Zane and Max and Rye wouldn't let their wives out of their sight, but Stef was willing to send her to France for years.

She couldn't help it. The tears started again.

Zane's wide green eyes were huge as he stared at Jen in abject horror. "Oh, wow, just let me kill him. Would that make her stop crying? I can't stand it."

Jen growled his way. Her friends were right. She didn't want to be around men right now. They all sucked. "I want to cry, asshole. You, go away."

Zane scooted out of the booth after kissing his wife on the forehead. He pointed toward the counter. "I'm going to be right over there, babe. Out of the line of fire."

He practically ran away.

Callie shook her head before reaching out to her. "I'm sorry. He means well."

"I know." Everyone meant well. Stef meant well, at least he thought he did. Meaning well had broken her heart. She could still see his face as he'd worked over her the night before, still feel his arms around her. God, how was she going to get through the rest of her fucking life without him?

"Jen, are you sure about this?" Now that Zane was gone, Rachel had softened, sympathy plain on her face.

"I have to be." She meant what she said. She couldn't spend the rest of her life with a man who was waiting for her to leave. "He planned out my whole future and made sure he wasn't in it. I don't know if he meant to talk me into leaving or just flat out shove me on a plane."

"I know." Callie had heard the whole story told to her in between Jen's sobs. "But you love him. He doesn't know what he's doing. Maybe if you talk to him..."

"And say what?" She'd thought about it, thought about going back to the big house and having it out with him again. "Look, I love him. I think I'm going to love him for the rest of my life, but I kind of love me, too. If I hang around for years and hope that one day he'll see that I'm worth the risk, I don't know if I'll be able to respect myself."

"She's right." Rachel rubbed her hands along her lower back as she spoke. Her back had been bugging her for the whole time they'd been together this morning. "What's she supposed to do? Put her life on hold because one man is a fool? Oh, I hate this."

Jen put aside her own misery briefly. "What's wrong?"

Rachel shook her head. "Stupid Braxton-Hicks. I've been having them for the last couple of weeks."

"That's false labor," Callie supplied. "A lot of women get it. It prepares you for real labor."

"It prepares you to want to kill yourself." Rachel tucked a piece of strawberry blonde hair behind her ear, a grimace of pain flashing across her face. "She's so bright-eyed about this. I was that way, once, before I gained four hundred pounds, started having to pee every five minutes, and waddled like an overstuffed penguin. And I have two more weeks of this."

Callie's face lit up. "And then you'll have a baby."

"Yeah," Rachel replied, her hand going to her stomach.

Stella walked up, coffee pot in hand. She was made up as usual, but there was something a tiny bit duller about her this morning. She'd obviously been crying. After hearing Sebastian's story, she had to think his being in town had brought up old emotions for Stella. Her heart had broken for the older woman with each word he'd spoken. As she'd stood there listening, she'd heard a bit of her own future in the story. The connection between Stella and herself had been clear. Stella always seemed so alive and happy. What heartache had she harbored all these years? She'd never married. As long as Jen had known her, Stella hadn't even dated. She'd built her life around this diner and Bliss and raising Stef.

Would that be her life, too? Would she throw herself into her work because she couldn't have the man she loved? It would be ironic if she ended up with the kind of career Stef wanted for her. And

empty, because he wouldn't be there to share it.

"Do you need some coffee, hon?" Stella asked, her smile not quite reaching her eyes.

"I'll take some. I'm the only one not on mommy restrictions." She held her cup out.

"God, I miss coffee." Rachel leaned over and breathed in the aroma.

"Stella, I thought you were working at the festival today? Aren't y'all selling lunch for the snowboarding competition?" Callie asked.

Jen hadn't thought about that. The whole place was being cleared out for the noon start of the finals of the competition. Everyone would be on the mountain watching it. Downtown would be quiet this afternoon. It would be a good time to check out the town hall. There was a bulletin board there with job listings and places to rent.

"I just talked to Zane about the festival," Stella explained. "He's going to help out. I'm shorthanded. He's a good man, your Zane. He's helping out with the short-order line while Hal makes sandwiches and salads."

"Ah, learning at the feet of the master," Callie said with a grin. "Zane doesn't consider it a favor. He loves it. He's been taking cooking lessons from Hal. Last week it was something French."

Zane stepped in beside Stella, a plate in his hand. "Beef bourguignon, babe. And it was a bit salty. I'll get it right next time. Here's your bacon, Rachel."

As Zane slid the plate across the table, Callie's face went slightly green. Her hand flew up, covering her mouth.

"Oh, I'm going to be sick." She slid out of her side of the booth and started to sprint for the bathrooms. Zane ran after her, not bothering to stop at the ladies' room door.

"Yep, she's pregnant." Rachel sighed and bit into her bacon. "The smell of bacon gets to some women. Not me. This baby boy likes meat."

A wistful smile stole across Stella's face. "Max and Rye were always like that. Their momma would have to fight to get them to eat a vegetable. Not Stef, though. He ate everything I put in front of him."

Jen felt her eyes tear up. At least Stella had Stef to lavish her love on. She looked up at Stella, wondering if there was still anything left

besides bitterness. "Sebastian came back for you."

Stella's shoulders squared after a moment of pure surprise. "That's what he said. But he's gone through something terrible. Many people make illogical decisions when they think they're dying."

Rachel's head moved back and forth, as though she was watching a tennis match. "Sebastian came back for Stella?"

"He loves you," Jen said. "He knows it was a mistake to leave."

"Oh, my god. Stella had an affair with Stef's dad? Does Callie know? Do I know something before Callie?" Rachel asked.

"You hush," Stella admonished. "This is old gossip. No one will care about it. I'm surprised Sebastian even talked about it around Jen."

"He didn't know I was there. He was telling Stef."

Stella blanched. "He told Stef we had an affair?"

"Yes," Jen said. "He told Stef that the worst mistake he ever made was walking away from you."

"It was." Sebastian's voice carried across the diner. Jen turned, and he was standing there in the aisle, hat in his hand. "It was the stupidest thing I ever did because I threw away the love of my life. I thought of you every day. You were my first thought in the morning and the face I pictured in my mind before I went to sleep at night. When I was in chemo, I sat in the chair and I pretended to hold your hand. I pretended you were there. I told myself that if I lived, I would come for you. I would come into this diner and sit here until I made you understand how much I love you."

Tears streaked down Stella's face, but she held her head high. "You might have pictured my face, but that isn't the face I have now, Sebastian. I'm an old woman now. That time is long past."

"Then I'll start a new time," he said, nodding resolutely. "And you aren't old, Stella. Never. You're still the most beautiful woman I've ever seen."

"I don't know if I can forgive you," Stella said, her hand clutching the coffeepot like a shield.

Sebastian's eyes studied her, and his lips curled up in a sad smile. "Well, I'll wait until you decide. I'll wait a day, or a month, or a year. I'll sit at the counter and hope you smile at me. I'll make a life in Bliss so I can be part of your world. I'll wait as long as it takes, and if

it takes longer than this life, then you should know, Stella Benoit, that I'll wait in the afterlife, too. I'll wait forever."

She set the coffeepot on the table. It clattered, utterly forgotten and useless because Stella was walking toward him.

"You better not change your mind, old man," she said as she walked into his arms.

"Never," he said, pulling her close. He buried his face in her hair, his arms closing around her, knitting them together.

"That was so beautiful," Rachel said, turning to Jen. Her face was bright red, and tears poured from her eyes.

Jen felt her own tears as she put an arm around her friend and let her cry.

It had been beautiful.

"I can't do it," Jen whispered, more to herself than anyone else.

Rachel smiled through her tears. "Of course, you can't."

She looked down, startled. "How do you know what I'm talking about?"

"I've been where you are. I know what you're thinking. You can't stand by and let him go. You have to fight. This isn't something you can let slide. He's your man. You fight for him. If you have even the smallest doubt in your head that this isn't over, then you go after him with everything you have. I never thought you were going to give up."

"Even when I ran away?" Jen asked, a light feeling stealing over her. She could still fight. If Sebastian could come to his senses after all these years, then Stef could, too. Not that she planned on letting nearly thirty years go by. His skull was going to soften up more quickly than his father's.

"Yes," Rachel said. "I knew you would come back. Tell me you hadn't thought about it."

She'd dreamed about it every night. If things hadn't gone horribly wrong, she would have been home by summer. The day before she'd been arrested, she'd sat down and written a long e-mail to Callie. She hadn't sent it, but she'd saved it. Eventually she would have sent it, and Callie would have replied, and she would have allowed herself to be "talked into" coming back. "I would have come back. I love him. I love him so much."

"I know. It'll work out, Jen. You'll see." Rachel wiped her eyes with her napkin. She turned in her seat to face the newly happy couple. "Hey, Stella, why don't you call someone in so you can take the afternoon off?"

Stella's face was vibrant as she faced Rachel. Sebastian's arms were around her, and she threaded her fingers with his as though she couldn't stand the thought of losing contact. "I have Holly. She can handle this crowd. I'll head out when she gets back."

The mention of that particular name reminded her she had to deal with the painting. "Holly's back?"

Stella nodded. "Yeah, she came in this morning. She wasn't scheduled, but you know her, she's always looking to take an extra shift. She has to pay that greedy ex of hers, or she never gets to see her kid."

Rachel was already moving. "Where is she? Does she know Nate's been looking for her?"

"No," Stella replied. "But I sent her to the Sheriff's Office. Maybe that's why she's taking so long."

Jen scooted out of the bench, following Rachel. It would be such a huge relief to get that damn painting back. Then she could concentrate on convincing Stef to give them a real shot. "Thanks. I'll send Holly back as soon as I'm done talking to her."

"I'm coming with you." Rachel grabbed her purse. "Don't you leave me behind. You'll be surprised how fast I can waddle."

Jen took her hand. "No, I wouldn't. I've seen you go after Max when he's obnoxious. Come on then. Let's find that stupid painting, and then I can find Stef."

It was a short trip from the diner to the Sheriff's Office, just three buildings in between and a hop over the street. The Sheriff's Office was housed in a small building off Main Street. Rachel walked behind her, only slowing her down a bit. The air was brisk, and the snow was falling lightly. The crowds had thinned out after the early morning rush. They would be on the mountain where the day's competition was getting started. It made the streets of Bliss nice and quiet. Only the park would be bustling at this point. The rest of Bliss was a bit of a ghost town. She made it to the front of the office first and pulled on the outer door. It was locked. She banged on it.

"Logan, wake up!" she yelled as she pounded on the door. Logan was not known for being the most dedicated deputy. He could often be found napping or reading comic books with his earbuds in. "Logan!"

"Stop that," Rachel said, frowning. Beside her, Q sat down and stared up at the women. "You're going to wake the poor boy up. I know where Callie hid a key. Nate throws Max in jail often enough that she let me in on the secret hiding place."

Rachel reached under the sign that proudly proclaimed this place to be the Bliss County Sheriff's Office and pulled out a small magnetic box.

"Only in Bliss would someone hide the key to the Sheriff's Office," she said, shaking her head.

Rachel slipped the key into the lock and turned it. She started to open the heavy outer door that led to the swinging doors inside. She stopped suddenly. "Why was the door locked? Didn't Stella say she sent Holly with breakfast? Logan wouldn't lock the door after Holly."

Jen paused as she stepped inside, Rachel behind her. "I don't know. Do you think something's wrong?"

As she got the words out of her mouth, the answer became apparent.

"You must to come in now, Miss Jennifer." Alexei stood in the doorway, his bulky body blocking the entrance, a gun fisted at his side.

Jen watched in horror as he leveled the gun, aiming it straight for her head. Yep, something was very, very wrong.

Chapter Eighteen

Jen couldn't quite catch her breath.

"It's a woman." Alexei's dark voice was tossed over his shoulder, but his eyes never left her. They were hard as steel. "What should I do with her?"

Utter confusion made her head spin. Alexei was out of his cage, and he had a gun in his hand. She could hear a conversation going on in the office, but she couldn't see past Alexei. Someone was speaking, his voice rough, almost guttural. It was a language she didn't understand. It had to be Russian. Oh, god, Alexei's mob friends were here. He'd tricked everyone into believing he was on their side, and now he'd taken over the station house.

"It's just one woman, Oleg. I think I can handle her."

Rachel took a quick step back.

He was letting Rachel go. He had to know she would go for help.

He looked past Jen at Rachel, and he gave her a barely perceptible nod before reaching out and grabbing Jen's arm. She turned her head as fast as she could and saw Rachel disappear as the outer door closed.

"You are not Jennifer," Alexei quietly whispered in her ear as he pulled her into the room.

"Jen?" Holly's voice trembled.

She heard Alexei curse under his breath, but it looked like whatever game he was playing, this piece was blown. Her heart pounded as she tried to assess the room. She saw Holly standing by Logan's desk, her face white as a sheet, but she appeared unharmed.

The shortest of the men stepped forward. He was dressed in a suit and tie, his graying hair slicked back. He was older, but by no means soft. He said something in Russian as he looked her over. Alexei replied, his manner slightly deferential, as though he was speaking to his boss. He finished and nodded slightly.

"Hello," the boss said. "My name is Dimitri Pushkin. You are Jennifer? Renard's Jennifer?"

Jen was somewhat startled at the sound of Renard's name. She knew she shouldn't have been, chided herself for it. He was the asshole who had gotten her into this situation in the first place. "I worked for him."

Alexei moved to Holly's side. His arm slid around her shoulder, hauling her close. All the while, he held the weapon casually at his side, yet his eyes never left the other two men in the room. It was like Alexei was watching two snakes, waiting to see which would strike first.

Had this man and his goons shown up, leaving Alexei with another decision to make? He'd let Rachel go so it felt like he was still on their side.

"Yes, and it seems you worked against him, too." Pushkin walked up to her, his finger lifting to her chin. She forced herself to stay still under his scrutiny. The Sheriff's Office wasn't exactly the biggest building in town. She found herself against the reception desk with no real place to run now that the doors were locked again. Her only hope was that Rachel still had the key. She glanced at the clock. 10:23 a.m. The streets were deserted, but Zane was still at Stella's. All Rachel had to do was get back there and get Zane. Zane would bring everyone else. She had to hold on. Her people wouldn't let her down. She had a whole family and they would come for her.

"I don't know what you're talking about, mister." Ignorance might buy her a few minutes.

"I am talking about the painting I purchased. I would like it

back."

"I don't know where the Picasso is." It was the truth. She had no idea, and it was apparent that Alexei didn't want Holly to talk. The minute Pushkin had started toward Jen, his hand had tightened on Holly's shoulders, as though in warning.

Pushkin's eyes narrowed. "I don't give a shit about the Picasso, and you know it. I want the painting I purchased from Renard. Your painting."

Now she wasn't feigning ignorance. She was truly confused. "My painting? But my painting is the one that Renard hid the Picasso behind."

Pushkin stared at her with cold, dead eyes. "Silly girl. That's what I told my employees. Trust me, what is hidden behind your work is much more valuable than any painting to me. Now, you can tell me where it is, or you can join the deputy."

That was when she heard it, a low moan coming from Nate's office. It sounded like an animal in pain. She tried to dismiss the notion that the person who made that low, utterly hopeless sound could possibly be happy-go-lucky Logan.

There was a humorless chuckle from Pushkin. "Americans. I see you are shocked. This is because you are the world's children, every one of you. You believe that life is innately fair when the rest of the world knows that it is not. You tell yourself that pain and horror, these are things that happen to other people. Certainly not to someone as privileged as yourself." He leaned in. She could feel the heat of his breath snaking over her skin, smell the stink of cigars on him. "But I am your teacher. The world is not fair, little girl. It is not some amusement park."

There was the sound of something thudding and then that long, low moan that ate at Jen's soul. She felt her jaw clench and angry tears prick at her eyes. "You're a monster."

The door to Nate's office opened, and a man stepped out. He looked something like the man backing up Pushkin. He had taken off his coat and jacket at some point in time, laying it over a chair. He was stripped down to a white T-shirt that was now splattered with blood. She didn't want to grasp the implications of that bright red blood. He said something in Russian and shook his head.

Pushkin grunted his reply before slipping back into English. His lips curled up in a satisfied smile. "You call me a monster? I am. Do you know anything about history, little girl? I find so few Americans do. Back in Rome when the gladiators would fight, the patron of the games would stand at the end of the fight, and he would decide the fate of the loser. If he gave a thumbs-up, the man would live. But that did not happen often. He would more likely give the thumbs-down, and the loser would fall. So much life lost on the simple placement of a thumb. But the Romans understood. There are only a few people in the world who truly matter. The powerful people of this world are the important ones. The rest are all slaves who have forgotten their places. Your deputy is learning this lesson right now. He learns that his control was an illusion. His life is not his own, and it never was. He was merely waiting for someone important to show him his place."

Impotent rage choked her. "You let him go."

"Now, why would I do that?" Pushkin asked. "He has offended me. He arrested my man, kept him from doing a very important job for me. More importantly, I don't care. He is nothing, a bug that I squash beneath my feet."

Logan, sweet, funny Logan, was at this man's mercy, and he had none. She couldn't help it. Her hand came out, and she slapped him for all she was worth. Flesh met flesh in a satisfying smack. The man who had been standing by the door was suddenly at her side, his thick, meaty hand tight around the arm she'd hit Pushkin with.

"Don't break the girl." Pushkin barked the order. He gave no indication that he was at all affected by her small act of violence. "Yet. This one has claws. I believe you will discover mine are longer and sharper than yours. You will tell me where the painting is, and I will give you a quick death."

All the more reason to be happy she had no idea where the damn thing was. Pain might be in her future, but Rachel would be back. Rachel would bring Zane and Nate and, god, she wanted Stef. She wanted to see him and hold him and have him tell her she was going to be okay. The thought of never seeing Stef again, never holding him, was too much to bear. She had to endure whatever this man handed out because she had to be alive when Stef came for her.

"I don't know." The world was fuzzy through her tears.

Pushkin frowned and turned to the man in the bloodstained T-shirt. "Luka, go and finish off the deputy. We need the space for another interrogation. This one will be more fun for you, no?"

Alexei whispered something to Holly, who turned her mouth up to his and let him kiss her, their mouths pressing together in a way that seemed staged to Jen. He stopped Luka with a hand to the other man's shoulder. "I would do this myself. I am the one he stuck in a fucking cage like dog."

Luka looked to Pushkin, who nodded his assent. "Let Alexei have his blood. You will have the girl's soon enough since her tongue seems unwilling."

Luka smiled at her, a dark, wicked thing. "I think I will use different strategy with such a pretty girl. We'll see if I can fuck the information out of her."

Pushkin laughed as the men disappeared behind the door.

It was only a moment before she heard the shot that ended Logan's suffering.

She heard Holly gasp and placed a fist in her own mouth to stop the wail that threatened.

She looked at the clock. Ten thirty.

Stef would be here. Stef would come for her. It was a mantra in her head. She closed her eyes and prayed.

* * * *

Stef slammed into the back of the café at exactly 10:25. He pushed through the doors from the alley and into the kitchen as Zane was carrying a distinctly green Callie out toward the parking lot and his truck.

"Hey, you okay, Cal?" Stef stepped around Hal, who was busy making sandwiches.

She smiled wanly from her big brute's arms. "I'm fine, Stef. Just a little pregnant."

"I'm going to take her home now that the morning's fun seems to be over," Zane said, looking a little green himself. "Tell Nate where we are if you see him."

"Sure thing. Where's Jennifer? Max said she was with Callie and Rachel." He tried to keep the panic out of his voice.

Zane shrugged. "Don't know. I left her with Rach. They must have left while Callie was heaving half her body weight in the bathroom."

"Gross." She smacked Zane in the chest, but Stef didn't miss the way she cuddled against him as though she could draw his strength into her body.

Zane kissed the top of her head before turning his attention back to Stef. "If I see her, I'll let her know you're looking for her. You try her cell?"

"She's not answering." He turned and saw Stella at the counter. She was talking to his father.

Zane and Callie continued out toward the parking lot. Stef stalked to the counter, pushing through the swinging doors, a restless feeling in his gut.

He didn't fail to notice that Stella's hand was in his father's, their fingers entwined. He was happy for them, but he couldn't let that take precedence over his need to find Jennifer and that painting.

"Stella, where did Jennifer go?" Stef asked, well aware that his voice was gruff.

Stella's face looked years younger as she turned to him. Her hand never left Sebastian's. "She was here a couple of minutes ago. She and Rachel went to find Holly."

A deep voice spoke up from Stef's left. "Holly came back?"

He glanced at the doctor, who was sitting at the end of the counter, sipping a mug of coffee, and it hit him. Who the hell else in this town would let Holly talk him into buying a painting for far, far more than it was worth right now? One day Jennifer's paintings would be worth more, but for now, they were only of interest to investment collectors. Holly couldn't know that it was worth anything. Who would she sell it to? Who else but the man who had walked into town and promptly fallen in love with her? Oh, Caleb hadn't made a single move on her yet, but the man brooded enough to let the world know he was crazy about her. As a man who had spent an enormous amount of time brooding over a female, he knew the signs and could diagnose the good doc's disease.

242

"Where did you stash the painting?" Stef asked, unwilling to waste a ton of time.

Caleb sat up straight. "The painting? I don't paint."

Stef bit back a moan of frustration. He'd already forgotten? "The one you bought from Holly?"

Caleb's eyes suddenly found his coffee mug as though he was seeking something there. "Oh, that. Yeah, I loved that painting. So beautiful."

"Cut the crap. Everyone knows you have a thing for Holly."

"No, I don't. I'm married." Caleb shook his head, running his hand across his face. "I mean, I was married. I…it's too soon to think about anyone else. Holly is just a nice girl."

Caleb's wife had been dead for five years, but Stef wasn't about to argue with him. "Where is it?"

He shrugged, as though content to put the other line of conversation behind him. "I put it in my office. It's in a closet. I haven't had time to hang it up."

It would have to do for now. "Good. Keep it there. Don't let anyone into your office until I get Nate off the mountain. Stella, try calling him. If that doesn't work, someone go down and wake Logan up. I have to find Jennifer and get her somewhere safe."

"Didn't Jennifer go down to the Sheriff's Office?" His father had already pulled out his cell and passed it to Stella.

The door to the diner slammed open and a dog barked, a deep and protective sound. He looked up as Rachel stumbled in, her hand on her belly. The minute he saw her, his gut clenched because she was in trouble. Rachel's face was red and Quigley danced around her, the big mutt's distress obvious. Everyone left in the diner was on their feet in a heartbeat. He managed to get to Rachel before she fell over.

"Oh, god, not again." She moaned as her whole body seized and pain contorted her face into a grimacing mask.

Stef held her up, feeling the way her whole body went tight.

"Rachel, how far apart are the contractions?" Caleb knelt beside her, his hand finding her wrist. For all his tics and odd mannerisms, the minute he needed to, he became a cool, calm professional.

She shook her head. "No contractions. It's just a little pain."

Stubborn. It described Rachel to a T. Stef tried to settle her

down. "Rachel, I see your stomach seizing. You're in labor. I can tell, and I don't have a medical degree."

"I can't have the baby now," she said, her voice hitching with every breath.

"I don't think he's going to wait." Caleb put a hand on her belly. "I need to get you back to the clinic. I don't know that we have time for a hospital. Besides, you have to have the baby. Your jeans are soaked. I have to think your water broke. No turning back now. I believe I explained to Max that it wasn't like someone dumping a glass of water on the floor. He didn't listen to me, hence the dog is still here. Come on. Let's get you to the clinic."

"No!" Rachel forced herself to sit up. She held on to Stef. "I have to get back to Jen."

The air around him seemed to go cold. "What's wrong with Jennifer?"

Rachel opened her mouth to speak, but her body wasn't her own again. A low wail came out. "Fuck. I hate this. I hate this. Please, I want my husbands. Please."

"Damn it." Caleb cursed for a few seconds and got to his feet. "Stella, we're having this baby here and now. She's probably been in labor all day and was too stubborn to admit it."

"It's too early. It's too early," Rachel said through her tears. "Please, Stef. They have her."

"Who?" He was trying to be patient. "Rachel, you have to tell me where Jennifer is and who has her."

She gritted her teeth as she tried to get up. "Sheriff's Office. We went to look for Holly, but the place was locked. I knew where the key was, and Alexei took Jen. He pulled her inside, but he let me go. He was talking to someone. I don't know how many are inside, but they have the building under their control."

He cursed inwardly. If only he'd walked around the front of the building, he might have seen Rachel and gotten to Jen sooner. Habit had brought him to the kitchen entrance. He'd come to Stella's this way since he'd been a child.

He had known he should have killed that son of a bitch. He wouldn't make the same mistake again. He would kill the Russian as soon as he could, and if he could make it painful, it would be for the

better.

Rachel doubled over and screamed in pain. Quigley whined and tried to lick her face, offering the only comfort he could. Stef reached over to a table that appeared to have been recently vacated, picked up the half-full glass of coke, and dumped it on the floor beside the dog. Quigley immediately took off, his huge body easily pushing through the swinging doors.

"There, Rach," Stef said. "Q will go get Max if we can't get him on the phone." He turned to the doctor, who was running antibacterial gel all over his hands and forearms. "I have to go."

Caleb nodded and took Rachel's hand. "I know you do, but I can't leave her. Stella is calling Nate, and she'll call Zane back if she can get him. You'll have backup as soon as possible."

Stella rushed forward. "Don't you dare go after her without this."

She passed her Colt .45 to him. He felt better having the weight of the gun in his hand. He checked the chamber and pocketed the extra ordnance she gave him. Stella went on her toes and kissed his cheek lightly.

"You come back with her. You understand me? You come back safe," she said tightly, her eyes glazed with unshed tears. "You're my boy. I don't care who gave birth to you. You're my boy."

"Yes, ma'am," he replied, a wealth of love for her filling his heart. She'd been his mother in every way that counted.

His father stepped forward. "Stefan, I'll come with you."

He looked at his father. His frail father was willing to go into god knows what with him. Jennifer had been right. It was past time to forgive him. Sebastian had made mistakes, but he was trying to fix them. One day his father wouldn't be here, and he wouldn't be able to work through their problems. The time to fix things was now. He put his arms around his father. "I appreciate it I do, but I'll move better on my own. Stay here. I'll come back. Dad, lock the doors after me. Shut the blinds. Unless you know the person, don't let anyone in. Stella's is closed for the day."

He jogged out the door. In the distance, he could see Max and Rye running down the street from the park, but he didn't have time to wait and wasn't sure he should. Their son was about to be born. He couldn't wait for Nate and Zane. He had to get to Jennifer, and he had

to do it fast.

His mind racing with a thousand horrific scenarios, he tried to narrow his focus as he moved between Stella's and the gallery beside it. He crossed the street and went behind the town hall to get to the alley behind the buildings. He couldn't go in the front door. It didn't make a lick of sense to grab the painting and try to negotiate. The mob didn't negotiate. And how exactly would he negotiate? No, he had one option and one option alone.

Kill them all.

He slowed as he reached the Sheriff's Office. He thought about the building. Nate's office was closest, and there was a small bathroom attached. The window was supposed to be permanently shut, but Rye had broken the lock years before during a summer heat wave when the air-conditioning had gone out. On quiet feet, Stef moved toward his destination. What had already happened to Jennifer? How much pain and fear had been handed to her by a bunch of monsters?

He forced himself to quell the panic threatening to overtake him. Rushing in and getting himself killed wouldn't help Jennifer. He wasn't sure how many of them were in the building, but they would all have guns. Mobsters had guns, probably more than one apiece. He would have to be careful and hope that Nate was careful, too. To that end, he quickly pulled out his cell and sent a text. God only knew if Nate would get it. The only sure way to get a hold of him while he was working was to call on his police radio, and the equipment for that was currently surrounded by the mob.

But he doubted they had all the bases covered. They could lock the front and back doors, but he knew how to work this particular entrance. As quietly as he could, he pressed in on the lower pane of the window. His ungloved fingers were bitten by the cold, but he had to move with great care or he might make a sound that would alert them. Jennifer was counting on him. Slowly, surely, he pushed the window open and gripped the sill, hauling himself up and over. It was tight, but he fit, lowering himself to the tiled floor of the bathroom. Someone was moving in the office, heavy footsteps slapping against the floor. There was the sound of a door closing and the footsteps moving away. Adrenaline pumping through his system, he eased the

safety off the Colt and listened at the door. He could hear people talking but couldn't make out exactly what they were saying. They were out in the main part of the station house. He gently turned the doorknob and opened the door slightly, wincing at the creak.

Nate's office had been trashed, his pictures and files tossed carelessly to the floor to make way for the body that lay atop it. Bile rose in his throat when he realized the body was in a bloodstained khaki uniform with a silver star on the chest.

Logan.

His chest rose just barely, as though only a thread of life remained.

Stef's hand tightened on the gun as the outer door opened.

He shrank back, waiting for the perfect time to pounce.

Chapter Nineteen

Alexei followed Luka into the small office, his every nerve vibrating with tension. He'd begged Holly to stay calm, whispering into her ear, promising her he would save her. How was he going to save her? Any way he looked at it, he lost, and that meant she would lose as well. The minute he revealed himself to be less than the perfect soldier, he would be killed, and his "woman" would be fair game.

Three against one. He had to find a way to even up the odds before he took the chance.

And then Pushkin had thrown it into his lap. He'd told Luka to kill the deputy.

This was his shot. No one would know that he'd killed Luka instead of the deputy until he walked out of the office, guns blazing. It would give the women time to run. It would give them a chance. That was all he could ask.

His heart was racing, his hand trembling. He had to do this right, or he would let them all down.

"The boy was utterly useless," Luka said in Russian as he approached the body on the desk.

The deputy's hands had been bound with the telephone cord. His

long legs dangled off the edge of the desk. They were still, so still it scared him. Was the deputy already dead? His face was a bloated mess, seemingly a mass of blood and bone and tissue with nothing to animate it. Alexei had seen this before, but now it made him sick. This young man had done nothing to deserve his pain.

"Ah, well, at least the girl will be more fun." Luka laughed as he pulled his gun. He put it to the young man's forehead. Logan lay still. If he knew how close to death he was, he didn't show it. Or perhaps he'd moved to a place where death was welcome.

He whipped up his own pistol to kill Luka before he fired, but the report of gunfire blasted through the room, making his ear ache. It hadn't come from him. Had he been too late? Had he already failed? His heart nearly stopped as Luka turned and fell to his knees. The gun fell useless at his side. He began to bleed from the back of his head as he slumped to the floor.

A man moved from the shadows where he'd clung like a wraith. Long and lean, the dark man slid into the room. His gun still smoked, heat flowing off it, but his eyes were arctic cold.

"Give me one good reason not to kill you."

He remembered this man. Jennifer was his woman. He'd come for his woman. Alexei dropped his arm to the side, along with the gun. He kept his voice very low. "Because they will believe one shot, not two."

"You were sent in here to kill Logan?"

He nodded. "I was not going to do it. I was going to kill Luka. You were faster."

"A nice fairy tale." The man's voice was as cold as his eyes, but he seemed to listen to reason since Alexei wasn't dead on the ground like Luka. "But I don't know why I should believe you. I doubt Logan would believe you."

"I don't blow the sunshine up your asshole." He had to make Talbot understand. There were two of them. They had a better shot if they worked together.

"Don't, Stef." The words were quiet, but Logan's lips moved, and his bound hands came up. He spoke through cracked, bleeding lips. "Don't kill him."

Talbot's face finally showed a flicker of emotion, a grimace of

pain for his friend. "Don't talk, Logan. I'm going to get you out of here."

"There's no way out. No way," Logan muttered and mumbled something unintelligible.

"We must to move quickly," Alexei said, fumbling for the English words. "Pushkin be expecting Luka. He is supposed to torture the girl."

Talbot's face hardened again, his will implacably marked there. "How many?"

He finally let out a breath. The man was willing to be reasonable. "Only two, but the women are out there. Holly and your woman are out there. Pushkin was interested in your Jennifer. He thinks she knows where his painting is."

"No, she doesn't, but I do." Talbot pulled a knife from his back pocket. It was a utilitarian knife, and he used it to free Logan's hands. The deputy groaned quietly as he tried to flex them.

"It will not matter. He will not make bargains with you. He will say one thing but do another. If you offer a trade, he will kill everyone. He has to." He'd seen Pushkin in action far too often. He was a snake, and he would turn on anyone if he saw a profit in it.

The dark-haired man nodded. "I thought as much. He can't leave us alive. He certainly won't believe we won't call the authorities. So we have to kill him. You willing to do that?"

A malicious joy lit Alexei's heart. He'd done the right thing. He had offered to give up his revenge, but now it landed in his lap as though the heavens had decreed it be so. He could save his soul and kill the man who had taken his brother. "Oh, I have waited many years to do such a thing. But I won't have women harmed. I would rather he go free than risk them."

"I would rather get the lay of the land. We can't just walk out shooting. We could hit one of the women."

"Holly knows what I do. She is supposed to cause some chaos. How about we cause some chaos of our own?"

Talbot hesitated, but Logan managed to reach out and take his hand. Talbot looked down at the deputy. He could only get one eye open. The other was swollen shut. Logan swallowed before he spoke. "You can trust him. They would have killed me and Holly. He told us

what to do."

"He's the reason we're all here," Talbot argued.

"Is there a problem, Luka?" The throaty Russian voice rang through the building.

Talbot's entire body tensed as Alexei clutched the doorknob. It was time to decide.

"Are you in the in door or going to the outs?"

Talbot snarled, but stepped forward. "If I live through this, you're getting English slang lessons. It's just 'are you in or out.'"

Alexei raised an eyebrow.

"Fine. I'm in."

Alexei opened the door. It was time to finish it. For good or bad.

* * * *

The shot was still ringing in Jen's ears as the fact of Logan's death washed over her. Logan. Sweet, funny Logan had been shot. How was he gone? Why had Alexei allowed it to happen?

"Stop crying, you sniveling bitch! Do you have any idea how much I hate you?" Holly stormed across the room toward her. The sweet-looking redhead had a scowl on her face normally reserved only for soap opera actresses in the middle of a big scene. "I hope Alexei kills you himself."

Holly launched herself at Jen, hitting her squarely in the torso, and both women hit the ground.

She was caught completely off guard and felt the breath knocked out of her.

"Sorry. I'm supposed to cause a distraction. Alexei was going to kill the other guy and save Logan. Get ready," Holly whispered in her ear before pushing herself up. She straddled Jen and pulled back her hand.

The younger man, Oleg, grabbed her fist, laughing. "You are a righteous bitch. Alexei chose well."

He hauled Holly up by the back of her shirt. Jen found herself up against Logan's desk, staring up at Oleg and Holly. Logan had left his drawer open, and as she attempted to get up, her hand slid across the comic books he kept there, causing her to fall again. She reached up

again, and her hands met something wooden. She couldn't see it, but she knew what it was. Logan's whittling knife.

"Calm yourself, girl." Pushkin stepped between Holly, who looked like she was auditioning for a ladies pro wrestling tour, and Jen. He snarled at the red-haired waitress. "Watch it. Alexei is not the boss here. I am. I don't like trouble, or the people who cause it."

While Pushkin made his speech, Jen grasped the knife in Logan's desk. It was small, with a one-and-a-half-inch blade and a wooden handle. Logan had brought it into the diner, swearing he was going to quit his deputy job and make a living whittling bears and wolves. He'd been awful at it, and the knife had disappeared.

She slid the blade, handle up, into the pocket of her jeans and then stumbled to her feet. It was tiny, potentially useless, but it was all she had.

"What is taking so long?" Pushkin asked, stepping toward her, a scowl on his face. He grabbed her arm. "Are they taking apart the body? Tell Luka to toss the body to the side. I want to get this done."

Oleg turned to the door. "Is there a problem, Luka?"

The door to Nate's office opened, and Jen felt her heart drop to the floor. Alexei moved out of the office. Stef—her beautiful, strong Stef—was in his grips. A gun was pointed straight at his dark head, the metal at his temple. Alexei had one of Stef's hands behind his back for leverage as he pushed him along.

"Yes, there was trouble," Alexei said. "I found this one lying in wait."

Oleg cursed and said something in Russian.

"I am sorry," Alexei said flatly. "He kills your brother."

Oleg spewed what had to be something vile. His face became a wicked shade of red. He pushed Holly aside and started toward Stef.

"Oleg!" Pushkin shouted across the room.

It felt like the world slowed down. One minute everything was far too fast and the next was horribly, painfully slow. She tried to run to him. She had no idea what she would do once she got there. She only knew she couldn't watch Stef die. He'd come for her, like she'd known he would, and the outcome of that act couldn't be his death. She took one step and then another before she felt a hand on her arm, pulling her back.

Oleg's gun came up, his movements jerky as though rage had taken over and there was clearly only one thought on his mind. She screamed, pulling against the hand that held her, but his strength ensured she couldn't get away. Futilely she tried, panic overtaking her, but the fist on her arm tightened, hauling her back as his other arm raised a pistol.

She heard Holly scream and hit the floor, covering her ears as a loud report boomed through the building. Gunfire cracked through the air, at least two shots going off, but it was Oleg who jerked backward as though he had hit a wall and bounced back. It was Oleg whose chest bloomed with blood.

Alexei pushed Stef lightly away as he shot Oleg again. Stef's right arm came from behind his back, and he had a gun, too. She watched as he aimed his gun, but his eyes lit with horror before he could pull the trigger. Stef stepped back as she felt an arm snake around her middle. Her back was suddenly pressed to Pushkin's chest, and his meaty arm was a manacle holding her down. He was using her as a shield. She squirmed, trying to do anything to get out. He hauled his weapon up and fired. Jen felt her eyes widen in horror as Stef took the bullet. A spot on his left side above his waistline started to bleed.

He staggered back for a moment, but managed to stay upright, his gun level at Pushkin's head. "Let her go."

She could feel the heat of Pushkin's breath against her ear as he spoke. "I don't think that is such a good idea. I believe I will keep the girl close, or I will end up like Oleg there."

"And if I told you I don't care about the girl?" Stef asked.

"I would not believe you," Pushkin replied. "You came for the girl. That is the only reason you are here. If you were simply working with the traitor, Alexei, you would have left the same way you came in. Tell me something, do you know where my painting is?"

Stef looked far too calm for a man who had just been shot. "I know enough to know you don't give a shit about the painting."

There was a low rumble from Pushkin that might have been described as laughter had there been an ounce of humor in it. "No, I don't care about the fucking painting. But I do want the bearer bonds behind it. Alexei, you appear unwell. Did Oleg's shot find purchase?"

Alexei did look a bit green. He put his hand over his gut and

came away with blood. He fell to his knees. Holly scrambled from her protected position to get to him. Even with a hole in his gut, Alexei pushed Holly behind him, trying to cover her body with his damaged one.

"I'm glad you're dying, you bastard. I never trusted you," Pushkin said. "There was something about you."

Alexei struggled as he spoke. "You kill my brother. I have worked, risen in your organization, to kill you. You will die here. Whether by my hand or others, you will die today, and you will take no more innocents with you."

Holly wept behind him, trying to get her hand on his wound.

Pushkin accepted the information as though it was a mere report of the weather and not a curse. "I did not know what was wrong about you, but I felt it better to keep you close. When I heard you changed course and were coming to Colorado, I was worried. I decided to come to the country in case something went wrong. When I couldn't raise Ivan, I became suspicious. That's why I brought along another three men. They should be here any moment. I've had them asking questions and looking for the painting. But I sent the signal for them to come to me. Soon, you and your friends will be a distant memory."

Jen heard the sound of gunfire, but this time it was from the outside of the building.

Stef's lips quirked up. "I have friends, too. We'll have to see who walks through that door, won't we? Or you can give me my woman, and I'll allow the sheriff to arrest you."

Pushkin took a deep breath, and the gun pressed to her temple. Such a small circle pushing against her head, and yet it could bring death in no time at all. She wouldn't even know it had happened. Pushkin could pull the trigger and everything she was would be gone.

"I love you, Stef." If she was going to die, those would be the last words she said because they were true. Nothing in this world had ever been as important as loving Stefan Talbot.

His stance hardened. "Jennifer, I will get you out of this. I love you. I will not let you go. You will not go to Paris without me. You will not move into that tiny loft at Callie's, and you will never leave Bliss."

Even with a gun to her head, she had to smile at the royal tone he

used. King Stef was in the building. "I already moved into Callie's place."

"Then get ready because I'm moving in. It's going to get crowded on that twin bed, but I won't sleep apart from you. You wanted me, well, you get me. I'm very possessive, and according to everyone in this town, I am also emotionally needy. I disagree, but the votes are against me. You should know I intend to love you forever, Jennifer. I intend to keep you with me or follow you when you go."

"I won't go, Stef. Not without you," Jen said, her heart filling up with love.

"That includes dying, Jennifer," Stef said sternly. "You are not allowed to die on me. I will take it as extreme disobedience, and there will be some punishment."

His voice was starting to shake, whether with emotion or pain or the combination of both, she wasn't sure, but it didn't matter. They were together. It brought her great strength. There was the sound of more gunfire outside, but the reports were getting further and further apart.

"It sounds like my men will be here soon," Pushkin said. "Now, tell me where my bonds are and I will kill you quickly. Otherwise, you will join that unfortunate deputy."

"Yes, I'd like to kill you for that, too." Stef snarled.

"Someone needs to do something," Holly said, crying. "I don't think he's going to make it."

Alexei's body was still, but his lips moved. He said something to Holly, who cried out and lightly slapped his shoulder.

She looked at Jen. "He won't move. He says I have to hide behind him. I can't get him off me, the big idiot. He's going to die."

"You are all going to die," Pushkin said.

"Not if I can help it." Logan's voice was ragged and his face brutalized past recognition, but he forced his body to move. He propped himself up in the doorway of the office and took aim. Logan's left arm hung at an odd angle, and his right trembled, but he held the gun level despite it all. "I don't have a shot from here, Stef."

"You don't need one," Stef said. "Nate is going to walk through that door any minute."

They were in a standoff and she wasn't sure who would win. All

the men on her side were injured and Pushkin was still healthy and whole.

She slipped her hand into her jeans pocket, her fingers curling around the whittling knife. Alexei had asked Holly for a distraction, but it looked like they needed another one. With Pushkin's eyes on Stef and Logan, he wouldn't notice that she was squirming a bit more. When she had the knife out, she held it at her thigh so Stef would notice.

"I tire of this," Pushkin said. Jen could feel that he was sweating now. He was starting to panic, and that could be bad for her.

Stef's eyes found the knife at her side, and he nodded, letting her know he was with her.

"I'm pretty fucking tired myself," Logan spat out.

"Jennifer, Nate is going to walk through that door," he repeated, as though his surety could make it happen. "He's going to come in here, and we're going to be fine. I love you with all my heart. Do you trust me?"

She nodded, far too emotional to speak. She heard the outer doors swinging open.

"Then do it now!" Stef commanded.

She raised her arm and plunged the small knife into Pushkin's leg. It didn't go deep, but it was enough that he howled and reached for his leg. It was enough that he let go slightly, and she was able to drop down.

She felt the bullets hit Pushkin's body. He jerked behind her once, and then twice, and then again. Jen covered her head, the ringing in her ears almost painful. She made herself as small a target as possible because Stef needed her out of the way.

The sound of bullets died away as the inner door burst open, and Nathan Wright's voice boomed through the building.

"Stand down!" Nate shouted.

"There's no one left to stand down, Sheriff. You are late to the party," Stef said.

She felt his hand on her shoulder and looked up into gray eyes. She jumped up and wrapped herself around him, relief pouring through her like a waterfall. He was here and alive, and that was all she could ask for. Stef's arms tightened around her body, so tight she

256

almost couldn't breathe, but she wouldn't complain. She needed him close.

"I love you, Jennifer."

"I love you, Stef. I love you so much."

Nate and several others were moving in. "Zane, call a bus."

"Why do we need a bus?" Jen asked, trying not to look at the bodies on the floor.

"It's cop slang, love. He's calling in an ambulance."

Max Harper strode into the room, a shotgun in his hands. "Is everything fine now? We killed everyone we needed to? 'Cause my wife is having a baby in the middle of a diner. I wouldn't be here except Rachel made one of us come down here to save Stef's butt, and she was yelling really loud. I'd like to make it back to see my son."

The doctor pushed through the double doors. He had an apron on and held his hands up as though he'd just sanitized them and didn't want to touch anything. "Better luck next time, Harper. You just had a girl. Sorry about that. I'm not real great with sonograms. Is there anyone left alive for me to fix?"

The doctor's face fell, and suddenly all of his bravado was gone as he saw Holly trapped under Alexei's body.

"Holly?" He ran to get to her.

Holly reached an arm out to the doc. "Please, Caleb. He saved me. You have to help him."

Chaos reigned as people poured into the small building. Zane helped Logan to sit. Nate checked the bodies. Max ran out, shouting something about his son not having a penis. Stef held her close, and she seemed far away from the horrors of the day.

"Don't ever leave me." His voice was a mere whisper in her ear.

"Never."

Chapter Twenty

Stef stretched slightly, trying to loosen up the tight feeling in his ribs. Jennifer turned and cocked a single eyebrow at him. He put his arm down.

"Hah!" Max said from his seat at Rachel's bedside. He sat in what must be one of the world's most uncomfortable chairs with a baby sleeping on his chest. "I saw that, Stef. You are just as pussy whipped as the rest of us. That is good to know."

"Maxwell Harper, that was rude." Rachel threw a stare at Max that might actually peel paint off the walls.

Max clutched his daughter and nodded at his wife. "Yes, baby. It was rude. I am so sorry." He turned back to Stef and pointed at himself. "See, we're all the same."

Jen chuckled beside him. "I don't want him to pull his stitches. The doctor told him not to move too much for a few days. I need him happy and healthy. He's supposed to take me to Paris for our honeymoon."

"Don't you have to get married first?" Rye Harper asked as he walked in the room, followed by Callie. Both carried trays of food.

Stef reached out and grabbed a cookie. He thought it looked like one of Laura's. She was famous for her chocolate chip cookies. Almost everyone in Bliss had been in and out of the hospital over the last two days. They had come to coo over the new baby or offer

support to Logan. They had come to sit with Holly while she held the hand of a man she barely knew, but had saved her life.

"Give them time, Rye," Callie said, offering Rachel a sandwich. "It takes a while to plan the kind of wedding Jen wants."

He turned to his fiancée. He had heard nothing about an elaborate wedding. "No Vegas, then?"

The smile on her face did funny things to his heart rate. "I suppose we could elope for some quickie wedding we'll soon forget. Of course, the honeymoon would probably match it."

He snorted. His woman never let her opinions go unstated. It was one of the things he loved about her. If he forced her into a quickie wedding, he would get quickie sex. While he was pretty damn sure he could change her mind about that, he was an indulgent husband-to-be. His father, on the other hand, hadn't been willing to wait. He smiled as he thought about the fact that his father was actually in Vegas. He'd married Stella, and they would come back to Bliss in a week. Stella and his father would live in the manor house. Stella was finally coming home. Yes, a big wedding was exactly what they needed. "We'll pull out all the stops then, love. We'll have a wedding like this town has never seen."

"That sounds like fun," Rachel said, happily munching on her sandwich. She scooted up so Rye could slide in behind her. His arms wrapped around his wife as she leaned back against him. "Callie and I can help."

Jennifer practically glowed. "You better. You're my bridesmaids. I need one more, though. I think I'll ask Laura. Maybe she'll teach me how to walk in five-inch heels."

"Nope," Stef said, pulling her close. God, it felt good to reach out and grab her whenever he wanted to. "I like you shorter than me."

"Unless this wedding takes place in the next month or so, I'm going to be a whale." Callie's face turned down as Nate and Zane walked into the room. It was getting full fast.

"Never, babe. You're going to be gorgeous all round and full of baby," Zane promised, towering over his wife. Zane softened around Callie. The hard lines of his face fell away.

He wondered if he looked like that when he stared at his Jennifer. He thought he probably did, but he didn't care. She was his. She

would be his always. It didn't matter that he had to wait for the wedding. He already had another ceremony in mind. He'd talked to his friend in Dallas and had a private collaring ceremony planned. Jennifer would never be a full-time submissive, and he didn't want that, but, oh, they would play. They would play for the rest of their lives.

"You want to see it?" Nate asked as he pulled out a file folder. In his hand was a small stack of what looked like certificates.

Whoa. Yeah, he wanted to see. He'd never seen a bond like that before, much less a stack. He ran his hand across the bonds that equaled enough money for Pushkin to kill for.

"That's twenty million dollars?" Jen asked.

"Yes, those are untraceable security bonds. It's a practice that dates back to the Civil War. It was the only way to get this much money in a neat, movable pile without involving a bank. The US Federal Reserve is trying to get rid of them, but they're still out there," Stef replied. "From what Nate, Zane, and I have managed to figure out, this was payment for a long-lost painting Pushkin sold on the black market to a collector here in the US."

"The Russian mob is making a fortune on black market masterpieces smuggled out of Germany during World War II. Pushkin used Renard to restore them, and then Renard acted as the middle man. He got the painting to the buyer and then smuggled the payment in bearer bonds to Russia via lesser paintings," Nate explained.

"Hey!" Jennifer crossed her arms over her chest.

"Nathan knows nothing about art, love," he said, kissing her neck. He loved the nape of her neck. It was soft and always smelled so good. He felt himself getting hard, but then he was always hard around her. "You have to discount his opinion."

Nate shrugged. "Sorry, Jen, but he was planning on using your painting. Apparently, he refused to ship twenty million dollars across two continents. Alexei and the dead guy were supposed to fly back with it. They couldn't put it in a suitcase because airport security does random checks. This was the way he'd found to work it. He hadn't counted on you changing the paintings."

"And that's why he had me arrested." Jen put two and two together. "He panicked. He had me arrested so he could search my

place and take the bonds back."

Renard had waited too long. "But I got there before he could. The minute I heard she'd been arrested, I had people at her place, packing her up to get her back to Bliss. Nate and I were there a couple of hours after the arrest. Renard tried to be clever."

He didn't like to think about what could have happened to her. He was damn grateful Renard had chosen the path he had. He could have simply killed her and taken the untraceable bonds the mob required as payment.

"It's all right," Jen said, as though sensing his thoughts. Her hand came up and smoothed across his cheek. "Everything is fine now."

"The feds are coming for Alexei tonight." Nate leaned against the wall. The long hours he'd put in the last few days showed on his face. Callie reached for his hand, and he pulled it up to his heart. The three of them were connected and content to be so. "They'll take the bonds into evidence and clean out our makeshift morgue. Is our doctor staying, or did we run him off with our latest clusterfuck?"

Max's eyes came open, and he put a hand over his sleeping daughter's head. "Will you watch your language, Sheriff? There is a child in the room."

"Sorry. After the way I heard she came into the world, I didn't suspect she would have delicate ears," Nate shot back.

Rachel wasn't at all embarrassed. "I did cuss a blue streak."

"And threatened grievous bodily injury on me and Max," Rye added.

Rachel waved them off nonchalantly. "Well, I was in a touch of pain. But the next one, I doubt I'll even go to the hospital. I'll probably just squat, have the baby, and then get back to work. I'm like a pioneer woman. I don't need a hospital. I'm only here because Caleb made me."

Rye and Max had both gone sheet white. "Don't you even think about it, Rachel Harper," Rye said.

"You're going into the hospital the minute you get pregnant. I won't have our next baby born in Stella's," Max said, patting the baby's back. "My poor little princess."

"I see Max got over the shock of having a daughter." Jen chuckled as she watched the huge badass man with a tiny baby girl.

"No, he hasn't," Rachel said with a sigh. "He's just moved on to paranoia mode. He's talking about setting up a defensive perimeter around our place."

Max gestured toward his daughter. "Well, look at her. She's gorgeous. Men are going to come sniffing after her, and I have to be prepared to kill them all."

Callie was grinning at the sight, too. "Wouldn't it be great if we had a boy and he and little Paige Stephanie got married?"

"That is not going to happen, Cal," Max shot back. "Paige is going to be a nun."

"We aren't Catholic, Max." Rachel turned to look at her more reasonable husband. "Tell him, Rye."

Rye nodded. "Max and I talked it over, baby. We're converting. Paige is definitely going to a nunnery."

Rachel shook her head and sighed. "And, I don't think we can scare Caleb off. He's too interested in a certain someone to leave."

Caleb had saved Alexei. His efforts had been heroic. He simply wouldn't give up on the big Russian. Alexei was alive because Caleb had willed it so. He had a bad feeling that Caleb might rue the day. Alexei seemed crazy about Holly, and Holly was obviously grateful, if not simply interested in him. Alexei had a long road to walk, though. He might be in prison. He'd promised to do what he could to help. He owed the man his and Jennifer's lives. Alexei would go with the feds and answer their questions, but Stef would try to make sure the man didn't spend the rest of his life in prison. If he wanted to go home, Stef would try to get him there. If he wanted to come back to Bliss, well, there was always room for one more.

"I'm glad the doc is staying. But Callie needs to beware. Don't let Doc do a sonogram," Max complained. "He can't tell the difference between girl parts and boy parts."

"And how is Logan?" Rachel asked, changing the subject.

"Healing," he said carefully. Logan's body was starting the process, but Stef didn't like where his head was at. He'd been silent and sullen and utterly unlike Logan. He hadn't flirted with the nurses. He'd sat in his bed, and it was easy to see he was building a wall around himself, letting no one, not even his moms, inside. Zane had tried to talk to him, but he'd been rebuffed. Stef would have to keep

an eye on him.

King Stef. He was doing it again, but now he didn't feel bad about it. Jennifer could tease him all she liked, but he was the King of Bliss in some ways. What he'd come to realize was that he hadn't earned the title by throwing money around. He'd earned it by loving this town and all of her citizens. He loved them even when it was hard. He would love them until the day he died, right here in Bliss.

"I'll make sure he has a nurse on call when they're ready to release him. And Nate, don't forget to have Hope file his paperwork. Anything he needs outside of what the county can pay for, send me the bill."

Jennifer turned her face up, and he knew what she was going to say. "You really are good, King Stefan."

"And I'll be even better with a queen at my side."

"Forever," Jennifer said, going up on her toes for a quick kiss. "I think I'll like being queen."

"So, let's plan a wedding!" Rachel said with a happy smile on her face.

Jen joined her friends and started planning the biggest day of his life. He would have his father at his side, and the woman who was his true mother would be there, too. He would have his family and all of Bliss.

The women planned, the baby slept, and the men talked about the events of the day. Stef sat back and watched, utterly content.

All was right in his kingdom.

* * * *

Holly, Caleb, Alexei, and the whole Bliss gang will return in *Lost in Bliss*, coming September 25, 2018.

Author's Note

I'm often asked by generous readers how they can help get the word out about a book they enjoyed. There are so many ways to help an author you like. Leave a review. If your e-reader allows you to lend a book to a friend, please share it. Go to Goodreads and connect with others. Recommend the books you love because stories are meant to be shared. Thank you so much for reading this book and for supporting all the authors you love!

Sign up for Lexi Blake's newsletter
and be entered to win a $25 gift certificate
to the bookseller of your choice.

Join us for news, fun, and exclusive content
including free short stories.

Go to www.LexiBlake.net to subscribe!

There's a new contest every month!

Siren in Waiting

Texas Sirens Book 5
By Lexi Blake writing as Sophie Oak
Coming September 4, 2018

Re-released in a second edition with new content.

Bethany "Mouse" Hobbes spent her entire life waiting, especially for the love of Bo O'Malley. But for the first time in her life, she is ready to start living, with or without him. She has found her dream, restoring a rustic farmhouse on the outskirts of town.

Trev McNamara left Deer Run a high school hero and has returned, his football career in ruins. When Trev meets Mouse, he discovers a passion strong enough to overcome his past. But can she accept his need for control?

Bo O'Malley has lived his whole life in the shadow of his brother, never committing to anything or anyone. When the woman he secretly loved all his life begins an affair with the man who betrayed his trust, Bo will do anything to claim her as his own.

Transformed by their love, will Mouse be enough woman for both of them?

* * * *

Bo turned back to his whiskey. It looked like he was going to need it after all. He reached for it, but Trev's hand whisked it away. He shoved it down the bar where Leo handed it back to the bartender.

"I think you can consider Mr. O'Malley's tab closed until further notice," Leo informed the bartender.

"Hey, I was drinking that," he protested.

"Not anymore you aren't." Trev sat down on the stool next to him. His face had softened.

"You don't have any right to tell a man what he can and can't do." What the hell was Trev doing here?

266

"I'm exactly the person to listen to about this. That whiskey isn't going to fix your problem. Let's get out of here. We can talk about Beth."

Fuck. Trev had obviously heard his message to Mouse. "I'm not going to talk about this with you. I'm not going to try to kiss her again if that's what you're worried about. She picked you. You win. I lose. Now leave me be."

"What if neither one of us had to lose?"

Bo stopped. What was Trev saying? Fuck. He knew exactly what Trev was saying. It wasn't anything he hadn't thought of himself in the hours since he'd realized Mouse wasn't going to leave Trev for him. How could he not think about it? He had living, laughing, loving proof paraded in front of him every day that a relationship like that could work.

"I don't like men." That was why it couldn't work. He wasn't bisexual. No matter what his father said. He didn't begrudge his brother and Lucas. Hell, Bo loved Lucas like a brother himself. Lucas was part of his family, but he didn't view other men as sexual objects.

Trev sighed. "I don't have sex with men, either. I know it seems like I've done just about everything decadent the universe has to offer, but I haven't done another dude. I don't have a problem with it. I'm simply not intrigued. Rest assured, I'm not after your dick."

Bo finally looked at Trev. "Fine. I don't like you."

Trev seemed nonplussed about that fact. "We got along once. We could get along again. For Beth's sake."

Crap. His cock twitched at the thought. Hadn't he had enough to drink that his cock should be asleep now? He had a sudden vision of Mouse, her gorgeous pale form surrounded by their tanned skin. She would be so fucking small in between them. They could turn her from one to the other, kissing her at will. She would be a pretty doll between them. They could lavish her with pleasure in a way one man alone couldn't.

"I don't think Mouse would go for that." No way was this going to happen. And even if she did want it, would he be able to do it? After what Trev had done? What had Trev truly done? He'd closed a door in Bo's face. And Bo had walked away. That was what he always did. He always walked away. And he never really tried. He

expected that it would all go bad. He expected that if he fought, he would lose.

Wasn't that what he'd done with Mouse?

His head was swimming with alcohol and possibilities.

"You are going to call her Beth. I won't allow you to call her by that nickname anymore," Trev said, his tone stern. "Her name is Beth. That's one of the rules."

Rules? There were rules now? "I think I'll call her whatever I like."

He tensed as a big hand went around his neck, and he was hauled off of his barstool.

Trev looked down at him, his eyes narrow and his face as hard as a rock. "You will show her some goddamn respect. Whether you end up accepting my proposal or not, if I ever hear you call her by that demeaning name again, I will beat the fuck out of you. You can't take care of her while you're putting her down. And you sure as fuck can't take care of her until you start taking care of yourself."

Bo put a hand on the barstool, trying to regain his balance. The whole world felt like it had tilted, and he wasn't sure where he was going to land.

Lost in Bliss

Nights in Bliss, Colorado Book 4
By Lexi Blake writing as Sophie Oak
Coming September 25, 2018

Laura Niles walked out the door and never looked back. As she left Washington, DC, her career was in ruins and her love life decimated. Her desperate flight eventually led her to Bliss, Colorado, where she managed to find a new home and a little peace. That will have to be enough because Laura cannot imagine finding happiness without the men she left behind.

For five years, Rafe Kincaid and Cameron Briggs have searched for the only woman they ever loved. When she disappeared, everything became crystal clear. For one night, everything had been perfect and instead of embracing what they had found, they let it all slip away. They had let worries about their FBI careers and what others might think destroy the most precious gift they had ever been given. Now they have finally tracked her down, and they want answers.

Laura is shocked when her former loves show up in her new home. When the full force of the FBI arrives with them, Laura knows that the quirky little town is in for a rough ride. The killer that ruined her life has been watching and waiting for the opportunity to strike again. For Rafe, Cam, and Laura it's time for second chances — to stop a monster, and to reclaim everything they lost.

* * * *

Rafe didn't miss the way Laura's body went still, her muscles stiffening where a moment before she'd been laughing with her friends. She changed the second she became aware of them. It wasn't the greeting he would prefer. Back when they were friends, when she would see him coming, her whole body would go soft and a welcoming smile would transform her face from something professional to an intimate visage, one only meant for someone close

269

to her. He'd taken great pride in the fact that he'd only ever seen that look on her face for one other person.

"Hello, *bella*."

She frowned at him. Even with her lips turned down, she was stunning. She looked only slightly out of place in her yellow heels. The rest of her outfit was charmingly Western. She had on a full cotton skirt, a yellow tank top, and a light denim jacket. It wasn't far off from what many of the other women were wearing, yet Laura made it seem elegant. Everything she did had an air of grace to it, even when she was bitching at him.

"I thought I asked you to stop calling me that."

He wasn't going to let her push him. He gave her what he hoped was an easy smile. "And I asked you to stop calling me asshole. I doubt you've done that. Dance with me."

Her eyes widened, a look of horror crossing her face. "No."

"Come on, baby. Don't say no." Cam crowded her, but she held her ground. Those heels were planted firmly in the grass beneath her. "I can't dance with you until you dance with him. I lost the coin flip."

"Oh, that's romantic." Her hands found her hips, and those gorgeously full lips pursed. "Every woman in the world wants to be won by the flip of a coin."

"We didn't have time to play cards," Rafe admitted. He was well aware that people were listening in. Oh, they were pretending to be doing other things, but they leaned over and then talked behind their hands. The citizens of Bliss seemed to be enjoying the drama. Damn, he couldn't get used to it. In DC, no one paid a bit of attention to what was going on around them. He tried to ignore it. "We weren't sure how else to handle it, *bella*. You have to teach us."

Her lips rose in a sarcastic grin. "See, that's easy. Let me teach you how to handle a situation like this. You both turn around and walk out the way you came in. You get in your car and drive to Alamosa and get on a plane back to DC."

Cam sighed. "That's not going to happen."

Cam ran a hand up her arm, and Rafe was satisfied with the way she shivered. She still responded to Cam. Would she respond to him? He reached out and took her hand, studying it. Her hand was small in his, her skin fair against his olive tone. Her nails weren't as long as

she used to keep them, but they were still manicured and painted a pretty pink. "Come on and dance with me. We came all this way. We've looked for so long. Can't you spare a moment of your time? I promise to behave."

He wouldn't behave. He had every intention of reminding her of the chemistry they'd had, but he wasn't going to announce it.

"Fine." She pushed off of the picnic table she'd been leaning against. "One dance and that's all."

"With both of us," Cam added quickly, pushing the advantage. "It's only fair. Otherwise, we'll both dance with you here and now."

There it was. Rafe's heart soared. Her eyes had flared momentarily, and it wasn't with disgust. When they had checked into the odd motel at the edge of town, they had decided it would be best to come at her together. She'd been turned on by sex with both of them. They needed to remind her of what they had to offer.

Cowboy Cross My Heart
Heart of Texas Book 1
By Donna Grant
Coming August 28, 2018

New York Times bestselling author Donna Grant takes you deep inside the Texas rodeo scene in the second book in her *Heart of Texas* series, *Cowboy, Cross My Heart*, where danger and desire ride side by side...

Naomi Pierce isn't the type to let a cowboy sweep her off feet. It's not her first rodeo, after all. But when she returns to her Texas hometown, she can't help but be swept up again in the rough-and-tumble world of hard-riding, bronco-busting good-ol'-boys she loved as a girl. She might be here to photograph her Rodeo Queen best friend. But it's one fine-looking cowboy who really captures her eye...

Brice Harper is all man, all muscle, and all heart. From the moment he rides into the stadium, he can't help but notice the beautiful stranger with a camera watching him from the stands. It doesn't take a zoom lens to see the sparks of instant attraction. But things really heat up when he meets Naomi up-close—and he discovers that someone is stalking her friend. Brice wouldn't be any kind of cowboy if he didn't offer to help the ladies out. But can the rough rider keep this spirited shutterbug out of danger—without risking his heart?

* * * *

Chapter One
March

Excitement rushed through everyone as the lights suddenly cut out in the arena. Naomi slid to the edge of the metal bench in the darkness, her heart kicking up a notch as silence fell over the crowd of several thousand. The only sound was the occasional stamp of a hoof from the animals or the jingle of a bridle.

A spotlight came on and swung to the gates. It had been years

since Naomi had been to a rodeo, but it took just a few seconds for the memories of that splendid time in her life to fill her.

Seemingly, as one, everyone rose to their feet and put their hands over their hearts. Her mind halted at the first strings of the national anthem that played loudly over the speakers. The first horse came walking out of the gates, with the American flag being held by none other than Naomi's best friend, Whitney Nolan.

Behind Whitney was another woman with the Texas flag. The two made their way around the edge of the arena several times, the horses moving from a walk to a trot to a gallop, and then a full-out run with the flags rippling in the wind. As Whitney neared her, Naomi flashed her a smile, the tears gathering.

Naomi blinked through them as her mind went back to high school and the third member of their group, Suellen, who had dreamed of being exactly where Whitney was. It was one reason Naomi had returned now.

Besides, it had been too long since she had done more than talk to her best friend over the phone or visit her mother.

Whitney and the other woman halted in the middle of the arena at the crescendo of music. The spotlight caught on the rhinestones of her friend's white chaps with writing claiming Whitney the Rodeo Queen of Baxter County.

Naomi grinned at the large crown fitted on the white Stetson hat atop Whitney's long, golden waves. When the anthem concluded, applause erupted as the lights came back on.

After a tribute to the military and a prayer had commenced, Naomi discreetly took pictures of everything. She resumed her seat and watched Whitney return through the gates as the event began.

Naomi laughed when the rodeo clowns rushed into the arena to get the crowd going. She snapped photos while enjoying the show. Part of her wished she had made it in time for the day rodeo when she could have seen the youngsters doing the steer racing.

It wasn't long before she was once more sucked back into a world she had left behind. She lost track of time as she cheered the events from calf roping, steer wrestling, and bareback riding.

When it came time for the barrel racers, Naomi's heart missed a beat. This had been her event. And she had loved every second of it.

With every rider that rushed through the gates and worked their horse around the barrels, she held her breath until they crossed over the finish line. When the final rider finished, the scoreboard went up, and her camera nearly slipped through her fingers.

Her time had yet to be beaten. There were some that came close, but somehow, she was still the rider to beat. Even after all these years.

She nearly forgot to raise her camera when the event shifted to team roping. Naomi paid no attention to the announcer as he spouted off the names of the first contestants while the clowns hurried to remove the barrels.

Naomi lifted her camera and looked through the viewfinder. She took rapid shots to get everything from the moment the gate was pulled and the steer rushed from the header box, to when the lead roper—called a header—got the rope around the steer's horns. Once the header had the steer turned, the heeler would rope its back legs.

It was a timed event, so it was always fun to watch who was the quickest. Naomi loved that women competed in the teams, as well. Some duos were mixed, some not.

Naomi swung her camera to the next two up for the event and snapped a couple of pictures.

"Ladies and gentlemen," the announcer said over the speaker. "The winners of the past three years are once more in the arena. Let's give a warm welcome to Brice and Caleb Harper."

The applause was deafening. Naomi looked down at her camera and pulled up the picture she'd just taken. She stared at the guy in a tan Stetson and a red and orange plaid button-down who looked at the arena as if it were his battlefield, while the other wore a mischievous grin that had obviously broken many hearts, along with a brown Stetson and a chambray shirt.

"These brothers are the ones to beat," the announcer finished.

Naomi had to admit, both were handsome, but there was something about the serious one that kept drawing her gaze. For the first time, she pulled her head away from her camera to the gates and watched as the cowboy maneuvered his horse into the header slot.

Somehow, she wasn't surprised that he was in that position. Was he the eldest? She imagined he might be.

She lifted her camera again and took picture after picture,

shocked at how skilled—and quick—the brothers were. No one seemed surprised when they won the first round of the event.

When she lowered her camera, her gaze remained on the serious one and strayed to his ass. Because there was just something about a man in Wranglers that she couldn't resist.

As he wound his rope, his eyes lifted and looked right at her.

Naomi's heart missed a beat. She smiled nervously. Right before he grabbed the reins, he tipped his hat at her and rode off.

At least she thought he'd been looking at her, but the women behind her giggled loudly, each wondering if she had been the object of his greeting.

Naomi laughed at herself and readied for the first round of bull riding, which was the main event at any rodeo. She'd once dated a bull rider. Briefly. She had been too young for their wild, reckless ways and how they eagerly put their lives in danger each time they climbed on a bull, hoping to hear the buzzer on that eight-second ride.

But people lived for the event. The crazier the bull, the louder the crowd cheered. Naomi took more pictures, her heart in her throat each time a cowboy was bucked off, and the bull went after them.

One of her pictures captured how close the bull's horns had been to gorging the cowboy. Yet, with each near-death experience, the crowd gasped then cheered both the rider for getting away and the rodeo clowns for coming between the bull and the contestant.

Her uncle had been a rodeo clown, and she knew their jobs were the hardest of everyone's. They were out there between each event and always at the ready for any participant or animal that got into trouble. They were also the ones with the most injuries.

In fact, her uncle had died when a bull's horn pierced his chest. But the cowboy her uncle had been helping got to safety. And that's what the clowns were for.

With the rodeo coming to a close for the night, Naomi was the first on her feet to give the clowns an ovation. As soon as the closing ceremony finished, Naomi made her way out of the stands to the back of the arena.

She paid only a passing courtesy to the many cowboys who murmured "ma'am" and tipped their hats as she walked past. When she finally reached the area where the pageant contestants were, she

easily found Whitney's white hat, sparkling crown, and blond locks.

Naomi watched her friend in her element for a long minute. Then Naomi whistled loudly. Whitney turned, her blue gaze scanning the people until she spotted Naomi. Whitley let out a loud squeal and rushed her. Naomi threw open her arms and hugged her friend tightly.

"It's been so long," Whitney murmured.

Naomi knew she was thinking of Suellen. "Too long."

Whitney leaned back and beamed at her. "I worried you might change your mind."

"Never. Weather delayed my plane, but I told you I'd be here."

"And you always keep your word." Whitney moved to her side and linked arms with her as they started walking slowly. "Well?"

Naomi shook her head as she glanced at Whitney. "Fine. I'll admit that I miss being involved in the rodeo."

"I knew it," her friend said with a pump of her arm.

"Don't get any ideas. I've got a nice life in DC, and that's where I'll be returning in a couple of days."

Whitney rolled her eyes. "You say that now, but I think if I can find the right cowboy for you, you'll change your mind."

"You forget I know all I want to know about cowboys."

"True," Whitney said with a twist of her lips. They both stopped and watched a couple of men walk past, their gazes on their fine asses. "Then again..."

Naomi swung her head to Whitney, and they both laughed. "If I do any riding, it will only be on a horse."

"Yeah, we'll see about that," Whitney declared with a grin.

"I mean it, Whit. I'm here to spend time with you and Mom. That's all."

Whitney nodded. "Yep. I hear you loud and clear."

Then why was it that Naomi suspected her friend had other ideas?

"Are you ready?" Whitney asked.

Naomi looked at all the women in rhinestones and hairspray ahead of them. Each beautiful and impeccably dressed in denim, boots, and rhinestone shirts. But anyone who believed rodeo pageants were like other talent and beauty contests was sorely mistaken.

The women were expert riders. While competing, they were

given a horse they had never ridden before and had ninety seconds to flawlessly complete an intricate routine.

But it went further than that. The girls weren't allowed to be married or have children. Each contestant also had a chaperone. Hell, even the judges had escorts. And the girls who competed were discouraged from even having boyfriends.

At her silence, Whitney raised a brow. "Is it too much?"

Naomi took a deep breath. "Yes. And no."

"Even after all these years, I still see Suellen everywhere," Whitney murmured.

Naomi tightened her hand on her friend's arm. Whitney, Suellen, and Naomi had been inseparable. They'd traded wins in barrel racing, and were always there to cheer each other on.

Suellen was the one who'd decided to do a rodeo pageant. Her dream was to win Miss Rodeo America and win the thirty grand prize. While neither Naomi nor Whitney had any interest in the pageant, they'd supported Suellen fully.

And when Suellen won her first title in a local rodeo, the three had gone out to celebrate. Suellen put the top down on her convertible. And they had the music blaring, singing loudly as they drove down the dark, winding roads.

They had the entire world before them. And they planned to conquer it together.

Until a car hit them head-on.

Naomi could still hear her scream mixed with the sounds of tires screeching. And the crunch of metal.

Whitney had suffered two broken arms and a broken collarbone. Naomi broke her femur, had several lacerations, and a concussion. Suellen...died.

Naomi had missed Suellen's funeral because of the surgery on her leg. She had tried to escape the hospital to go, and in the end, they had to sedate her. She didn't talk to her parents for four days after that.

"Suellen would be so proud of you," Naomi said to Whitney.

They shared a look, tears gathering before Whitney sniffed and hurriedly looked away. Then Whitney pulled her toward the corral where her horse was. "When was the last time you rode?"

"A horse?" Naomi teased.

Whitney threw back her head and laughed. Naomi took a quick picture of her friend. The sound was loud and glorious and infectious. Everyone paused and looked at her because they had no choice. Suellen had been fearless and bold, but Whitney was captivating and charming.

"Oh, you are as naughty as always," Whitney said with a wide smile. "God, I've missed your humor."

Naomi put her elbow on the railing. "I've not been on a horse since I left for college."

"And men?" Whitney asked with a twinkle in her blue eyes.

Naomi forced the smile to stay in place. "None since Johnny."

"That was over a year ago."

As if she needed a reminder of how long it'd been since she called off her engagement. It had been the right thing to do. Johnny was an amazing man, but she knew marrying him would be a mistake. So she'd saved them heartache—and a divorce. Though he didn't see it that way.

"Well," Whitney said with a sigh. "By the way the men here are looking at you, you should be riding soon."

Naomi rolled her eyes as she laughed. Maybe she would use this time to explore her options. What did she have to lose?

Your heart.

She laughed off her inner voice. As if that would happen.

About Lexi Blake

Lexi Blake lives in North Texas with her husband, three kids, and the laziest rescue dog in the world. She began writing at a young age, concentrating on plays and journalism. It wasn't until she started writing romance that she found success. She likes to find humor in the strangest places. Lexi believes in happy endings no matter how odd the couple, threesome or foursome may seem. She also writes contemporary Western ménage as Sophie Oak.

Connect with Lexi online:

Facebook: Lexi Blake
Twitter: authorlexiblake
Website: www.LexiBlake.net

Sign up for Lexi's free newsletter!

DATE DUE

PRINTED IN U.S.A.